Royal Bournemouth
Hospital Library

‖‖‖‖‖‖‖‖‖‖‖‖‖‖‖‖‖‖‖‖‖‖‖‖
B2015305

ⒼYⵏSO

WITHDRAWN

Appreciative Healthcare Practice

LIBRARY
ROYAL BOURNEMOUTH HO
BOURNEMOUTH
BH7 7DW
TEL: 01202 70427(
library@rbch.nhs.u

Full the full range of M&K Publishing books please visit our website:

www.mkupdate.co.uk

Contents

Preface

This book aims to fill the gap between the combined science courses, which are commonly used in the early secondary years, and the courses which lead to public examinations in the fifth year. This gap most frequently occurs in the third year, and it provides the last opportunity for wide ranging studies before teachers meet the constraints imposed by examination syllabuses.

A wide variety of interesting material is included. It is not linked directly to the examination syllabuses but it does provide a sound introduction to the subject for those who will continue to study biology. On the other hand, for those who will give up the subject at this stage the book provides a complete course. The material encourages students to look beyond the boundaries of their own country and their own experiences and towards other countries and wider issues.

There is more material in the book than can easily be covered in a single year, enabling teachers to select the sections most suitable for their students. Some of the activities are easier than others, and within many exercises some questions are harder than others. Teachers can therefore choose work appropriate for their classes, or for individuals within a class, if there is a wide ability range.

Reference skills are encouraged by the inclusion of a special Students' Reference Section. There is also a Teachers' Guidelines Section for each chapter with notes on reagents, advice and references. Teachers may find it convenient to photocopy the headings for some of the results tables for students to use. The publishers have agreed to waive copyright on the results tables illustrated. All other material in the book is protected by copyright.

There are many people without whose help this book would never have been written. I am especially grateful to my parents who encouraged and fostered my early interest in books and natural history. Their generosity provided me with many opportunities to extend my interests. Among those who taught me I am indebted to Noel Wilkinson, John Dancy, Terry Kermode, George Shaw and Barrie Juniper for their advice and guidance, and I owe much to former colleagues, especially John Leonhardt, James Boyes, and Colin Ranger. However, it is to my colleagues at the Netherhall School, and at other schools in the Cambridge area, that I am particularly grateful. It was while working with them that the idea for this book was born. Brian Gillinder and Rita Spaxman have been especially kind and helpful.

Many other people have assisted me during the book's preparation. They include Miss S. Marchand, Miss C. Corning, Mr P. Dickinson, Dr J. A. Hill and Dr D. R. Jones (Ministry of Agriculture); Dr E. M. J. Kirby and Miss M. Appleyard (Plant Breeding Institute, Cambridge); Mrs A. Fox-Robinson (Community Dental Service, Cambridge); Dr. C. D. R. Flower, Mr I. MacDonald, Mr S. I. M. Robinson and Mr R. E. Robinson (Addenbrookes Hospital, Cambridge); Miss P. Schofield (Centre for Overseas Pest Research); Dr I. Hardy (Papworth Hospital); Dr R. H. Ellis (St. Bartholomew's Hospital, London); Miss B. Dunbar (Action on Smoking and Health); Mr D. C. Cameron (Cambridgeshire County Council); Mr B. Leith (Natural History Unit, BBC Radio); Dr C. Watsham (Newmarket General Hospital). I am very grateful to all of them. It is also a pleasure to acknowledge the great stimulus given to the teaching of biology by the Nuffield Foundation Science Teaching Project.

In thanking my publishers, Cambridge University Press, I acknowledge with much gratitude the help and skill of many people in the editorial, design and production departments.

The largest debt of gratitude I owe to my wife who read much of the manuscript and provided a number of helpful suggestions particularly on medical matters. The realisation of this book was made possible by her patient encouragement and provision of suitable working conditions amid the clamour of family life.

In thanking all of these people, however, I must add that I alone am responsible for any shortcomings that remain.

Richard Price
Cambridge
March, 1982

'Knowledge is of two kinds. We know a subject ourselves, or we know where we can find information upon it.'

Samuel Johnson (1709–1784)

Acknowledgements

The author and publishers are grateful to the following for permission to use their photographs: Walther Rohdich: 1.1. David Rae (Nature Photographers Ltd.): 1.2. Nigel Luckhurst: 1.3, 2.1e, 2.7, 3.7, 4.3a, 5.2, 5.3, 6.4a, 6.4d, 6.4e, 6.4f, 7.5, 9.10, 9.11, 10.3, 11.14, 11.15, 11.16a, 11.16b, 11.16c, 11.16d, 11.16e, 11.16f, 12.1a, 15.1c, 15.3a, 15.3b, 18.1, 13.9. Bill Paton (Nature Photographers Ltd.): 2.1a, 13.6a. S. C. Bisserot (Nature Photographers Ltd.): 2.1b, 2.1c, 13.6b. Tony Seddon: 2.1d, 3.3. Chris Mylne (Nature Photographers Ltd.): 2.1f. Arthur Christiansen: 2.1g. Hans Beste (Ardea, London): 2.1h. WHO Photo: 3.1a, 3.1b, 3.1d, 5.7, 10.1b, 10.5, 14.1, 14.2, 14.3, 14.5, 14.6, 14.7, 14.13. Public Health Department, Corporation of Glasgow: 3.1c. Health Education Council: 3.8a, 3.8b. Department of Medical Illustration, Addenbrookes Hospital, Cambridge: 4.3b. Michael Gore (Nature Photographers Ltd.): 5.5, 8.1. Royal Commonwealth Society: 6.1. Dr E. M. I. Kirby: 6.4b, 6.4c. C. Ashall: 7.1a, 7.8. Centre for Overseas Pest Research: 7.1b. Peggy Heard (Nature Photographers Ltd.): 7.13. Keven Carlson (Nature Photographers Ltd.): 7.14. FBC Ltd.: 7.15, 7.16, 18.2. Phillip Coffey: 8.4, 17.10. Aerofilms Ltd.: 9.8, 9.9. Imperial Tobacco Ltd.: 10.1a. Anglian Water Authority: 11.3. All-Sport Photographic Ltd.: 11.4. Dr J. R. Harris: 11.5, 11.6. Associated Press: 12.5. Dr J. Aitken: 13.2. Tom Willock (Ardea, London): 13.6c. Lynwood Chace: 13.6d. Ake Lindau (Ardea, London): 13.7. Dr M. J. Hare: 13.18, 13.19. Derek Widdicombe: 13.21a, 13.21b. C. James Webb: 14.8a, 14.8b, 14.9a, 14.9b, 14.10. A Shell Photograph: 14.17. Popperfoto: 15.1a, 15.11. Richard McBride: 15.1b, 15.1d. Roy Edwards: 15.1c. Independent Newspapers Ltd.: 15.8. Michael W. Richards, Royal Society for the Protection of Birds: 15.9. University of Cambridge Committee for Aerial Photography: 16.2. Colin Jones (The Observer Magazine): 16.3. Times Newspapers Ltd.: 16.4. Cambridge Instruments Ltd.: 17.3, 17.4. Dr J. Nagington: 17.5. Bruce Coleman Ltd.: 17.11.

The author and publishers are also grateful to the following: Careers Research and Advisory Centre for permission to refer to their publication *Your Choice at 13+*, The Advisory Committee on Oil Pollution of the Sea for permission to quote from their 1980 Annual Report, The Royal College of Physicians for permission to quote from their report *Smoking or Health*, The Ministry of Agriculture, Fisheries and Food for permission to quote from the Advisory leaflet No. 534 and the Manual of Nutrition (1978), Guinness Superlatives Ltd., for permission to refer to the 1981 27th edition of the Guinness Book of Records, The World Health Organisation for permission to quote from *World Health* magazine, and Phillip Harris Biological Ltd., for permission to reproduce the chromosomes shown in Figure 13.9.

1 Photosynthesis

1 Survival

What does the word survival mean to you? Look at Figure 1.1. It is obvious that animals must eat in order to survive.

1 What else must animals do to survive?
2 Look at Figure 1.2. What must plants do to survive?

These are some of the questions which biology, the study of life, tries to answer. This book starts by asking some questions about plants.

Fig. 1.1 Why is this lizard eating?

Fig. 1.2 Why do these plants have leaves?

2 Using iodine solution to test for starch

Activity

a ▶ Put a small drop of iodine solution onto a piece of paper.

1 What colour does the paper go? This colour is always seen when iodine solution is added to something which contains starch.
2 Does paper contain starch?
3 What is paper made from?
4 What colour is the iodine solution in the reagent bottle?
5 If there was no starch in paper, what colour do you think the paper would have gone after adding iodine solution?

3 Do plants have starch in their roots?

Activity

One of the easiest plants to study is the geranium.

a ▶ Take a piece of geranium root about 20 millimetres (mm) long. Cut it in half.
b ▶ Put one piece in a watch glass. Flood it with iodine solution. Label this A, and leave it while you carry on with the next part.
c ▶ Cut and crush up the other piece of root into very small pieces.
d ▶ Put these into a test tube labelled B. Add water to a depth of about 40 mm.
e ▶ Boil the contents of tube B gently, then cool.
f ▶ When it is completely cool, add a few drops of iodine solution.

1 What colour is seen when iodine solution is added to B?
2 Does the geranium root contain starch?
3 Compare the whole piece of root A, with the other piece, B. Which treatment gives the best result with iodine solution?
4 Why do you think that one treatment gives a better result than the other?

Starch belongs to a large group of chemical substances called **carbohydrates**. 'Carbo-' means that they contain the element carbon, '-hydr-' means that they contain the element hydrogen, '-ate' means that they contain the element oxygen. Starch is stored in many plants, especially in their roots. This is the reason why we eat the roots of some plants. Starch is also stored in other parts.

5 Give the names of some plant roots which we eat.

g ▶ If you have time, use the iodine solution to test some more pieces of plant root for starch.

4   Where else is starch found in the geranium?

Starch is not found in the soil so it is unlikely that plants get their starch from there.

1 What parts of a plant are found above the soil?

Activity

a ▶ Take one leaf from a variegated geranium.
b ▶ Make a quick sketch of the leaf to show which areas are green and which are white. Figure 1.3 shows you how to do this, but make sure that you draw your own leaf. Do not just copy Figure 1.3. Leaves are tested for starch without cutting them up as you did the root in the Activity in Section 3.

Fig. 1.3 A variegated geranium leaf and a simple sketch of the same leaf showing the green and white areas

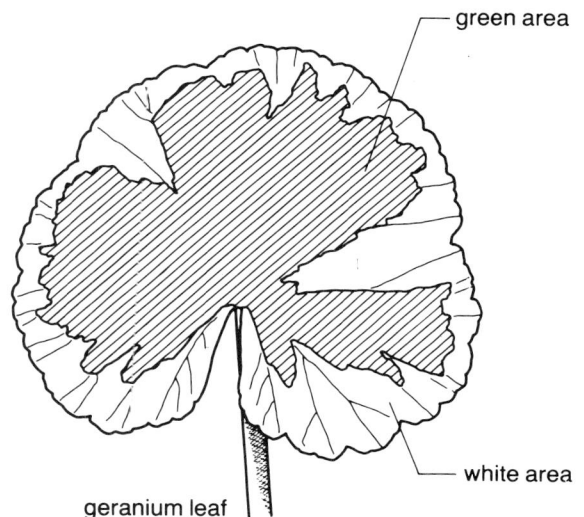

green area

white area

geranium leaf

c ▶ Put your leaf into boiling water. This kills the leaf and softens it so that the iodine solution can get into it.

d ▶ Boil the leaf for about one minute. Then turn the burner out.

e ▶ Take the leaf out of the hot water. Put it into a test tube.

f ▶ Add about 50 mm of ethanol to the tube with the leaf in. Make sure that the ethanol covers the leaf.

g ▶ Heat this test tube in a water bath (see Figure 1.4). Make sure that the burner is turned off. Ethanol is highly inflammable.

h ▶ Look at the leaf from time to time while it is in the ethanol.

2 What is happening to it?

i ▶ When the leaf has lost all or most of its green colour remove it carefully from the ethanol. Wash it gently in water. This makes the leaf less brittle.

j ▶ Spread the leaf out on a tile or in a shallow dish. Flood it with iodine solution. Wait for about five minutes. Add more iodine solution if necessary. Then wash the leaf again in water.

3 Describe what happened to the leaf when iodine solution was added to it.

4 Does the leaf contain starch?

5 Draw a quick sketch of the leaf and label it to show exactly where the starch is.

6 Compare this drawing with your drawing of the same leaf before it was boiled. What do you notice about the part that was green and the part where the starch is found?

The Activities in Sections 3 and 4 show that starch is found in the roots and in the leaves of a geranium. The question is, where does this starch come from? The Activity in Section 5 helps you to answer this question.

5 Is starch found in the leaves of a geranium plant which has been kept in darkness?

Activity

a ▶ Set up the experiment shown in Figure 1.5. Each box

Fig. 1.4 Heating ethanol. Always use a hot water bath to heat ethanol – never a burner

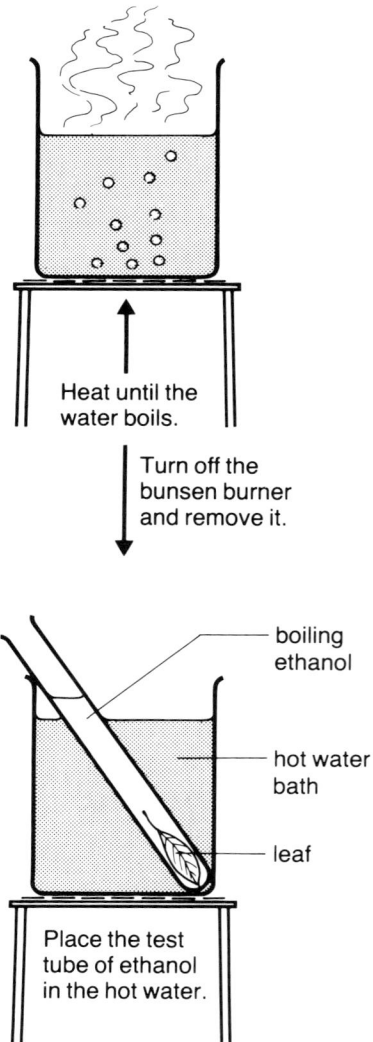

Heat until the water boils.

Turn off the bunsen burner and remove it.

boiling ethanol

hot water bath

leaf

Place the test tube of ethanol in the hot water.

should contain a potted geranium of about the same size. The boxes should be identical except that A is lightproof, and B has one side replaced by a piece of clear transparent material. This lets light in to the plant. Suitable materials include acetate, Clingfilm, glass or Perspex.

b ▶ Leave the plants, in their boxes, by a window for at least 48 hours (longer in cold weather).

c ▶ After a suitable length of time prepare a container of boiling water. Carry out the next two steps quickly but carefully.

d ▶ Take a leaf from plant A. Cut off the stalk. Quickly put the leaf into the boiling water. Throw away the stalk.

e ▶ Take a leaf from plant B. Do not cut off the stalk. Put the leaf quickly into the boiling water with leaf A.

f ▶ Then carry on with the starch-iodine test on both leaves as in the previous Activity.

1 Why were you told to cut off the stalk from one leaf but not from the other?

2 Describe what happens to leaf A when iodine solution is added to it.

3 Describe what happens to leaf B when iodine solution is added to it.

4 Is there any starch in either of the leaves? If so, in which one is the starch seen?

5 What do geraniums need in order to make starch in their leaves?

The plant in box B (in the light) is called the **control** experiment. It was set up to try to make sure that the only difference between plants A and B was the presence or

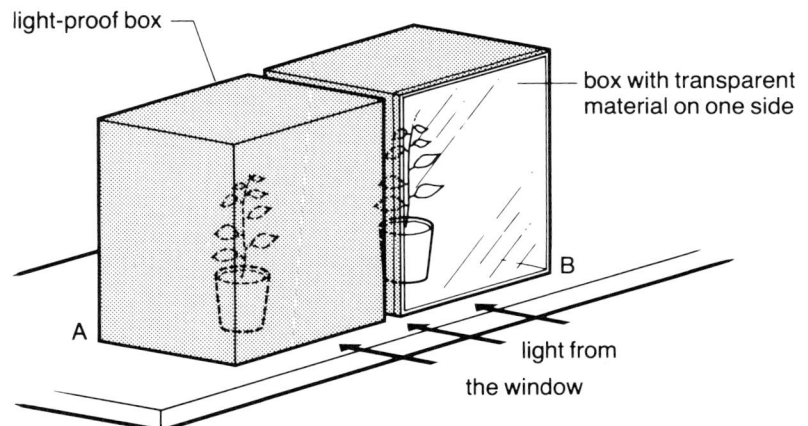

light-proof box

box with transparent material on one side

B

light from the window

A

Fig. 1.5 Set up your plants near a window

absence of light. In all other ways the plants were treated in exactly the same way. This means that any difference between the leaves at the end of the experiment must be due to the presence or absence of light, and not to something else.

Control experiments are widely used in biology. Careful thought goes into the design of good control experiments. The experiment with two plants in boxes, described above, might have been done by putting plant A in a dark cupboard and plant B on a window sill.

6 This would not be such a good experiment as the one using two boxes. Explain why.

Geraniums make starch in their leaves when they are kept in the light. Starch disappears from their leaves in darkness. Starch is stored in their roots. These three things are also true of many other plants. Plants need energy to make starch in their leaves. Section 6 explains where this energy comes from.

6 How green plants capture energy

The sun's energy reaches the surface of the Earth in two forms: heat energy and light energy. Plants and animals are warmed up by the heat energy. However they cannot capture and use this heat energy for their life processes.

Fig. 1.6 Photosynthesis

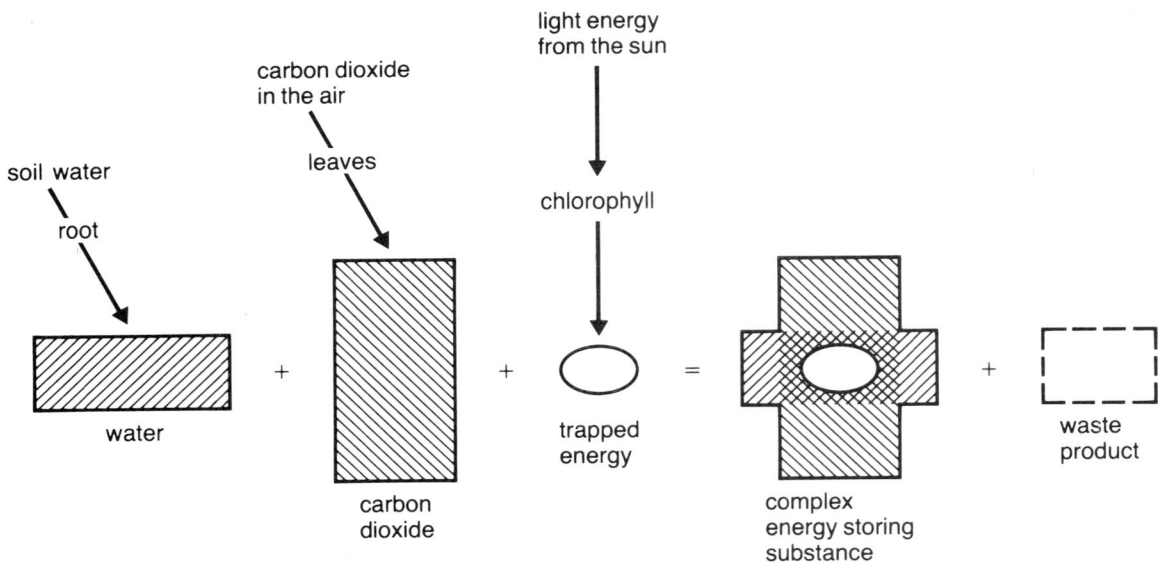

soil water

root

water

+

carbon dioxide in the air

leaves

carbon dioxide

+

light energy from the sun

chlorophyll

trapped energy

=

complex energy storing substance

+

waste product

sunlight

luxuriant
swamp forest

trees become
flooded and die

trees become
covered by sediment

sediment layers
build up

trees compressed
to form coal

coal layers become
folded and may
even be exposed

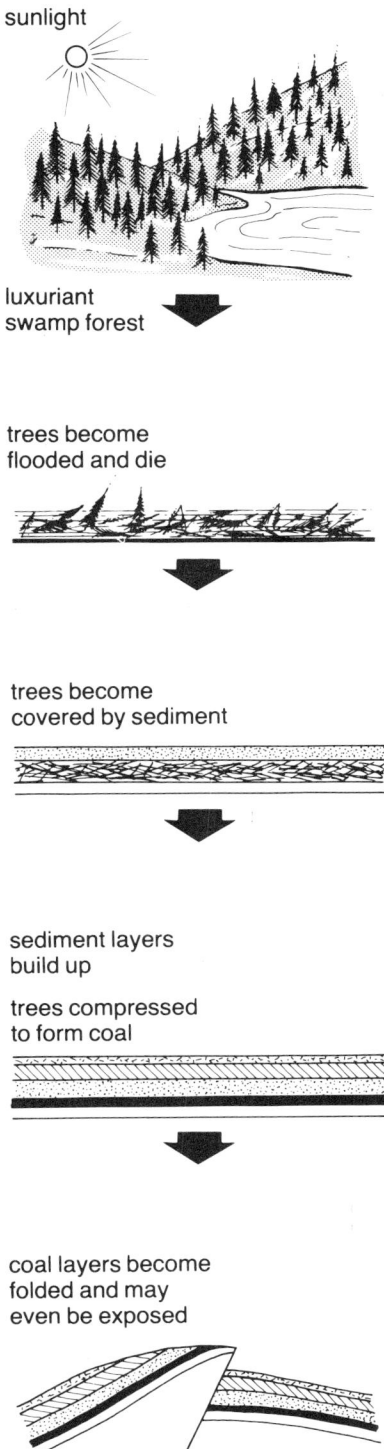

Fig. 1.7 *The formation of coal from forest trees*

Plants are the only living things which can capture the light energy. This is because they contain a special energy-capturing substance called **chlorophyll**. Plants make use of the light energy which is trapped by their chlorophyll. They use the energy to make water and carbon dioxide combine together to form a complex energy-storing substance. This process is called **photosynthesis**. The word photosynthesis means 'putting things together with light'. The process is shown in Figure 1.6. Some of the light energy is changed into chemical energy. This chemical energy is stored in the complex energy-storing substance which is shown in Figure 1.6.

1 Look at your answer to question 6 in Section 4. What colour do you think chlorophyll is?
2 Look at your answers to questions 4 and 5 in Section 5. What do you think the complex energy-storing substance might be?

Most plants are green because they contain chlorophyll. Some plants, such as the copper beech and the red and brown seaweeds, do not look green. However they can still capture the sun's energy. Their chlorophyll is hidden by other coloured substances.

Green plants are called **producers**. This is because they make their own food. They use simple materials to make complex substances. Energy is needed. This comes from the sun.

Animals cannot do this. Some animals get their food by eating plants. Other animals eat animals which feed on plants. For this reason, animals are called **consumers**. All animals therefore get their energy from plants, which in turn get their energy from the sun. Plants are very important to all of us. If there were no plants, the sun's energy could not be trapped. There would be no food for animals.

All living things need energy to carry out the millions of chemical reactions which keep them alive. These reactions make possible life processes such as growth and reproduction.

When we eat a potato we take in some of the energy captured from the sun by the potato plant when it was growing. When we burn coal, oil or gas we release energy which was captured, by plants, millions of years ago (see Figure 1.7).

7 ▶ What is the waste product of photosynthesis?

Figure 1.6 shows that two things are made during photosynthesis. One is starch and the other is a waste product. In land plants this waste product is difficult to identify. However, it can easily be seen and identified in a water plant. A good water plant to use is the Canadian pondweed.

Activity

a ▶ Shine strong light on an aquarium or beaker containing the pondweed. Bubbles will be seen rising from parts of the weed. These bubbles contain the waste product of photosynthesis. The waste product is a gas which is found in air.

1 Make a list of the common gases which are found in air. (Look them up in the Reference Section at the back of the book if you find this difficult).
2 One of the gases in air makes lime water turn milky (and bicarbonate indicator solution turn yellow). Which gas does this?
3 Another of the gases in air will relight a glowing splint. Which gas does this?

b ▶ Collect some of the bubbles from the pondweed (see Figure 1.8).
c ▶ Test the gas with lime water or bicarbonate indicator solution.
d ▶ Collect a second sample of the bubbles.
e ▶ Use this to try to relight a glowing splint.

4 What result did you get when you tested the gas with lime water or bicarbonate indicator solution? What conclusion can you draw from this?
5 What result did you get with the glowing splint? What conclusion can you draw from this?
6 What is the name of the gas which the pondweed produces?

This gas is important to all animals. Without it we would all die. **Oxygen** is produced by all green plants during photosynthesis.

Fig. 1.8 Apparatus for collecting bubbles from pond weed

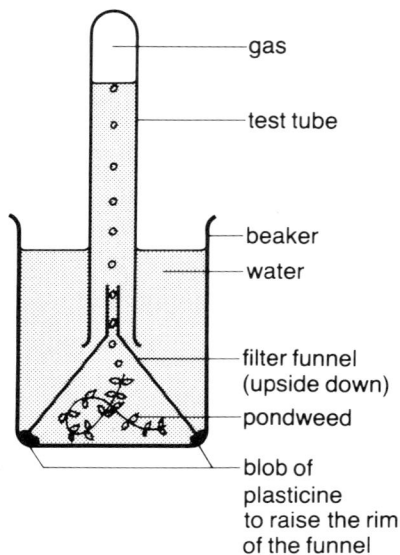

gas

test tube

beaker

water

filter funnel (upside down)

pondweed

blob of plasticine to raise the rim of the funnel

2   Food chains

1   Introduction

Chapter 1 shows how plants use chlorophyll to trap the sun's light energy. This energy is then used by the plants to make simple materials combine together to form complex substances. Chlorophyll is green in colour.

1 Are most animals green, like plants?
2 Do you think that animals contain chlorophyll?
3 Do you think that animals can capture the sun's light energy?
4 How do you think that animals get their energy and other food materials?

2   Food chains

Most animals must eat often to stay alive and healthy. They need energy and many other food materials. These are needed for life processes such as growth, movement and reproduction. Apart from water and oxygen, animals take in few simple materials from their surroundings. They get their energy and other materials either by eating plants, or by eating other animals which have eaten plants. Perhaps the most important difference between plants and animals is in the way they get their energy.

Activity

a ▶ Watch any animal feeding. It may be a wild animal, or a laboratory animal such as a locust, a gerbil or a fish. It may be a pet animal at home, a farm animal or an animal shown in a film or film loop.

b ▶ Sometimes it is difficult to see animals actually feeding. However, you can often see evidence that they have been feeding. For example, leaves damaged by caterpillars are easy to find. You may see a collection of broken snail shells near a stone (see Figure 2.1f). This shows where a bird called a thrush has been breaking the shells to get the soft parts of the snail out. The thrush eats these.

Fig. 2.1a A lion eating a zebra

Fig. 2.1b Some snails on a leaf

2.1c ▶

Fig 2.1d A zebra eating grass

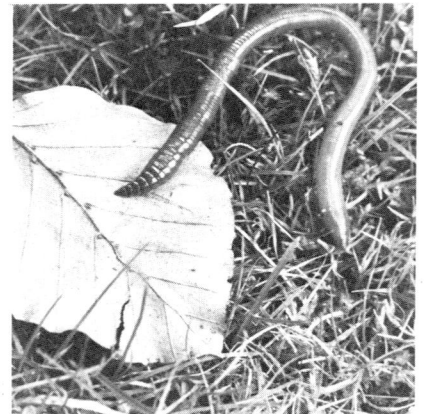

Fig. 2.1e A worm on a leaf

2.1f ▶

Fig. 2.1g (below) A blackbird collects a worm

Fig. 2.1h (below) A mouse eating a locust

Fig. 2.1c A locust eating grass

Fig. 2.1f A thrush anvil. The bird holds the snail in its beak and breaks the shell against the stone

1 Make a list of the animals which you have watched or studied while they were feeding. Beside each animal write down what it was eating.

2 As far as possible try to find out what the food eaten by each animal comes from. For example, thrushes eat snails. What do snails eat? If the animal eats part of a plant, try to find out the name of the plant.

3 Do any of the animals you have been studying get eaten by other animals? For example, are thrushes killed and eaten by something else?

4 When you have gathered as much information as you can, try to draw some food chains of your own. For example,

plant leaves ⟶ snail ⟶ thrush ⟶ ?

5 What difficulties did you have when seeking the information to answer questions 1 to 4 above?

6 Look at Figure 2.1d. The zebra is eating grass. In which direction is the energy passing; from the grass into the zebra, or from the zebra to the grass?

7 Look at Figure 2.1a. In which direction is the energy passing; from the lion to the zebra, or from the zebra to the lion?

8 Arrows are used to show the direction in which energy passes when an animal eats food. Copy down and complete this food chain. Put in arrows which point in the correct direction.

grass   zebra   lion

9 Draw a second food chain using three of the other living things shown in Figure 2.1.

10 Draw a food chain which includes man, grass and beef cattle.

11 Look at the food chains which you have drawn. What sort of living thing is found at the beginning of each chain?

12 Food chains often have more than three living organisms in them. The following might all be found in an oak wood:

shrew   oak beauty moth caterpillar   oak leaves
hunting beetle   red fox

Put them in the correct order, with arrows, in a food chain.

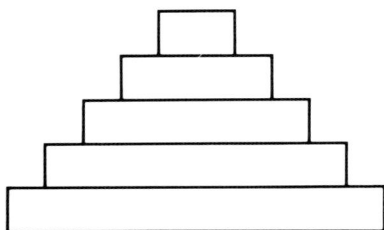

Fig. 2.2 Pyramid of numbers

13 In your food chain from question 12, which do you think there are more of:

oak leaves or oak beauty moth caterpillars?
hunting beetles or shrews?
oak beauty moth caterpillars or hunting beetles?
shrews or foxes?

Answer this question by copying down Figure 2.2. Put the name of each one in the correct place in the pyramid. The greater the number, the bigger is the box. This is called a pyramid of numbers.

14 If all the shrews suddenly died, what would you expect to happen to: **(i)** the foxes, and **(ii)** the hunting beetles? In each case say why you think that your answer is right.

3 How energy is lost in food chains

When the oak beauty moth caterpillar eats an oak leaf, energy-containing material passes into the caterpillar. Figure 2.3 shows what happens to this material once it gets inside the caterpillar.

Leaves are flat and thin, and of roughly even thickness. We can therefore assume that the area of a leaf is a measure of the amount of energy-containing material in the leaf. The oak leaf shown in Figure 2.3 has a total area of 50 squares.

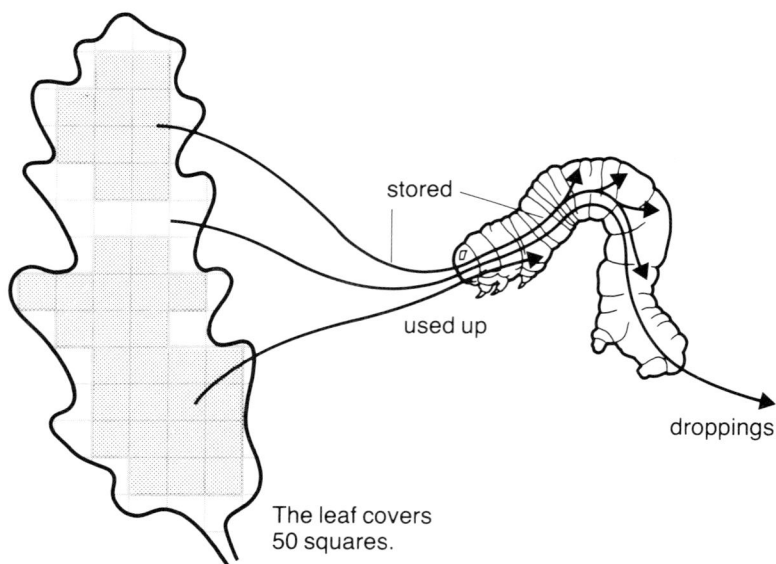

Fig. 2.3 Oak beauty moth caterpillars eat oak leaves. Assume this caterpillar eats the whole leaf

stored

used up

droppings

The leaf covers 50 squares.

Leaf material	Number of squares	% (Figure in last column × 2)
Amount wasted (droppings)		
Amount used up (movement etc.)		
Amount stored (growth)		
Total amount eaten by caterpillar	50	100

Table 2.1

The caterpillar eats the whole leaf. Copy down Table 2.1. Write your answers to questions 1, 2 and 3 in the table.

1 By counting the squares, work out how much of the leaf material in Figure 2.3 is wasted by the caterpillar. Put this in your table.
2 How much is used up by the caterpillar?
3 How much is stored by the caterpillar?
4 Fill in the percentage column of your table.
5 What percentage of the leaf material eaten by the caterpillar goes into the growth of new caterpillar material?
6 What percentage is used up and wasted? Add them together.

When the caterpillar eats an oak leaf, only a small amount of the oak leaf energy-containing material goes into the growth of new caterpillar material. Of the rest, some cannot be digested by the caterpillar. This passes out as solid waste, the droppings. The largest amount is used up just to keep the caterpillar alive and able to move.

When the hunting beetle eats the caterpillar the same thing happens again. Only a small amount of the caterpillar material, eaten by the beetle, goes into the growth of new beetle material. The rest is used up or wasted. This happens

oak leaves

caterpillars

becomes
new
caterpillar
tissue

beetles

becomes
new
beetle
tissue

shrews

becomes
new
shrew
tissue

fox

used up
and wasted

used up
and wasted

used up
and wasted

used up
and wasted

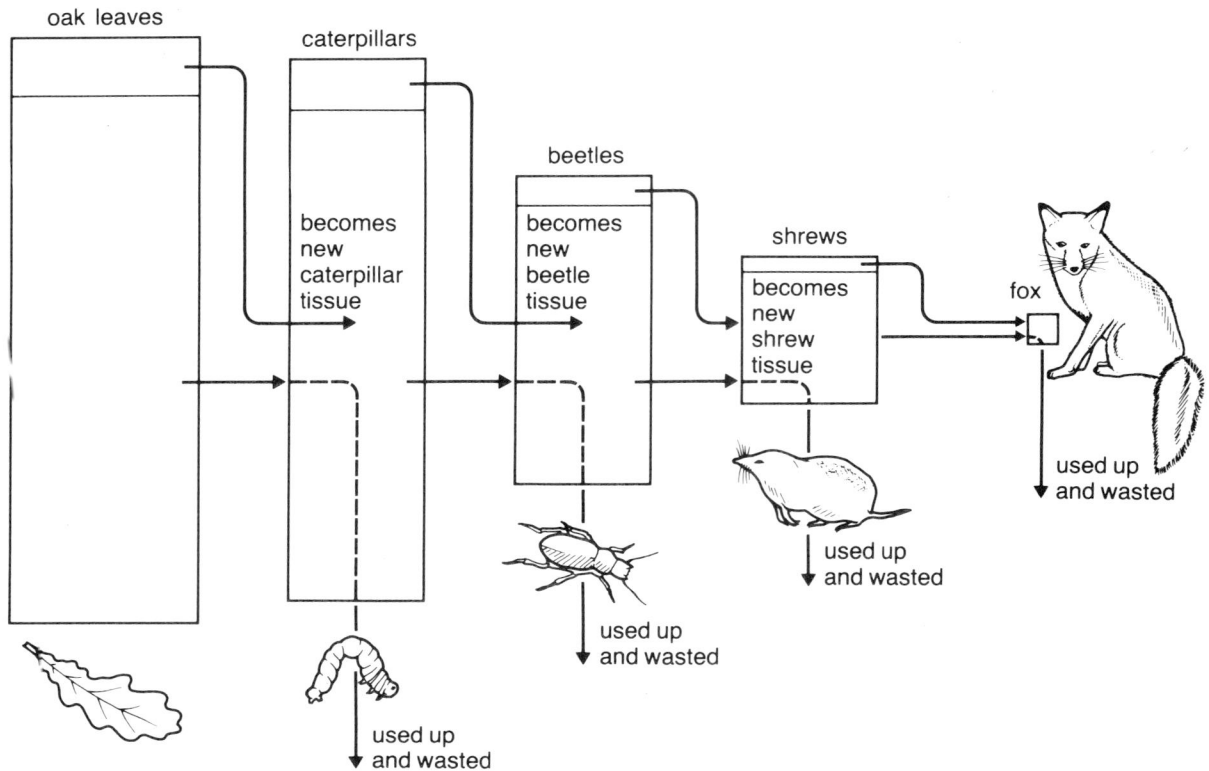

Fig. 2.4 A woodland food chain. Notice that only a small part cf the oak leaf tissue becomes new caterpillar tissue. Only a small part of the caterpillar tissue becomes new beetle tissue and so on

at each stage in a food chain (see Figure 2.4). The amount of energy-containing material passed on gets less and less at each stage.

7 The food chain shown in Figure 2.4 has five stages or links. Food chains do not often have more than four or five links. What do you think is the reason for this?

4 Food chains which end with man

Many of us enjoy eating meat and other animal products. We also depend on plants for a large amount of our food. The meat comes from animals which, in turn, have eaten plants.

Cereals such as wheat and maize can be used to feed man in two different ways. They can be eaten by man. For example, wheat flour can be used to make bread. Secondly, the cereals can be fed to cattle, pigs or poultry. These animals are then eaten by man (see Figure 2.5). Both food chains in Figure 2.5 start with the same amount of wheat. They therefore start with the same amount of energy.

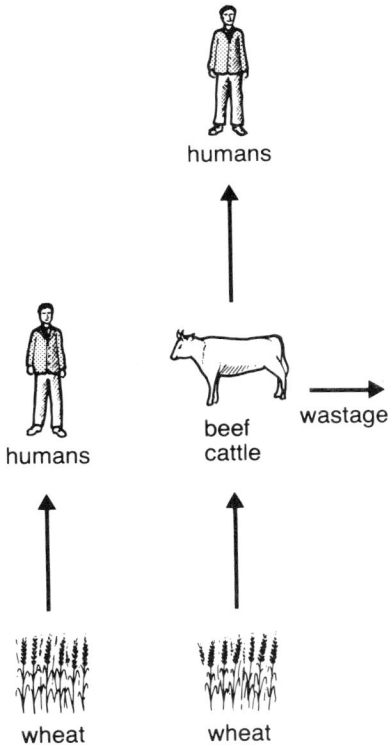

Fig. 2.5 Two food chains with humans at the top

1 Which food chain in Figure 2.5 gives man the most energy?

In fact, cattle are worse than caterpillars at converting plant material into their own body material. When beef cattle eat grass, the figures are:

Total amount eaten	100%
Total amount used up (providing energy or wasted)	96%
Total amount stored as new body material	4%

2 Think about food energy only. Which is it more economical for man to eat, cereals such as wheat, or meat from cattle?

If we ate less meat in Britain we could still have a healthy diet. Less cereals would be needed for animal feed. This would leave more cereals for those who do not get enough food.

5 Food webs

grass ⟶ rabbit ⟶ red fox

Food chains are not often as simple as this. For example, it is very likely that other animals such as grasshoppers, are eating the grass. Secondly, young rabbits are also eaten by hawks, and so on. Therefore, our food chain may be combined with other food chains to form a **food web**. (See Figure 2.6.) It is usually a very difficult task to work out all

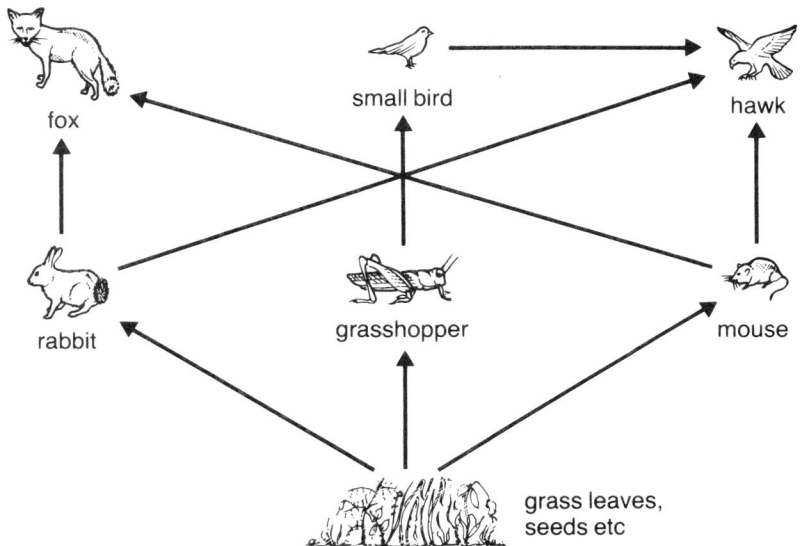

Fig. 2.6 A food web (the animals are not all drawn to the same scale)

the details in a food web. Often, the picture is far from complete. It may also change throughout the year.

1 How many individual food chains can you find in the food web in Figure 2.6? Write them out separately.
2 Which animals in Figure 2.6 may not be found during the winter?

There are several ways of working out the links in a food web. Firstly, some of the links can be identified by direct observation. For example, rabbits can be seen eating grass. Grass which has been nibbled by rabbits looks different from grass grazed by other animals such as sheep. Binoculars are useful when watching wild animals feeding.

3 Which other links in Figure 2.6 might have been observed directly?

In question 3 above you might be tempted to say that all of the links could be worked out by just watching the animals. However, if you are lucky enough to see a hawk swoop onto a small animal, you are unlikely to be near enough (even with binoculars) to see whether the animal is, in fact, a mouse, a shrew or a vole.

Secondly, other links are worked out by catching animals and looking at their stomach contents. For example, it would be difficult to see wild mice feeding because they are very timid and often come out only at night. However, they can be trapped and their stomach contents will show what they have been eating. Figure 2.7 shows a trap which is commonly used to catch small mammals such as mice, voles and shrews.

4 Which links in Figure 2.6 might be identified by looking at the stomach contents of animals?

Fig. 2.7 Longworth traps. The trap on the left is open, but the door will spring shut when a small mammal enters

Thirdly, many birds **regurgitate** (bring up and spit out) a pellet which contains the parts of their diet which they cannot digest. These parts might include bones, seed husks, fur, feathers and the hard bits of insects. Birds which produce pellets include:

> garden birds, such as robin, hedge sparrow and starling;
> water birds, such as heron, kingfisher and herring gull;
> farmland birds, such as rook, carrion crow and yellowhammer;
> birds of prey, such as shrike, owl, falcon and hawk;
> game birds, such as partridge and pheasant.

The pellets can be found at nest sites, roosts (places where the birds rest), and at feeding sites.

5 Which links in Figure 2.6 might have been identified by looking at bird pellets?
6 What sort of mistakes might be made when using this method alone for identifying the food which such birds eat?

If you want to know more about where to look for bird pellets and how to identify what you find in them, write to the Royal Society for the Protection of Birds. The address is given in the Reference Section.

3 Diet

1 Malnutrition

Have you ever thought about the sort of things that you eat? Scientists call this your **diet**. Most of us eat a large variety of things. A healthy diet contains a variety of foods. A poor diet often leads to **malnutrition**. This may cause serious ill-health. Much sickness, all over the world, is caused by malnutrition. Some examples of ill-health caused by malnutrition are shown in Figure 3.1.

One of these four nutritional diseases is caused by a general lack of food in the diet. Another is caused by eating

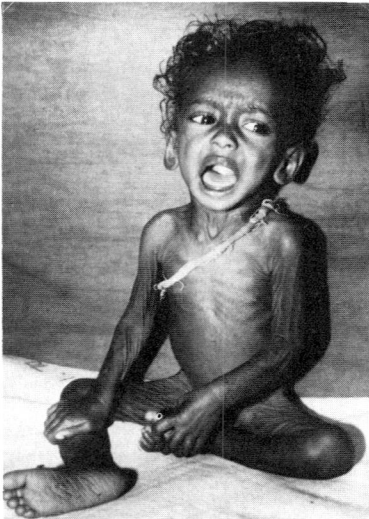

3.1a ▲

3.1b ▲

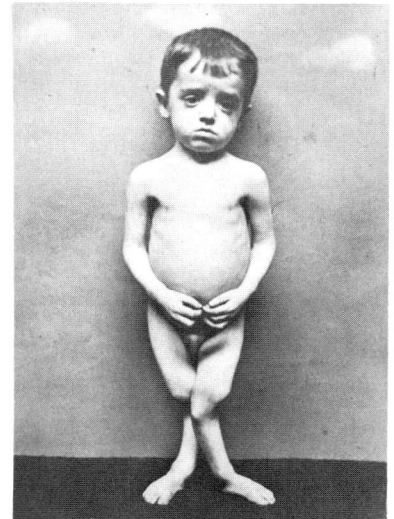

3.1c ▲   3.1d ▼

Fig. 3.1a A 13 month old child suffering from malnutrition

Fig. 3.1b Obesity

Fig. 3.1c A young boy suffering from rickets

Fig. 3.1d Xerophthalmia is a disease of the eyes which can cause blindness

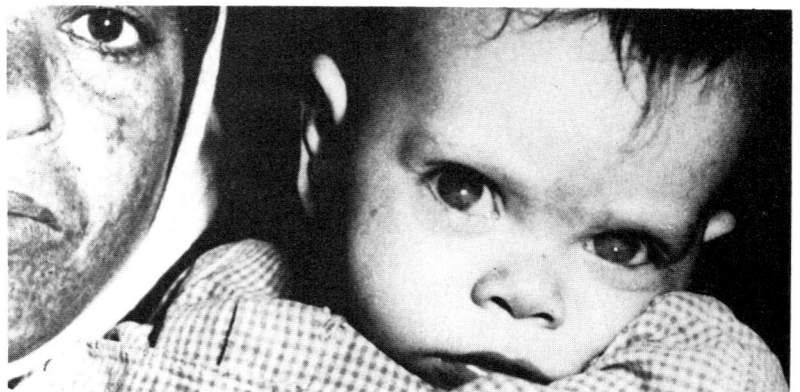

18

too much food. A third is caused by the lack of a substance called vitamin D in the diet. A lack of vitamin D causes the bones to become soft. The legs may bend under the weight of the body. A fourth is caused by a lack of vitamin A in the diet, and can cause blindness.

1 Copy out Table 3.1 and fill in the column headed *Caused by*. Then read the passage which follows before you fill in the rest of the table.

Name of disease	Caused by (lack of ——— or too much ———)	Effect on health	Part(s) of world where the disease is common
Marasmus			
Obesity			
Xerophthalmia			

Table 3.1

Nutritional diseases may not actually kill those who have them. However, they do make their sufferers more likely to get other diseases. For example, an **obese** (overweight) person is more likely to suffer from heart disease than someone who is not overweight. Heart disease kills more people than any other disease in the developed countries of Europe and North America. Obesity is common in these countries, and causes more ill-health than all the vitamin deficiency diseases put together.

Children with **marasmus** suffer from a general weakness and do not grow properly. They are more likely to suffer badly from the infectious diseases which healthy people can get over quite easily. These include coughs and colds, as well as childhood diseases such as mumps and chickenpox. Three of the four diseases shown in Figure 3.1 are common in many of the developing countries of Asia, Africa and Latin America.

2 Now complete the last two columns in your copy of Table 3.1.

There are many other nutritional diseases. Most are caused by a lack of something in the diet. A few are caused by eating too much. Writing in 1977, Dr Halfden Mahler, Director-General of the World Health Organisation (WHO), had this to say about malnutrition:

'It bears hardest on small children, contributing to the massive death toll among the young and . . . it interferes with the adequate growth and development of the survivors. It reduces their capacity to learn during childhood and to earn during adulthood. The inevitable result is a downward spiral in which poor malnourished parents produce malnourished children who in turn will become poor and malnourished parents.'

(World Health, May 1977)

Dr Mahler was thinking about the deficiency diseases such as rickets and marasmus when he wrote this. However it is important to realise that a diet consisting mostly of such foods as chips together with sausages, fish fingers or hamburgers is equally unhealthy. Fresh fruit and fresh vegetables are also needed, and less of the fatty, fried foods.

Scientists agree that a healthy diet should contain the right amount of each of the following:

Carbohydrates. These provide energy. They can also be converted into body fat.

Some **Fats**. These provide energy. They can also form body fat. They also help the body to take in some vitamins.

Proteins. These help to make new body tissues during growth. They also help in the repair or replacement of worn or damaged parts of the body. Proteins can be converted into carbohydrate and used to give energy.

Minerals and **Vitamins**. They are needed in small quantities. They help to control body processes such as respiration, and to keep the body healthy.

Water. Water makes up about two thirds of an adult's body weight.

Fibre or roughage.

Most foods contain many of these things. For example, 100 grams (g) of boiled potatoes contain about 20 g of carbohydrate, 1.5 g of protein, 78.5 g of water, and very small quantities of various vitamins and minerals (see Table 1 in the Reference Section). If the potatoes are fried they will also contain fat.

Man can survive for many weeks, without food, on water alone. The record for the longest survival without food **and** water probably belongs to a young Austrian man. He was a passenger in a car which was involved in a traffic accident. The police put him in a cell on 1st April 1979. They then forgot about him. He was rediscovered, nearly dead, on 18th April 1979. (*Guinness Book of Records, 27th Edition, 1981*)

3 How long had this Austrian man been without food and water?

Scientists agree that a healthy diet should contain the right amount of each of the seven items listed above. However, the right amount is not the same for all people. The next section looks at the way in which different people need different amounts of energy.

2 Energy: why we need it

1 Measure and write down your body temperature.
2 How does your reading compare with the readings obtained by other members of the class?
3 Look up normal human body temperature in the Reference Section. How do the class results compare with this?
4 Measure room temperature by placing a laboratory thermometer where the bulb is surrounded by air. Keep your hands well away from the bulb of the thermometer. After about two minutes, write down what the room temperature is.
5 Which is warmer, the air in the room or you?
6 What is the difference between the two readings?
7 In which direction will heat energy be travelling, from the air to you, or from you to the air?
8 If a beaker of hot water is left in the room, heat energy passes from the hot water to the air. What happens to the temperature of the water in the beaker. Does it rise, fall or stay the same?
9 You might expect the same to happen to human body temperature. Instead, it stays the same even though heat energy is being lost all the time. What must be going on all the time, in your body, to stop the temperature from falling as heat energy is lost?

The simple experiment described above shows one reason why energy is needed by the human body. The energy is needed to make heat. This heat replaces the heat that is lost by the body. It helps to keep body temperature constant at 37 °C. Energy is needed for other things as well.

10 When a healthy person lies completely still, what is going on inside their body which might need energy? You may be able to think of several things.

11 If the person starts to move about do they need more energy or less energy? Give a reason for your answer.

12 Do you think that all of us need the same amount of energy? What sort of people need more energy than others? Explain why.

13 Look at Table 3.2. Why do you think that men generally need more energy than women, even when they are doing similar things, for example, light work?

Table 3.2 Energy is measured in kilojoules. One kilojoule is the amount of energy needed to raise the temperature of 239 grams of water by one degree centigrade. These tables show the energy requirements for some activities and the recommended daily intakes of energy in kilojoules per day

	Activity	Kilojoules per minute
Energy requirements for 25-year-old man, weighing 65 kg (10 stone):	Sitting	6
	Standing	7
	Walking slowly	13
	Walking up stairs	38

	Age (years)	Children (both sexes)	Males	Females
Recommended daily intake of energy (in kilojoules per day) for children:	0–1	4200		
	2–6	6800		
	7–11		9 650	9200
	12–15		12 000	9600

	Activity	Males	Females
Recommended daily intake of energy (in kilojoules per day) for adults:	lying in bed	7 300	6 300
	light work	11 550	9 450
	heavy work	14 700	12 600
	being pregnant		10 000
	breast-feeding a baby		11 300

14 How much more energy does a pregnant woman need compared with a woman doing light work? Why does she need this extra energy?

15 Why do you think that boys aged twelve to fifteen need more energy each day than girls of the same age?

3 Measuring the amount of energy in a piece of food

In Chapter 1 you discovered that when you eat food, such as a potato, you take in some of the energy captured from the sun. This energy was captured by the potato plant when it was growing.

Table 3.2 shows the energy needs of various types of people. In order to make sure that we take in enough energy we must, therefore, find out how much energy there is in the foods which we eat. For most foods this is not easy. It requires the use of very complex equipment and very accurate measurements. However, a rough answer can be obtained for a peanut by setting light to it. The heat it produces is then used to heat up some water. The rise in temperature will give some idea of the amount of energy in the peanut.

Activity

a ▶ Copy down Table 3.3. Leave room to include the results of other people in the class. This will help you to compare all the results at the end.

Table 3.3

Name of group or person	(2) Mass of peanut	(3) Temperature of water before heating (°C)	(4) Temperature of water after heating (°C)	(5) Temperature rise (°C)	(6) Energy produced (kJ)	(7) Energy produced by 1 gram of peanut (kJ/g)

From my experiment, the amount of energy in 100g of peanuts = ...

From Table 1 in the Reference Section,
                    the amount of energy in 100g of peanuts = ...

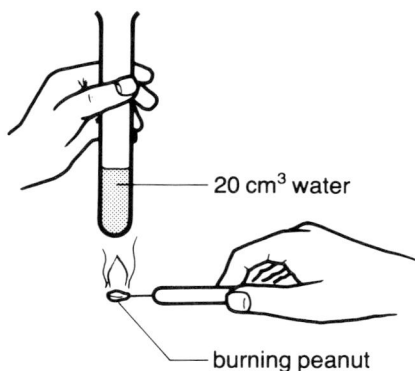

20 cm³ water

burning peanut

Fig. 3.2 Heating water with a burning peanut

c ▶ Put a thermometer in the boiling tube and leave it there while you go on with the next two steps.

d ▶ Collect a weighed half peanut. Write down its mass in the results table.

e ▶ Light a bunsen burner, but keep it well away from the boiling tube.

f ▶ Measure and write down the temperature of the cold water in the boiling tube. Then remove the thermometer and put it safely away from the burner.

g ▶ Stick a mounted needle firmly into the half peanut. Be careful not to split it.

h ▶ Hold the boiling tube upright in one hand. With the other hand set fire to the peanut by holding it in the flame of the burner.

i ▶ As soon as it is alight, put the burning peanut under the upright boiling tube (see Figure 3.2). Keep it there until it has finished burning. Relight the peanut quickly if the flame goes out. Keep the flame just touching the bottom of the boiling tube. Do not let it spread around the sides.

j ▶ As soon as the peanut stops burning, put the thermometer back into the boiling tube. Stir gently, and record the highest temperature reached by the water. Write this temperature down in your results table.

1 1 cm³ of water weighs one gram. You used 20 cm³ of water. How many grams of water did you use?

2 Complete column 6 of your results table like this:

Energy produced =

$$\frac{(\text{mass of water used}) \times (\text{temperature rise}) \times 4.2}{1000} \text{ kilojoules.}$$

3 Complete column 6 for the results obtained by other members of the class.

4 Do some pieces of peanut seem to give more energy than others? There is one obvious reason for this. What is it? (Look at column 2 in the results table.)

5 Complete column 7 of the results table like this:

$$\frac{\text{Amount of energy produced}}{\text{by one gram of peanut}} = \frac{\text{energy produced (kJ)}}{\text{mass of peanut used (g)}}.$$

6 Calculate this figure for each group and enter the figures in column 7.

7 Why is the figure in column 7 a more useful one than the figure in column 6?

8 Multiply your figure in column 7 by 100. This gives the amount of energy in a 100 g portion of peanuts. Write this figure at the bottom of your results table.

Scientists have used very accurate methods to work out exactly how much energy different foods contain. The figures are given in Table 1 in the Reference Section. For each food the amount of energy in a 100 gram portion is shown.

9 Look up the energy value of peanuts in Table 1 in the Reference Section. What figure does the table give for the amount of energy in 100 grams of peanuts? Write it down at the bottom of your results table.
10 How does this compare with the figure which you got?
11 Your class results will probably be very different from the figure given in Table 1. What errors were there in the way you did the experiment which might have caused the difference?
12 Suggest some ways in which the experiment could be improved if you did it again.
13 Look again at Table 1. Make a list of the main energy foods which you ate yesterday.
14 List six foods which contain very little energy.
15 How much energy is needed each day by a man doing light work? See Table 3.2.
16 Did people in Mozambique get more or less than this amount in 1975–77? Compare Table 3.2 with Table 3.4.
17 Did people in Britain get more or less than the recommended amount of energy each day? Compare Table 3.2 with Table 3.4.

Fig. 3.3 This young African girl probably has a diet much lower in protein content than many girls in Britain

	Mozambique (kJ per day)	Britain (kJ per day)
Energy from plant foods	7 833	8 639
Energy from animal foods	273	5 242
Total energy intake	8 106	13 881

Table 3.4 The average amount of energy taken in by an adult in Mozambique and Britain (estimates for 1975–1977).

4 Protein and a healthy diet

The protein content of many different foods is given in Table 1 in the Reference Section. Table 3.5 gives the recommended daily intake of protein for various people.

1 Why should a diet contain protein? See Section 1 if you need help with this question.
2 Look at Table 3.5. Why do you think that twelve to fifteen year olds need so much protein?
3 A woman who is breast feeding her baby needs to eat more protein than usual. Why is this?
4 What good protein foods did you eat yesterday? Look at Table 1 in the Reference Section.
5 How much protein is needed each day by a man doing light work? See Table 3.5.
6 Did people in Mozambique get more or less than the recommended amount of protein each day in 1975–77? Compare Table 3.5 with Table 3.6.
7 Did people in Britain get more or less than the recommended amount of protein each day? Compare Table 3.5 with Table 3.6.
8 Where is Mozambique? Look at the world map in the Reference Section.

Table 3.5 Recommended daily intakes of protein in the United Kingdom. The figures in brackets are the minimum recommended amounts of protein required for good health, assuming that the diet contains sufficient other food items, especially energy containing ones

Age (years)	Children (both sexes) (grams per day)	Females (grams per day)	Males (grams per day)
0–1	20 (15)		
2–6	41 (25)		
7–11		56 (33)	58 (34)
12–15		58 (43)	71 (47)
Adults			
light work		55 (38)	68 (45)
heavy work		63 (38)	90 (45)
pregnant woman		60 (44)	
mother breast-feeding		68 (55)	

Table 3.6 The average amounts of protein eaten by an adult in Mozambique and Britain (estimates for 1975–1977)

	Mozambique (grams per day)	Britain (grams per day)
Protein from plant foods	31.6	35.7
Protein from animal foods	4.3	56.0
Total protein eaten	35.9	91.7

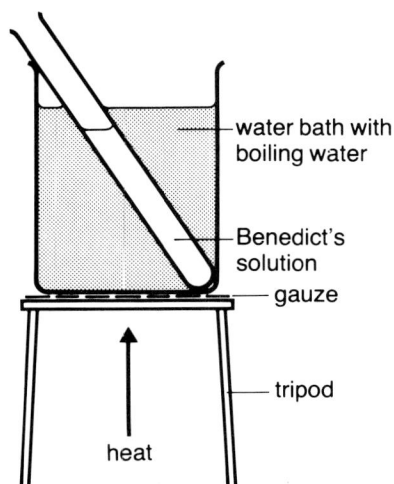

Fig. 3.4 Always heat Benedict's solution in a water bath. If you heat it directly in the flame, the liquid tends to spit out. This is dangerous and it leaves you without a result

5 Testing food to find out what it contains

In Section 3 you found out how much energy there is in peanuts. Look at Table 1 in the Reference Section.

1 What does the energy in a peanut come from mostly, protein, carbohydrate or fat?

You can see that energy will come from protein, from carbohydrate and from fat. If we just measure the amount of energy in a piece of food, it does not tell us which of these three is providing the energy. We need to know this when working out balanced diets for different people.

There are simple tests for two carbohydrate foods. One identifies simple reducing sugars such as glucose. The other identifies a carbohydrate called starch. There is also a simple test for protein. A flow diagram showing how to carry out these tests is given in Figure 3.5. However, before you carry out the tests you must learn how to heat Benedict's solution safely (see Figure 3.4).

2 Why is a water bath used for heating Benedict's solution?

Activity

a ▶ Copy out Table 3.7.
b ▶ Read carefully through the flow diagram in Figure 3.5. Make sure that you understand all the steps.
c ▶ Collect a sample of food to test.
d ▶ Write down its name at the top of your results table.

Name of food tested :		
Reagent used	Results (what happened)	What does this show? (eg. starch present or starch absent etc.)
Iodine solution		
Benedict's reagent		
Sodium hydroxide and copper sulphate (Biuret test)		

Table 3.7

```
┌─────────────────────┐        ┌─────────────────────┐
│  For solid food     │───────▶│  Take a pea-sized   │
│  start here.        │        │  piece of food.     │
└─────────────────────┘        └─────────────────────┘
                                          │
                                          ▼
                               ┌─────────────────────┐
                               │  Cut or crush it up │
                               │  into very small    │
                               │  pieces.            │
                               └─────────────────────┘
                                          │
                                          ▼
┌─────────────────────┐        ┌─────────────────────┐
│  For powdered food  │        │  Put the pieces in  │
│  start here.        │───────▶│  a test tube.       │
│  Use a 5 mm depth   │        │  Add 5 cm depth of  │
│  of solid in a      │        │  water.             │
│  test tube.         │        │  Boil gently.       │
│                     │        │  Cool – this is     │
│                     │        │  very important.    │
└─────────────────────┘        └─────────────────────┘
                                          │
                                          ▼
┌─────────────────────┐        ┌─────────────────────┐
│  For liquid food    │        │  Divide into three  │
│  start here.        │───────▶│  equal portions in  │
│  Use a 5cm depth    │        │  3 test tubes.      │
│  in a test tube.    │        └─────────────────────┘
└─────────────────────┘
```

Test for starch.	Test for simple (reducing) sugars.	Test for protein.
Add a few drops of iodine solution.	Add 1 cm depth of Benedict's solution (or Fehling's A & B)	Add a 2cm depth of sodium hydroxide solution. Mix it gently.
	Boil in a water bath (see figure 3.4).	Add copper sulphate solution drop by drop, while shaking gently.

If a dark/black colour is seen this shows that there is starch in the food.

If the solution stays yellow (the colour of the iodine solution), there is no starch.

If a simple sugar is present the following changes will be seen while heating. The solution will go cloudy (a precipitate). This will be green at first, then yellow, then orange, and finally red or brown.

If the solution stays blue or blue-green, there is no simple sugar.

If a purple or lilac colour is seen this shows that there is protein in the food.

If the solution stays pale blue (the colour of copper sulphate solution) there is no protein.

This is called the Biuret test.

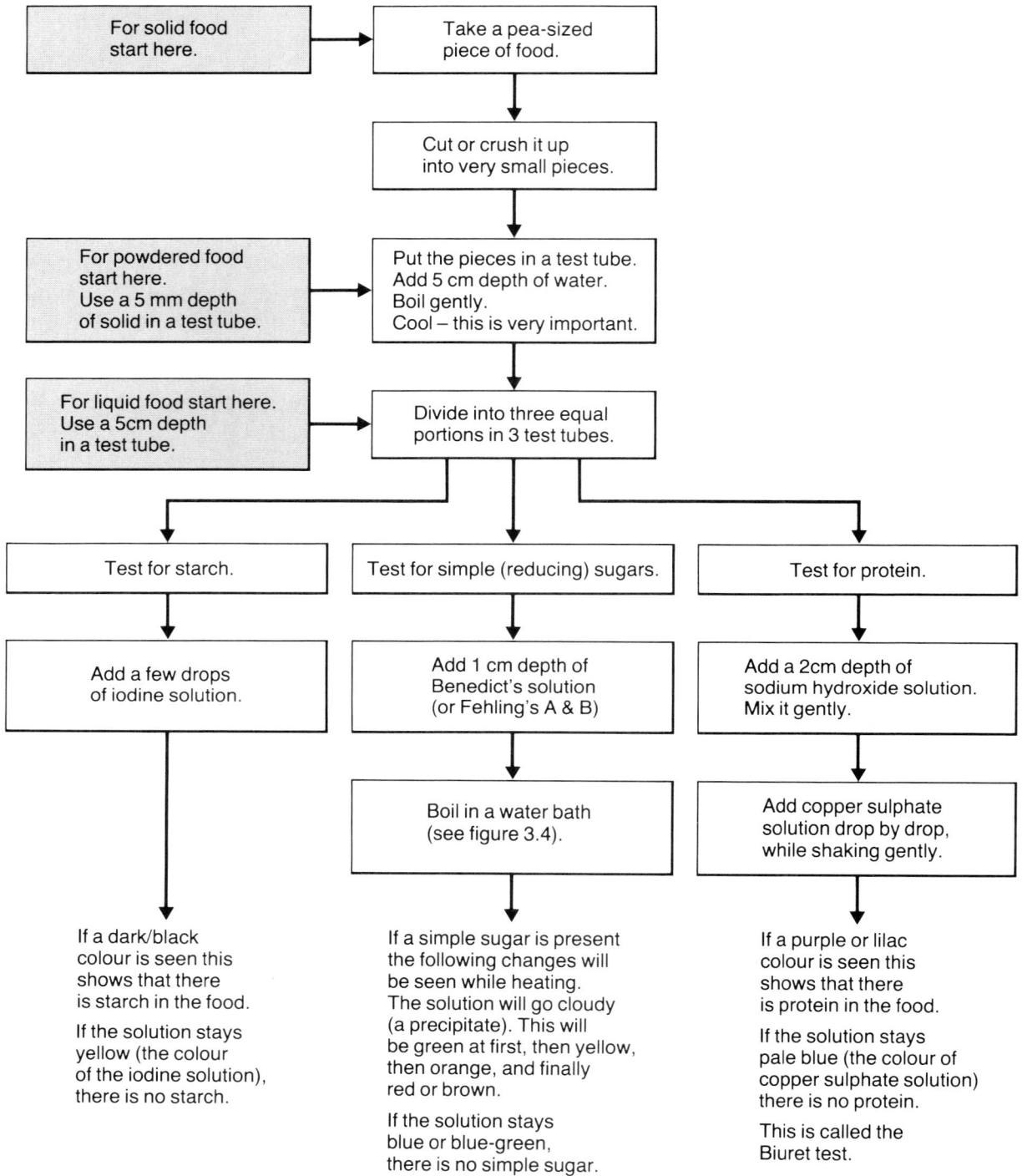

Fig. 3.5 Testing food. Start at one of the shaded boxes with solid food, powdered food or liquid food, and follow the steps

e ▶ Work your way through the flow diagram in Figure 3.5. Follow the instructions carefully. Record your results as you go along.

f ▶ If there is time, collect another sample of food. Wash your test tubes thoroughly. Repeat the tests. Record the results in another results table (use Table 3.7).

g ▶ If other members of the class have tested different foods, summarise the results in a copy of Table 3.8.

Names of foods tested	Name of group testing it	Starch (present or absent)	Simple sugar (present or absent)	Protein (present or absent)

Table 3.8

You have done some simple tests on various foods. These tests do not tell you how much of each nutrient the foods contain. This requires the use of very complex equipment. The nutrient content of some foods is given in Table 1 in the Reference Section.

3 Find a food in Table 1 in the Reference Section which contains a lot of protein, but little carbohydrate or fat.

4 Find another food which contains a lot of fat, but little protein or carbohydrate.

5 Find a third food which contains a lot of carboyhydrate, but little protein or fat.

6 Vitamins

There is a summary of some information about vitamins in Table 3.9. Vitamins are chemical substances which must be present in small amounts in our food. They are essential for growth and health. There are a number of different vitamins. The list may still be growing as more is learnt about them.

Vitamins are of two main types. There are those which dissolve only in fat. For example, vitamins A and D are fat soluble. The second type includes those that dissolve only in water. For example, vitamin C and the B vitamins are all water soluble. Use Table 3.9 to help you to answer questions 1, 2 and 3.

29

Table 3.9 Vitamins. There are two main types of vitamin, those soluble in fat and those soluble in water

Fat soluble vitamins

Vitamin	Function in the body	Effect of deficiency	Good food sources
A retinol	Essential for night vision. Protects eye surfaces, skin, and lining of airways.	Night blindness, Severe eye lesions (xerophthalmia), Complete blindness, (keratomalacia).	Fish liver oils, liver, butter, carrots, dark green vegetables. Added by law to all margarine sold in Britain.
D calciferol	Essential for uptake and use of calcium and phosphorus for bone and tooth growth.	In children, weak deformed bones which may bend under the weight of the body. This is called rickets.	Fish liver oils, dairy products. It is made in the skin by the action of sunlight. Added by law to all margarine sold in Britain.
K	Normal blood clotting.	Deficiency is unlikely.	Spinach, cabbage, cauliflower, peas, cereals. It is synthesised by gut bacteria.

Water soluble vitamins: There are at least 12 vitamins in the B group.
The three listed here are the best known.

B_1 Thiamin	Essential for the release of energy from carbohydrate	Beri beri (nervous paralysis and muscle weakness).	Meat, liver, milk, eggs, wholemeal flour. Thiamin is added by law to all white flour sold in Britain.
B_2 Riboflavin	Essential for energy utilisation.	Restricted growth and poor skin.	Milk, meat, liver, eggs. Riboflavin is destroyed by UV light, so don't leave milk on the doorstep.
Nicotinic acid (Niacin)	Essential for energy utilisation.	Skin becomes dark and scaly. This is called Pellagra.	Meat, cereals, vegetables, milk. Niacin is added by law to all white flour sold in Britain.
C Ascorbic acid	Maintaining healthy skin.	Slow healing of wounds, bleeding from the gums—scurvy.	Fresh fruit and vegetables, especially potatoes, green vegetables and citrus fruits. But vitamin C is easily lost by storage or cooking.

1 List six different foods which are good sources of the fat soluble vitamins.
2 List six different foods which are good sources of the water soluble vitamins.
3 Which vitamins must, by law, be added to foods sold in Britain? Which foods are they added to?

A knowledge of vitamins is very important for those whose job involves preparing and cooking food. Consider the following facts.

Vitamin C and the B vitamins are water soluble. Most of them are destroyed if they are heated for long periods (more than a few minutes). Vegetables may be cooked in either a little or a lot of water. Some people cook vegetables for a short time, so that they are just cooked. Others cook them for much longer. Sometimes vegetables are cooked and then kept warm for several hours before being served.

4 Why is it best to cook vegetables in a small amount of water rather than a large amount?
5 Why is it best to cook vegetables for as short a time as possible, until they are just cooked?
6 Why is it not a good thing to keep vegetables warm for long periods before serving them, or to reheat them if they get cold?
7 Why is it a good idea to use the water in which vegetables have been cooked for making gravy instead of throwing it away?

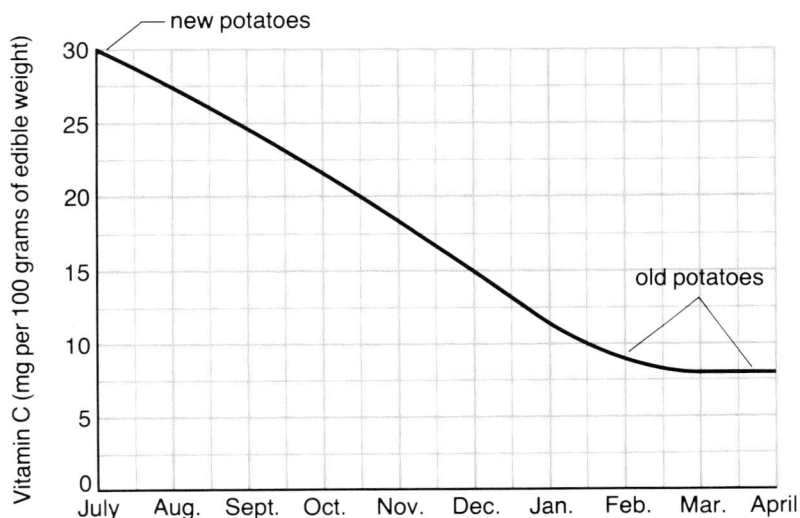

Fig. 3.6 The vitamin C content of new and old potatoes

When foods are stored, the amount of some of the vitamins in them may change as time goes by. Figure 3.6 shows what happens to the vitamin C content of potatoes when they are stored.

8 What is the vitamin C content of new potatoes?
9 What is the vitamin C content of old potatoes in April?
10 What happens to the vitamin C content of potatoes during storage?

The *Manual of Nutrition* (1978) issued by the Ministry of Agriculture, Fisheries and Food has this to say about vitamin C:

'Vitamin C is not widely distributed in foods. Small amounts occur in milk, especially breast milk, and in liver, but virtually all the vitamin C in most diets is derived from fruit and vegetables. As many of these are difficult to store and are comparatively expensive when out of season, and since vitamin C is readily lost from them during storage, preparation and cooking, this vitamin remains one of the few nutrients in which British diets can be deficient.'

7   A case for the doctor

Read the following passage and answer the questions which follow it. You may find it useful to refer to Table 3.9 while you are doing this.

An elderly man has been feeling rather tired for some months. He has not bothered to tell anyone because he thinks that it is just a sign of old age. However he tells a neighbour that it has become very painful when he eats. The neighbour persuades him to go to his doctor. The doctor examines him carefully and discovers that the old man has swollen gums, which are bluish in colour and bleed rather easily. The doctor asks him various questions and gets him to talk about the way he lives. The old man complains that the cuts and scratches which he gets while working in his garden do not heal up as well as they used to.

1 What other questions do you think the doctor asks the old man?

The doctor discovers that the old man's wife died six years ago. He has been living alone since then. A few of his close relatives used to visit him at first. They do not visit him now. The old man insists that he eats well. Careful questions show that he seldom bothers to prepare and cook fresh vegetables.

2 What other types of food do you think might be absent from his diet?
3 What do you think is wrong with him? If necessary, look at Table 3.9.
4 What sort of treatment do you think the doctor gives him?
5 When the old man is better, what sort of advice do you think the doctor gives him?

A recent medical textbook has this to say about scurvy:

'There are now in our cities an increasing number of old people who live alone and have neither the opportunity nor the aptitude (ability) to feed themselves properly, so that they sometimes develop scurvy. The social problem of ensuring the satisfactory nutrition of old and solitary people has yet to be solved.'

Fig. 3.7 Could this old man suffer from nutritional disease?

8 Rickets in Britain

Look very carefully at the information about vitamin D in Table 3.9. Doctors have discovered that the people most likely to get rickets in Britain today are the children of parents who come from India and Pakistan. The strange thing is that these parents feed their children on the same sort of food as those who live in India and Pakistan, where rickets is much rarer in similar families.

1 What do you think is the reason for this difference? Table 3.9 will help you to find the answer.
2 What special advice about the diets of children should be given to parents from India and Pakistan when they come to live in Britain?

آپ کے بچے کو وٹامن ڈی کی ضرورت ہے

**Your child needs
Vitamin D**

Fig. 3.8a The Health Education Council produces posters to help people learn about vitamins

When the *sun* shines on the child's skin, the body makes its own Vitamin D.

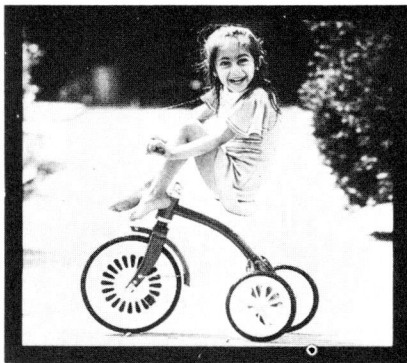

جس وقت آپ کے بچے کی جلد پر سورج کی شعاع میں پڑتی ہیں، اس کا بدن خود بخود وٹامن ڈی بنالیتا ہے۔

But there is not much sun in this country.

لیکن اس ملک میں سورج زیادہ نظر نہیں آتا۔

Fig. 3.8b Part of this poster is written in Urdu, an Asian language. This is because vitamin D is especially important to Asian people who live in this country

9 Mineral nutrients

Some information about the main mineral nutrients needed in the human diet is given in Table 3.10.

1 Which minerals must, by law, be added to foods sold in Britain? Which foods are they added to?
2 Which minerals are needed for the growth of healthy bones and teeth?
3 What sort of food is a good source of iron?
4 Why should the diet include iron?

Recently a medical expert said this about iron:

'Next to obesity, iron deficiency anaemia is the most important nutritional cause of ill-health in Great Britain and other prosperous countries.'

There is more information about another mineral nutrient known as fluoride in Chapter 4.

Minerals	Average man intake in grams/day	Total body content (g)	Function and/or where it is found in the body	Good food sources
Calcium	1.1	1000	Bones and teeth. Absence causes rickets.	Milk, cheese and green vegetables. Calcium is added by law to all white flour sold in Britain.
Phosphorus	1.4	780	Bones and teeth. Essential for energy release in the cells.	Present in nearly all foods.
Sulphur	0.85	140	Found in muscle, skin etc. Used in making protein.	Protein foods.
Potassium	3.3	140	An essential mineral in all cells and body fluids. Involved in nerve impulses.	Vegetables, meat, milk and fruit.
Sodium	4.4	100	An essential mineral in all cells and body fluids. Used in nerve impulses. Lost from body in sweat.	Salt, bread, cereals, meat products (e.g. bacon, ham), milk.
Chlorine	5.2	95	An essential mineral in all cells and body fluids. Lost from body in sweat.	Found in the same foods as sodium. Added to many manufactured foods.
Magnesium	0.34	19	Bones and all cells.	Green vegetables.
Iron	0.016	4.2	Red blood cells. Absence causes anaemia.	Meat and some vegetables. Iron is added by law to all white flour sold in Britain.
Fluorine (fluoride)	0.0018	2.6	Bones and teeth. Absence may increase dental caries.	Tea, fish bones (in tinned sardines), drinking water, if it has been added.
Iodine	0.0002	0.013	Thyroid gland. Used to make the hormone thyroxine.	Sea-foods, iodized table salt.
Other trace elements	As well as fluorine and iodine, there are at least five other trace elements required in minute quantities.			

Table 3.10 Minerals

4   Teeth

Why do we need teeth? Could we manage without teeth?

1   Introduction

Most of us enjoy eating, but would we enjoy it as much if our teeth were loose, painful or missing? A healthy diet contains many foods which must be broken up into small pieces before they can be swallowed.

Your teeth should last as long as you do, if you take care of them. If you do not look after them, you may suffer from painful toothache and gum disease. You will find it uncomfortable to eat. You may find it difficult to smile. You may be ashamed to open your mouth to laugh. You may find it difficult to speak properly.

1 Make a list of foods which you could still eat easily even if you had no teeth.
2 When we speak, the tongue touches the teeth to help make some sounds. For example, say the word 'tooth'. How many times did your tongue touch your teeth?
3 Make a list of other words which are pronounced with the tongue against the teeth.

In one survey of fifteen year old children in Britain, only fourteen in every hundred (14%) had no filled or decayed teeth.

4 In a school of 1000 teenagers, how many would you expect to have filled or decayed teeth?

In another survey in Britain, one third of all people over the age of 16 years had lost all of their natural teeth.

Everyone should know how to look after his or her teeth. You should know how teeth grow and what they are made of (Sections 2 and 3); What can go wrong with teeth (Sections 4 and 5); and how to stop things going wrong with them (Sections 6 and 7).

2 How teeth grow

The teeth of a new-born baby are not visible, but they are already growing inside the gums and jaws. When the baby is about six months old, the first tooth erupts through the gum. The baby is **teething**. In most children, by the age of three, all twenty of the **deciduous** teeth will have erupted. These teeth are sometimes called milk teeth or baby teeth. The child's jaw goes on growing while the deciduous teeth do not. If the deciduous teeth stayed in place they would be far too small for an adult. This is the reason why they are replaced by the larger **permanent teeth**. The change begins at about the age of six. The permanent teeth grow up under the deciduous teeth. The roots of the deciduous teeth dissolve and the crowns become loose. Finally the crowns drop out. Then the permanent teeth erupt in their place.

By the age of thirteen or fourteen, twenty-eight of the permanent teeth have normally erupted. The four remaining molars usually erupt between the ages of seventeen and twenty-one. These are called the **wisdom teeth**.

1 How many permanent teeth should you have when all of them have erupted by the age of twenty-one?
2 Give two differences between deciduous teeth and permanent teeth.

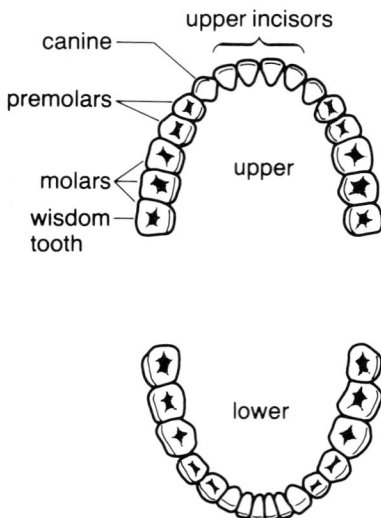

Fig. 4.1 The full set of human permanent teeth

3 What teeth are made of

The full set of human permanent teeth is shown in Figure 4.1.

1 Altogether (upper and lower jaws together), how many of each of the following teeth are there? Incisors, canines, premolars, molars.
2 With the help of a mirror or a friend, count your own teeth (or your friend's teeth). Write down the number of each type of tooth, and the total number of teeth. Include teeth with fillings but do not include any false teeth. There is a more detailed survey in Section 5.
3 Section 2 will have told you how many teeth you should have for your age. How does this compare with the number of teeth which you have found in your mouth? If there is a difference, do you know what the reason for it is?

The structure of a typical molar tooth is shown in Figure 4.2. Enamel is the hardest substance in your body. It is even harder than bone.

4 Why does enamel need to be so hard?
5 If the enamel is damaged, which part of the tooth may become exposed?
6 What holds the root of a tooth firmly in place in the jaw?

Enamel and dentine both contain large amounts of the minerals calcium and phosphorus. They also contain smaller amounts of other minerals including fluoride.

7 Look at Table 3.10. Which foods are good sources of calcium and phosphorus?
8 Which vitamin is essential for the uptake of calcium and phosphorus (see Table 3.9).

Fig. 4.2 A human molar tooth

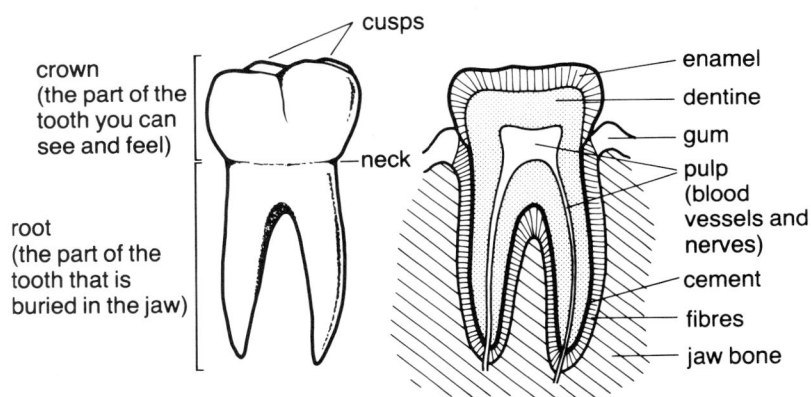

Fig. 4.3a Healthy teeth give you a nice smile

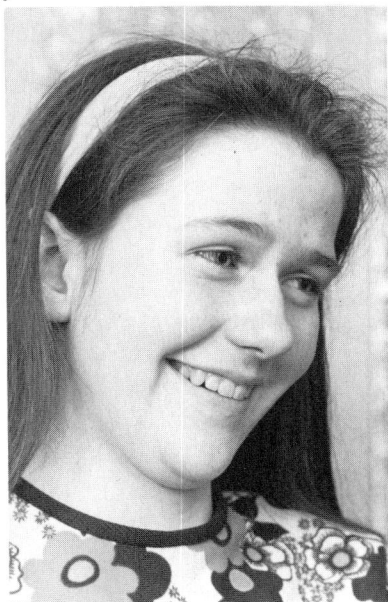

4 What can go wrong with teeth: dental caries

Good teeth remain strong and healthy for many years as long as the enamel on them is not damaged. If the enamel is cracked or destroyed, the much softer dentine gets exposed. The tooth will then decay rapidly. These areas of decay are called dental caries.

A tooth can be repaired by drilling out the damaged and decayed parts. The hole is then filled to seal the enamel layer again. If this is impossible the whole tooth must be removed because the decay could spread into the jaw bone.

Enamel is destroyed by acids, and this is the cause of dental caries. This may puzzle you. You don't eat many

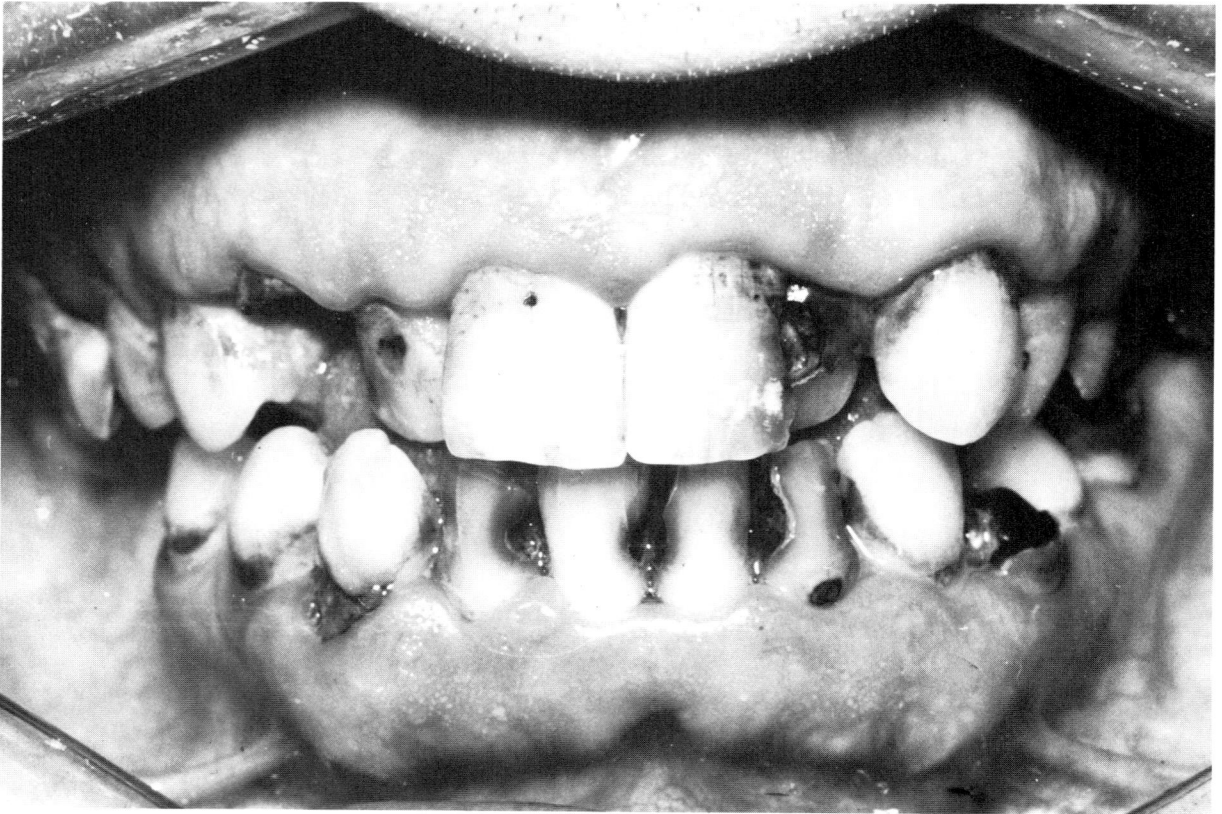

Fig. 4.3b Unhealthy teeth are painful and ugly

things which contain acids, so where do they come from? The rest of this Section will help you to find out the answer.

First look at Figure 2 in the Reference Section. Then answer questions 1 to 5.

1 At what pH (acid level) does tooth enamel start to dissolve?
2 What is the pH range of saliva?
3 Is saliva alone likely to dissolve tooth enamel?
4 What is the pH of sugar?
5 Will sugar alone damage enamel?

There are millions of bacteria living in your mouth. On their own they are harmless. They are found in the mouths of even the healthiest people. These bacteria combine with saliva to form an invisible material called plaque. Plaque will cover up the enamel on your teeth, if you let it, especially near the gum line and between the teeth. Like all living things, these bacteria must feed. They feed on sugar, and produce waste which contains acid. It is this acid which dissolves the enamel.

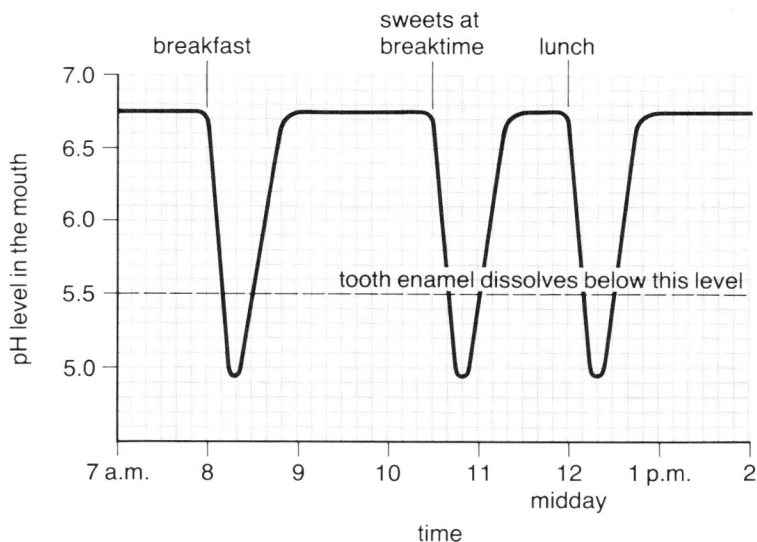

Fig. 4.4 Graph to show the pH levels in the mouth at different times during the day. Notice that the pH falls rapidly each time food is eaten, and that eating a few sweets has the same effect as a full meal

6 What is plaque?
7 How can you stop it from collecting on the surface of your teeth?
8 Make a list of all the sugar-containing things which you eat.
9 Are the things which you listed in question 8 essential, or could you do without some of them?
10 What is the normal pH of the mouth between meals?
11 Is this acid, alkaline or just about neutral?
12 What happens to the pH in the mouth when food is eaten?
13 Compare the pH change at breakfast with the pH change when a few sweets are eaten. Is there any difference?
14 At what pH does tooth enamel start to dissolve?
15 For how long is the pH in the mouth at or below this level (i) at breakfast, and (ii) while eating a few sweets?
16 Suppose that after breakfast you ate a sweet every 10 minutes until 10 a.m. What would happen to the pH in your mouth during this time?
17 Which is better for your teeth, eating a few sweets at odd times throughout the day, or eating all sweets only at the end of a meal. Give reasons for the answer you choose.

5 A survey of teeth

Activity

a ▶ Copies of Figure 4.5a are needed for the survey.

b ▶ The work can be done in pairs in class. Each member of the pair examines the teeth of the other and records the details on a copy of Figure 4.5a. An example of a completed form is also shown in Figure 4.5b.

c ▶ The survey can be extended to include other classes in the school or other members of families.

d ▶ Figure 4.5 shows that, in each case, age and sex can be recorded. Extra space is given so that more information can also be recorded, for example, how often the person cleans their teeth, what type of toothpaste they use, what type of toothbrush they use, how often they buy a new toothbrush, and whether they are right or left handed.

1 Can you think of any other questions to ask people? If so include these in your survey.

e ▶ Find out if fluoride is added to the water supply in your area. Record this on the survey forms.

f ▶ A summary of the class results will be interesting. This can be done in a number of ways. For example, one of the simplest ways is to record the total number of decayed, missing or filled teeth of each type in a copy of Table 4.1.

Fig. 4.5a Use this form for your teeth survey. Remember that the wisdom teeth shown here do not appear until the late teens

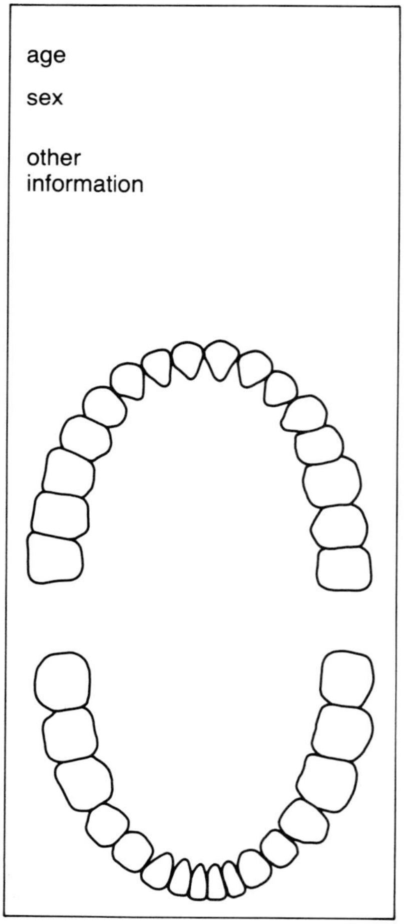

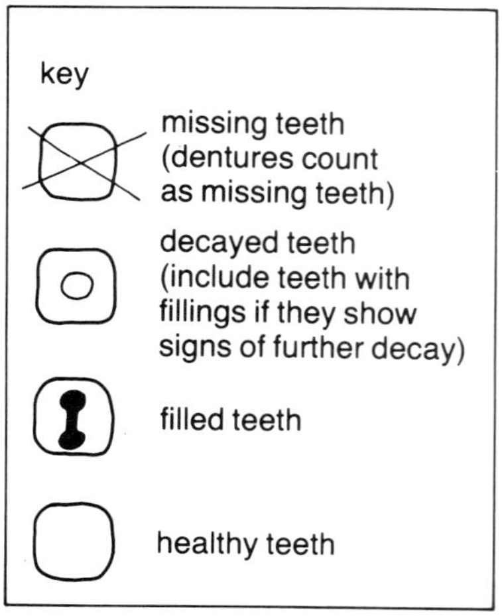

Table 4.1 Summary of class results of the survey

Person	Age	Number of each type of tooth decayed, missing or filled						
		Upper incisors	Upper canines	Upper molars and premolars	Lower incisors	Lower canines	Lower molars and premolars	Total
1.	15	1	O	4	O	O	6	
2.								
3.								

Fig. 4.5b An example of a completed survey form. The teeth marked W show where the wisdom teeth will appear

age 13

sex Male

other information 6 months since last visit to dentist. Cleans teeth once a day — usually!

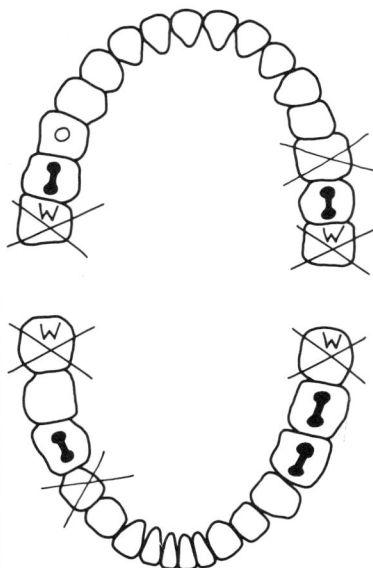

2 Which of the six types of teeth in Table 4.1 seem to be least likely to be decayed, missing or filled?
3 Which type seems to be most likely to be decayed, missing or filled?
4 Did you find anyone with no decayed, missing or filled teeth? If so, there may be a good reason for this. Try to find out what it is. The survey form will help.

6 How to prevent dental caries: diet

Dental caries is widespread throughout the world. However it is rare in some groups of people. In some parts of the world caries used to be rare or unknown, but it is now common. Consider the following facts, then answer the question which follows.
(i) When Captain Cook visited Tahiti, a remote Pacific Island, 200 years ago he was greatly impressed by the beautiful white teeth of the local people.
(ii) In 1965, one visitor to Tahiti described the teeth of the Tahitians as 'catastrophic'. There was very widespread dental caries. Many of the teenagers had no teeth at all.
(iii) Until about 70 years ago, dental caries was unknown among the Eskimos. It is now increasing among them.
(iv) Today dental caries is increasing among the people in many of the world's poorer countries. In earlier times, caries was rare or unknown in these places. However, differences within some countries are still seen. For example, dental caries is often more widespread among the richer people (especially those living in towns), than among the poorer people living in rural areas.
(v) The traditional diet of Eskimos was bear and seal meat.

43

(vi) Traditional diets in Tahiti, among the Eskimos, and in most poorer developing countries do not include sugar or sweets.
(vii) Sugar and sweets are now readily available in developing countries, especially in the towns, but they are expensive.

1 Imagine that you are a dental health expert who has been called in by the government of a developing country to report on the people's teeth. You discover that dental caries is widespread in the towns, but almost absent in the rural areas, especially among the poorer people. You are asked to write a report for the Minister of Health. The Minister is particularly puzzled by the fact that the wealthiest people in his country appear to have more decayed teeth than the poorer people. Using the information in (i) to (vii) above, write a 200 word summary of your findings. It should contain brief details on the cause of dental caries and the reason why it is probably more common among the wealthier people.

7   How to prevent dental caries: fluoride

1 Look at Figure 4.6. Which children have less decayed, missing or filled teeth; those who drink water with no fluoride in it, or those who drink water with one part per million (1 ppm) of fluoride in it?

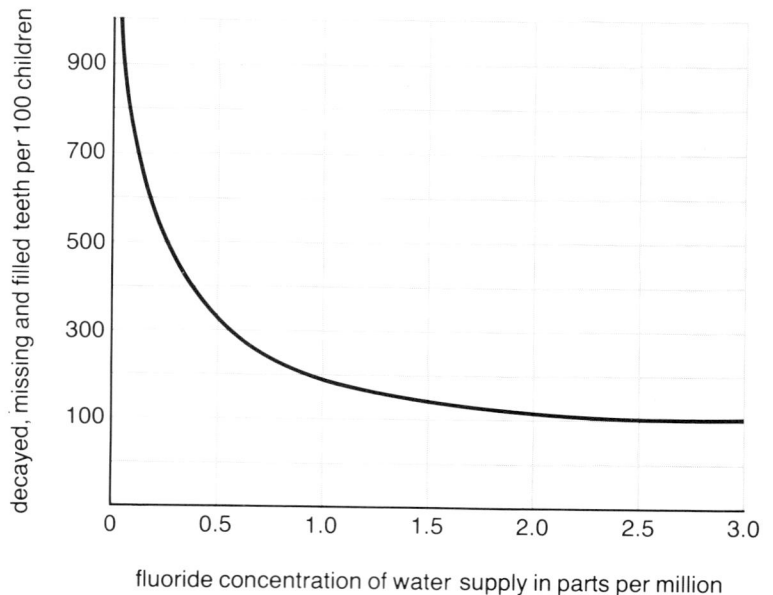

Fig. 4.6 *The effect of fluoride on tooth decay*

decayed, missing and filled teeth per 100 children

fluoride concentration of water supply in parts per million

Some people think that fluoride should be added to the drinking water in all places where the amount of naturally occurring fluoride is less than one part per million. They believe that this will reduce the amount of dental caries.

Other people disagree. They say that adding fluoride to water is too expensive. They also say that the health of those who drink fluoridated water may suffer. They say that fluoride is dangerous.

Fluoride is added to the water in some parts of Britain, but not in others. Many dentists recommend that children should take fluoride tablets if they live in areas where there is no fluoride in the water supply.

No one knows exactly how fluoride acts to reduce dental caries. It seems likely that it does so by making the enamel less soluble. Fluoride is deposited in the enamel and dentine of the teeth mostly before they erupt. However fluoride is also absorbed onto the surface of newly erupted teeth, but only during the first few weeks after they have erupted. Therefore it is the teeth of children which benefit most from the addition of fluoride to the diet. One common source of fluoride in the diet is tea. When it is made with fluoride free water, tea averages one part per million of fluoride.

Sections 6 and 7 show that there are two ways to stop tooth decay. The first is to eat less sugar and sweets, to cut down on snacks between meals and to clean your teeth regularly. The second is to add fluoride to drinking water or take fluoride tablets.

2 Which method of preventing tooth decay seems best to you? Remember, adding fluoride to water costs money, and some people think it is not good for health.

It is important to try to control dental disease, because it costs the country a lot of money. In 1977, the cost of treatment for dental disease was estimated at £140 000 000 per year, in England alone. Dental disease is responsible for the loss of approximately 2 million working days each year.

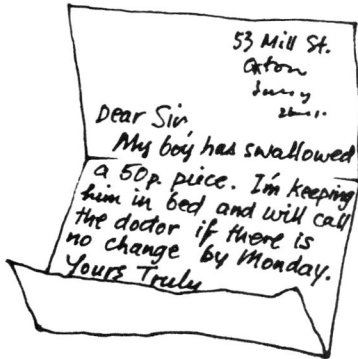

Fig. 5.1 A parent's letter

Given a healthy diet and good teeth, what does the body do with the food which we eat?

Food enters the body through the mouth. Waste leaves the body in a number of ways. For example, it comes out as liquid from the bladder, called urine. Waste also leaves the body through the anus, as solid material called faeces.

1   The gut

Many children accidentally swallow small objects such as coins or marbles. These objects come out in the faeces after about 24 hours.

1 What must there be between the mouth and the anus?

Fig. 5.2 A dissection of a rat and a drawing made from the dissection

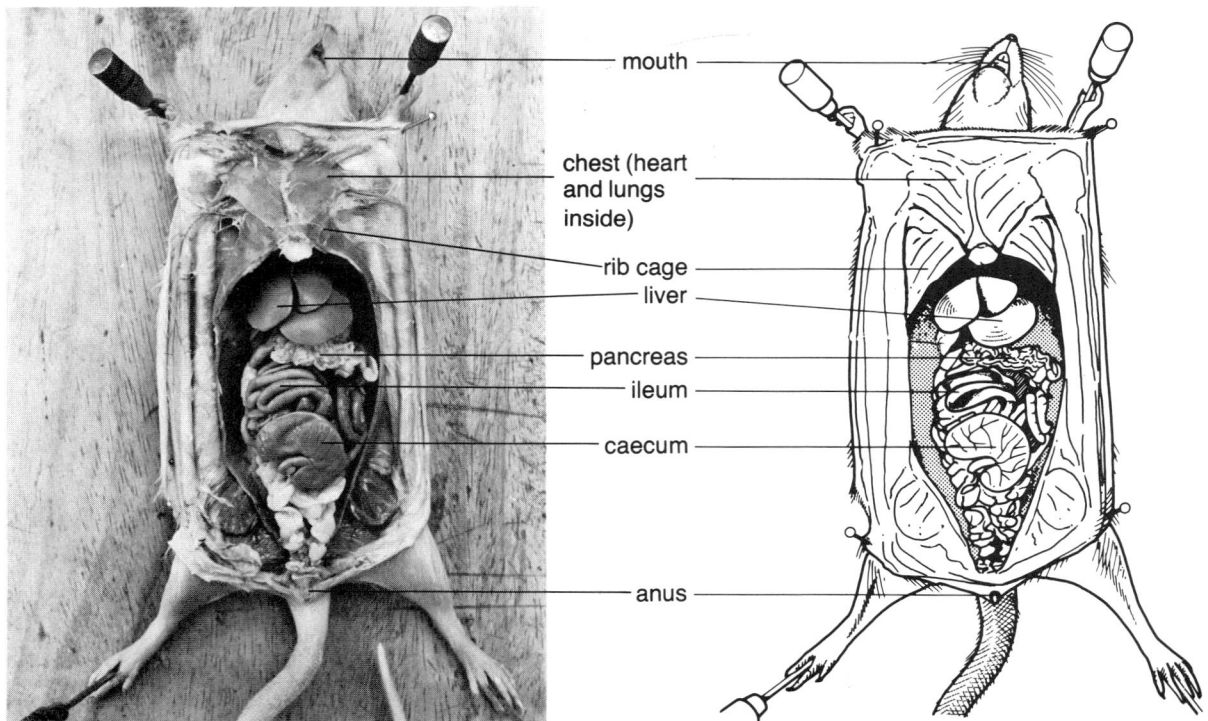

What is true of human beings is likely to be true of other animals such as rats. When dead animals are opened up, a long tube is seen passing through the body. It passes from the mouth to the anus. This tube is called the gut, and is found in a very large number of different animals, including man.

In Figure 5.2 a rat has been opened up. In Figure 5.3, the gut of the same rat has been spread out to show the different parts more clearly.

2 With the help of Figures 5.2 and 5.3, list the following parts of the gut, in the correct order, to show the path followed by the food as it goes through the gut: anus, caecum, colon, duodenum, oesophagus (gullet), ileum, mouth, stomach, rectum.

Fig. 5.3 The gut of the same rat has been laid out

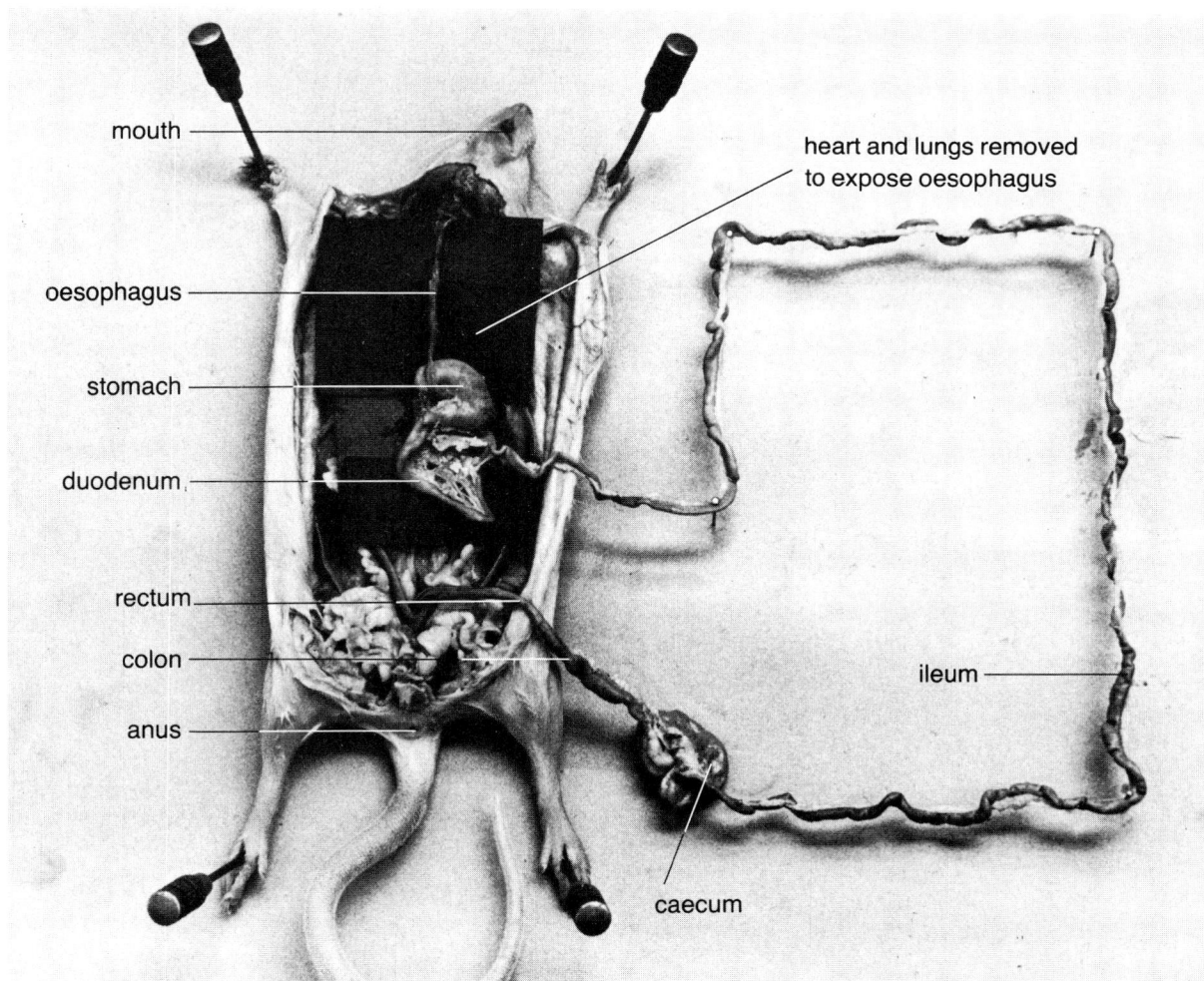

Fig. 5.4 The human gut

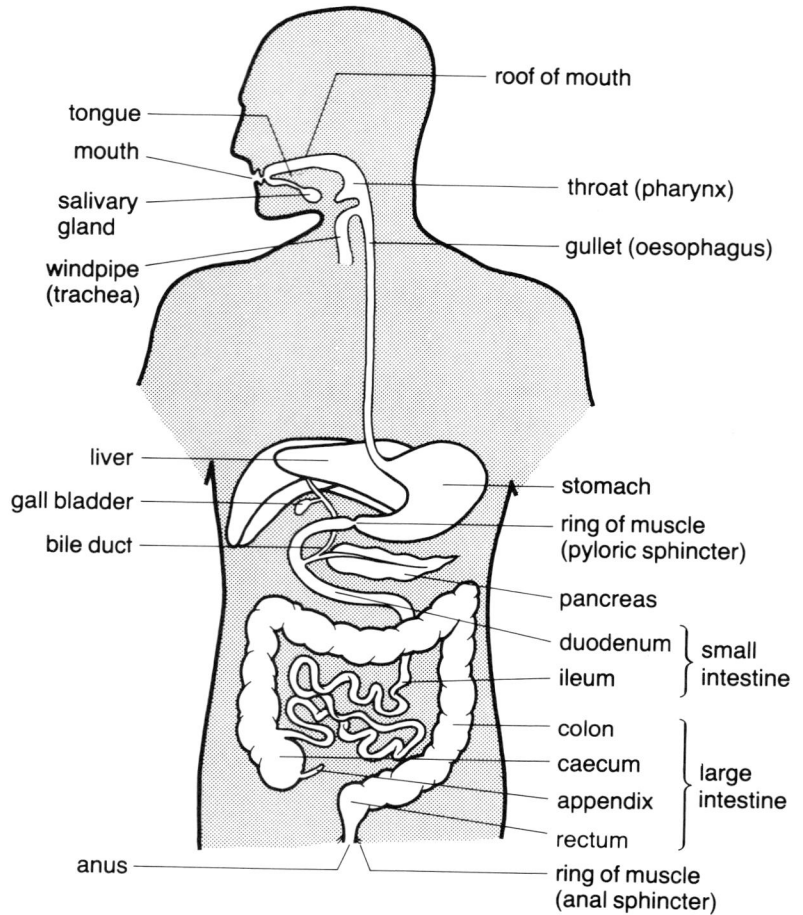

In a living adult person, the total length of the gut, from mouth to anus, is about 10 metres (m). A diagram of the human gut is shown in Figure 5.4. We are normally sitting upright when we eat, so it is easy to imagine that the food passes down the gut helped by the force of gravity.

3 Can you swallow food when lying flat on your back? Is it easy? Is gravity a help in this case?

A person can swallow food, including liquids, when placed upside down. However it is easy to choke when trying to do this. The gut is packed into the body in such a way that, in some parts, the food actually passes upwards over short distances. Look at Figure 5.5. Many mammals lower their heads to drink or feed.

4 Does food flow through the gut on its own, or is it moved along by some internal force?

Fig. 5.5 For a giraffe, having a drink might be a problem

Fig. 5.6 Peristalsis. The muscles contract one after the other along the gut. This wave of contraction pushes the food along

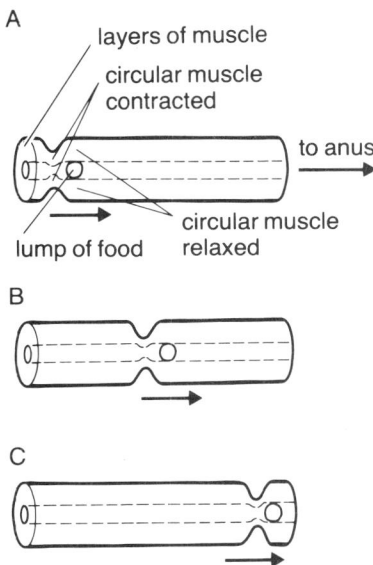

The process shown in Figure 5.6 is called **peristalsis**. It pushes the food along from the mouth to the anus. A model can be used to show how it works.

2 Making a model to show how peristalsis works

Activity

a ▶ Put a little oil or grease on a small marble. The oil or grease represents the slippery fluid called mucus which is produced by the walls of the gut. Mucus helps to lubricate the movement of food through the gut.

b ▶ Put the marble into one end of a short piece of rubber tubing.

c ▶ Hold the tube upright with the marble at the bottom.

d ▶ Pinch the tube below the marble so that it slides up inside the tube.

The food which we swallow is never usually as hard as a marble. However, it does need to be bulky so that the circular muscles in the gut wall have something to push against. It is for this reason that a healthy diet should contain enough fibrous food, often called fibre or roughage. The following foods contain a lot of roughage: wheat bran, whole (unrefined) cereals, peas, beans, raisins and spinach. If a diet

49

Fig. 5.7 *Obesity is a serious nutritional disease in America and Europe*

contains very little fibre, food may take as long as a week (instead of about one to three days) to pass from the mouth to the anus. Some scientists say that the diets of people in many developed countries, such as Britain and the USA, contain far too little fibre. It is possible that this lack of fibre in the diet is one reason for widespread ill-health. Fibrous foods generally contain less energy and more bulk than an equal amount of non-fibrous food. This makes people feel fuller and they do not have to eat so much before feeling satisfied. Enough fibre in the diet may help people to avoid becoming obese (overweight).

3 Large and small molecules

Food that stays in the gut and passes through to the anus is of no use to the body (apart from fibre). To be of use, the food must get through the gut wall and pass into the blood. It can then be carried to all parts of the body.

A simple model shows what has to happen to food before it can pass through the gut wall and into the blood. See Figure 5.8. The length of visking (cellulose) tubing represents the gut. The starch/glucose mixture inside the tubing represents the food. The distilled water represents the blood.

Fig. 5.8 *Visking tubing can be used to make a model gut*

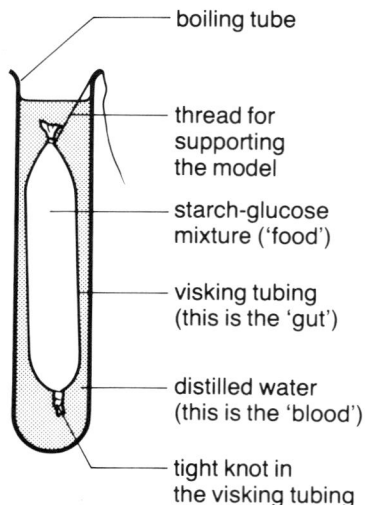

Activity

a ▶ Use a piece of visking tubing that is about 14 cm long.
b ▶ Wet the tubing with tap water to make it soft.
c ▶ Tie one end into a firm leakproof knot.
d ▶ Use a pipette or syringe (no needle) to fill the tubing with the starch-glucose mixture. Be careful not to puncture the tubing.
e ▶ Close the top end of the tubing by tying it off with strong thread. Leave about 10 cm of loose thread still attached to the knot.
f ▶ Carefully rinse the outside of the tubing under the tap.
g ▶ Lower the tubing into a boiling tube. Fill the boiling tube with distilled water (see Figure 5.8).
h ▶ Immediately, remove a sample (about 4 cm³) of the water with a pipette and divide it into two portions. Test one sample for starch and the other for simple (reducing) sugar (see Chapter 3, Figure 3.5). Record your results in a table. Make a copy of Table 5.1 for this.

Results of tests on the water surrounding the visking tubing				
Time (in mins)	Colour after adding Iodine Solution	Amount of starch in the water – write none/some/a lot etc.	Colour after boiling with Benedict's solution	Amount of simple sugar in the water none/some/a lot etc.
O				
10				
20				
30				
40				

Table 5.1 Results table

i ► After 10 minutes, take another 4 cm³ sample. Test this for starch and simple sugar as above. Record your results in the table.

j ► Repeat this procedure, at 10 minute intervals, for about 40 minutes. Record your results as you go along.

1 Why was the outside of the visking tubing washed thoroughly?

When the model was set up, there was a mixture of starch and glucose inside the visking tubing, and only distilled water on the outside. Starch is made of very large molecules. It is almost insoluble in water. Glucose is made of much smaller molecules. It is soluble in water.

2 Visking tubing has tiny invisible holes in it. Which one, starch or glucose, would you expect to pass through the holes more easily? Give a reason for your answer.

3 Which of the following is shown by your results?

A Both starch and glucose pass through the tubing equally easily.

B One gets through more easily than the other (if so, say which).

C One gets through while the other does not.

D Neither starch nor glucose gets through the visking tubing.

4 Using the information given above, about starch, glucose and visking tubing, try to explain why you got the result you did.

5 Does this experiment need a control?

6 Which of the two substances, starch and glucose, do you think will be able to pass through the wall of the gut and into the blood? Give reasons as far as you can.

7 Most of the foods that we eat are made of insoluble substances, with large molecules, like starch. What must be done to these large molecule foods so that they can pass through the gut wall and into the blood?

4   Finding out what saliva does to starch

The mouth contains several **salivary glands**. These glands produce the liquid which we call saliva. There are three main pairs of salivary glands and some smaller ones. Try to find at least one pair of salivary glands in your mouth. Use your tongue to help search for the glands and to feel the saliva as it comes out. If you think of, or watch, someone sucking an orange it may make the saliva flow faster. This makes the glands easier to find.

1 Whereabouts in your mouth are the salivary glands which you have found?

The total amount of saliva produced in 24 hours by an adult is probably about 600 cm³. However, it is difficult to measure and varies from one person to another. Some estimates give a figure as large as 1500 cm³ of saliva each day.

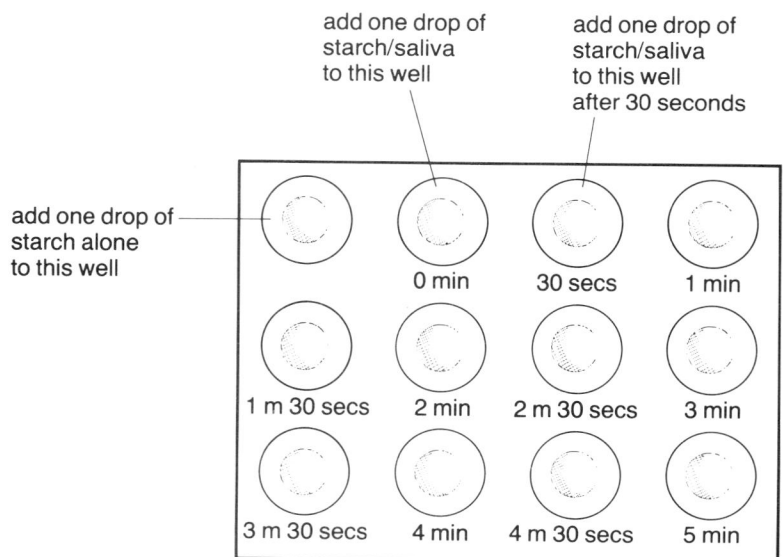

Fig. 5.9 Put one drop of iodine into each well on a spotting tile

Table 5.2 *Record your results in a table like this one*

Starch alone Black (starch present)	Mixture straight after mixing Black (starch present)	Mixture after 30 secs ___ ___	Mixture after 1 minute ___ ___
After 1½ mins ___ ___	after 2 mins ___ ___	after 2½ mins ___ ___	after 3 mins ___ ___
after 3½ mins ___ ___	after 4 mins ___ ___	after 4½ mins ___ ___	after 5 mins ___ ___

Activity

a ▶ Collect a beaker of starch suspension. Label it 'starch'.

b ▶ Arrange a spotting tile with one drop of iodine solution in each little well (see Figure 5.9).

c ▶ Make a copy of Table 5.2.

d ▶ Add one drop of starch suspension to the iodine in the first well.

e ▶ Use about 20 cm³ of distilled water to rinse your mouth. Spit this out into a sink.

f ▶ Use another 20 cm³ of distilled water. This time, swill the water around in your mouth with your tongue and teeth for about a minute. You now have a solution of diluted saliva in your mouth. Collect this carefully in another beaker. Label it 'dilute saliva'.

g ▶ Use a clean 5 cm³ syringe to suck up 2 cm³ of the starch suspension. Carefully rinse the outside of the syringe with distilled water. Keep the starch inside the syringe.

h ▶ Quickly use the same syringe to suck up 2 cm³ of diluted saliva. You now have a mixture of starch and saliva in the syringe.

i ▶ Lift the syringe out of the saliva. Point the end of the syringe upwards and suck in a little air. Mix the contents by turning the syringe up and down a few times. Go on to the next step quickly.

j ▶ Squeeze the plunger very slowly so that one drop of the mixture falls onto the iodine solution already in the second well. Do not let the syringe touch the iodine. Make a note of the time.

k ▶ After 30 seconds, add a drop of the starch-saliva mixture in the syringe to the next well.

l ▶ Go on adding single drops to the wells on the spotting tile until there is no further colour change. Record the colour in each well in the results table. Keep the mixture in the syringe for use later.

When starch is added to iodine solution, a black colour is always seen. This is the usual test for starch (see Figure 3.5). In this experiment, you added the mixture of starch and saliva to iodine on the spotting tile.

2 If you see a black colour in a well, what does this tell you?

3 If you do not see a black colour, what does this tell you?

4 If you see a pale purple colour in the well, what does this tell you?

5 Go through your results table adding, in brackets under the colour, one of the following: 'starch', 'some starch' or 'no starch'.

6 What has the saliva done to the starch during this experiment?

m ▶ You still have some of the starch-saliva mixture in the syringe. Carefully put 1 cm³ of this into a test tube. Test this with Benedict's solution to see if it contains any simple (reducing) sugar, (see Figure 3.5).

7 Does the starch-saliva mixture from the syringe contain simple sugar?

8 Was there any simple sugar in the syringe at the beginning of the experiment? How could you find out?

The experiment which you have just done shows that saliva will break up starch into simple sugar. In this reaction the starch has been digested. The reaction is possible because saliva contains a chemical substance called an **enzyme**. An enzyme is a substance which makes a chemical reaction go much faster, and take place at a lower temperature than it would without the enzyme. Saliva contains three main things. They are water, mucus and salivary amylase.

9 Which of these do you think is the enzyme which breaks down starch?

You have found out that large, insoluble food molecules are broken down into small, soluble food molecules. These small

Fig. 5.10 The digestion of starch

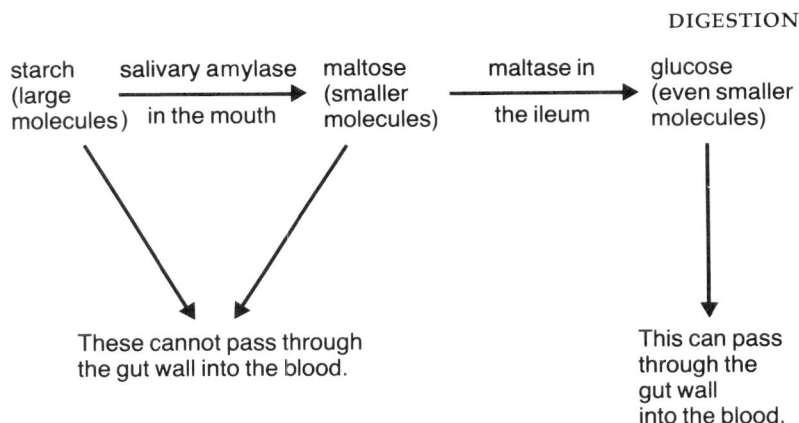

starch (large molecules) → salivary amylase in the mouth → maltose (smaller molecules) → maltase in the ileum → glucose (even smaller molecules)

These cannot pass through the gut wall into the blood.

This can pass through the gut wall into the blood.

molecules can pass through the gut wall and into the blood. The Activity above shows that starch digestion begins in the mouth. The simple reducing sugar which is produced when salivary amylase acts on starch is called **maltose**. The molecules of maltose are smaller than starch molecules. However, they are still too large to pass through the gut wall and into the blood. Another enzyme is mixed with the food when this reaches the duodenum and ileum. This enzyme is called **maltase**. Maltase breaks down maltose into **glucose**. Glucose is a sugar with smaller molecules than those of maltose. Glucose passes through the gut wall and into the blood (see Figure 5.10).

10 How many enzymes are needed to complete the digestion of starch into glucose? What are their names?
11 Why can't starch pass through the wall of the gut and into the blood?
12 Why do we need digestive enzymes?

There are many other enzymes which digest the other insoluble foods which we eat. These other insoluble foods include proteins and fats. The soluble products of digestion, such as glucose, pass through the wall of the ileum and into the blood. The undigested matter, including fibre, passes on through the colon. It collects in the rectum. It is pushed out from time to time as the faeces. This usually happens once each day.

5   Digestion in another animal

Human food needs to be bulky so that the muscles in the gut wall have something to push against during peristalsis (see Figure 5.6). A healthy human diet, therefore, contains plenty

Fig. 5.11 The gut of a cow showing the four chambers. Note that food is swallowed into the rumen first and it is then regurgitated and chewed before going down to the second chamber and the rest of the gut

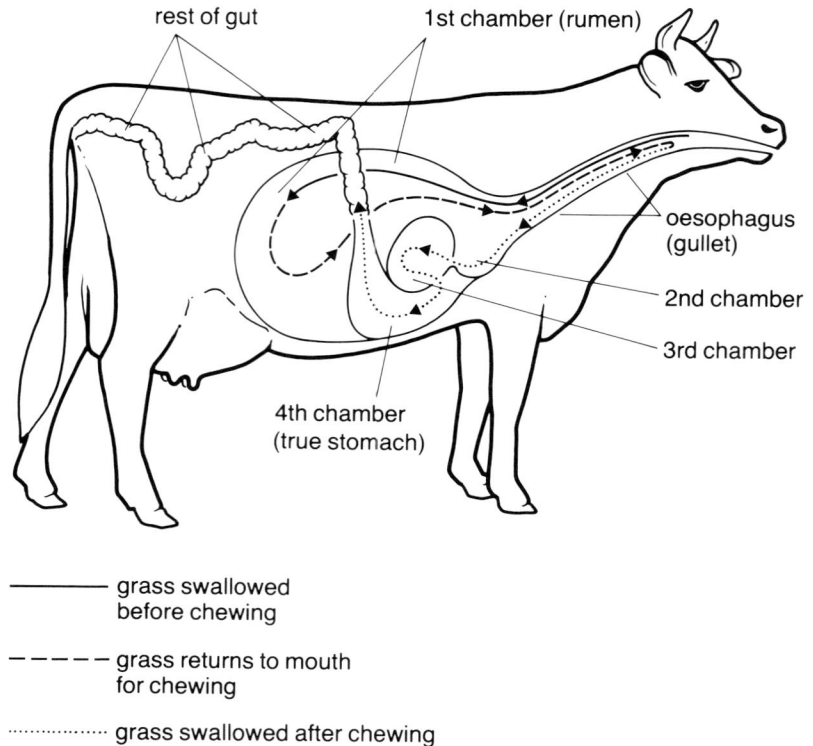

———— grass swallowed before chewing

– – – – – grass returns to mouth for chewing

·············· grass swallowed after chewing

of fibrous food (roughage), which provides the bulk. The fibre in these foods is made of a substance called **cellulose**. None of the digestive enzymes produced in the human gut can digest cellulose. This is why fibrous foods pass through the gut undigested. However, some animals, such as cattle and rabbits, feed on foods which contain a lot of cellulose. For example, grass contains a lot of cellulose. The digestive enzymes produced by cattle and rabbits cannot digest cellulose. These animals rely on the help of millions of microbes (bacteria and protozoa) which live in their gut. These microbes make an enzyme which digests cellulose. The soluble products of this digestion are released into the gut of the animal. The microbes feed on some of them. The rest of the soluble products of cellulose digestion pass through the gut wall of the cow or rabbit and into its blood.

The cow and rabbit both benefit from the microbes in their gut. Without these microbes, they would be unable to digest most of their food. The microbes also benefit. They have a safe warm home in the animal's gut. When two different organisms live together so that both of them benefit, we call this **symbiosis**.

The cow is an interesting and important example of an

animal which relies on microbes to help with cellulose digestion. The cow has a stomach made of four parts (Figure 5.11). The microbes live in the first chamber, which is called the **rumen**. All types of cattle are called ruminants because they have a rumen. Other examples of ruminants are goats, deer, antelopes, giraffes and sheep. Rabbits are not ruminants. They have a different way of making use of microbes for cellulose digestion, but that is another story (see Reference Section).

Cows feed on grass. Grass contains a large amount of cellulose. Cows themselves cannot produce an enzyme which will digest cellulose. However, cellulose digestion takes place in the cow's gut.

1 Rearrange the following phrases, in the correct order, to show how food which contains cellulose is digested in the gut of a cow. Use Figure 5.11 and the text above to help you.

(i) Cellulose digestion continues in the 2nd and 3rd chambers.

(ii) Microbes start to digest cellulose in the rumen.

(iii) Food enters the 4th chamber and then passes into the rest of the gut.

(iv) Food enters the rumen and is mixed with microbes.

(v) Cow eats grass and mixes it with saliva.

(vi) Food returns to mouth for chewing. Digestion of cellulose continues.

(vii) Food, consisting of grass and saliva, is swallowed.

(viii) Food is swallowed again and passes along a special groove into the 2nd chamber.

6 Crops

1 Man as a hunter-gatherer

Our earliest human ancestors were hunters. They lived in camps. When food became difficult to find they moved off and built another camp elsewhere. No crops were planted. These people got their food by hunting animals and by gathering the edible parts of wild plants. There are a few people who still live like this today, for example, the Kung bushmen of Botswana in southern Africa. (Look at the world map in the Reference Section and Figure 6.1.) Scientists have made a careful study of the energy used by the bushmen

Fig. 6.1 A family group of bushmen in southern Africa

Activities consuming energy	Energy required, in kJ
Walking 4.8 km from camp to nut forest (1.2 hrs)	1 130
Collecting nuts (3 hrs)	2 826
Return trip to the camp (1.2 hrs)	1 934
Sleep (10.6 hrs)	1 980
Other activities (8 hrs)	3 350
Total energy required for 24 hrs	11 220
Energy value of nuts collected, in kJ (1.75 kg of shelled nuts)	43 964

Table 6.1 The Kung bushmen use up energy in collecting their food and other activities. The table shows the average figures for one adult in 24 hours

58

when they go out to gather food. They have also found out how much energy there is in the food which was gathered (see Table 6.1).

The most important energy food for the bushman is the mongongo nut. They also eat other plants as well as some meat. When the nuts are ripe the bushmen move into the nut forests and set up camp. They will live in one camp for between a week and a month. They start by collecting and eating the nuts closest to the camp. After a week they will have eaten all of the nuts within 1.6 kilometres (1 mile) of their camp; after two weeks 3.2 kilometres (2 miles) and after three weeks 4.8 kilometres (3 miles). The children and elderly do not help to collect the nuts. They stay in or near the camp.

1 During which week, the first, second or third, will the bushmen be using up most energy? Give a reason for your answer.

The bushman walks 4.8 kilometres to get the nuts and the same distance on the return trip. Each trip takes 1.2 hours. You can assume that the trip is over level ground (no hills).

2 Which trip needs the most energy? (See Table 6.1.)
3 How much more energy does this trip need compared with the other?
4 Why does this trip use up more energy than the other?

Bushmen do not collect nuts every day and they collect more nuts on some days than on others. The average energy content of nuts collected by one adult is about 96 720 kilojoules per week. The average energy needs of a nut gatherer are about 59 857 kilojoules per week.

5 How much surplus energy is there after the nut gatherer has eaten?
6 This surplus energy is needed. Who do you think consumes it?

Adult bushmen (men and women) spend on average 2.2 days per week collecting nuts. The remaining 4.8 days are spent doing a variety of things. These include collecting firewood, moving about, constructing shelters, making clothes, caring for children and leisure activities such as dancing.

2 The first cultivated plants

In the past people believed that the crops which they grew had been given to them by their god or gods. Now most scientists think that our crop plants are descended from wild plants. This process must have begun when man started to collect and to cultivate the seeds of useful wild plants. We think that this first started in about 7000 BC in an area called the Fertile Crescent. (Look at the world map in the Reference Section.)

The first plants to become cultivated crops were probably wheat and barley. Many more crops have followed since. The wild plants from which these are descended can often still be found. The main crops of the world and the areas where it is thought that they came from originally are shown in Figure 6.2.

1 Make an outline trace of the world map. Mark in the place where the following groups of plants are thought to have come from. Use a different colour for each group: cereals, peas and beans, soft fruits, root crops and potatoes.

There are still some people living today who live the same sort of life as the first cultivators must have lived in about 7000 BC. For example the people who live in the mountains of New Guinea (see world map) collect and eat wild plants, hunt wild animals and keep pigs. They also grow a few crops, such as sweet potatoes and bananas.

Fig. 6.2 The main crops of the world and the areas from which they originally came

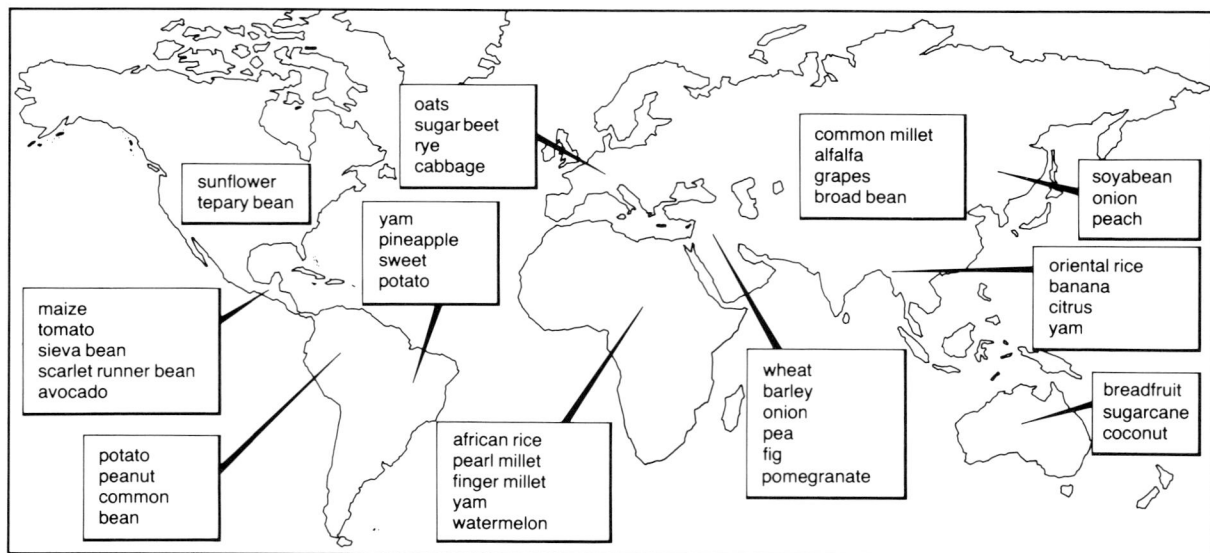

2 What farming activities do these people do which bushmen do not do?

A village in the New Guinea mountains was studied by
scientists. They looked at the amount of energy which the
villagers used up when cultivating a certain area of crops.
They compared this with the amount of food energy which
the villagers got from the crops in the same area (see Table 6.2.)

Table 6.2 The energy used by New Guinea farmers in farming their crops and the energy value of the crops. The figures are given for one hectare, which is a little more than the size of a football pitch

Activities consuming energy	Energy required, in kJ/hectare
Clearing ground, felling trees and burning	504 952
Fencing and soil retainers	249 545
Planting and weeding	932 026
Other work	229 448
Harvesting	347 940
Carrying harvested crop to the village	609 627
Extras	221 325
Total energy required	3 094 863
Energy value of food crops, in kJ/hectare	47 666 742

Table 6.3 compares the bushmen's energy surplus with
the New Guinea farmers' energy profit. The bushmen's energy surplus is eaten by the elderly and by the children. There
is no energy left over after everyone has eaten. However the
energy surplus of the New Guinea cultivators is much larger.
They produce from their crops more energy than they need

Table 6.3 Energy profits for the bushmen and the New Guinea cultivators

Hunter gatherers

Energy produced by one adult Bushman	43 964 kJ
Energy used up by one adult Bushman	11 220 kJ
Ratio of energy produced to energy used up	= 43 964 : 11 220 = 4 : 1 (approx)

New Guinea cultivators

Energy produced from one hectare of crops	47 666 742 kJ
Energy used up cultivating 1 hectare of crops	3 094 863 kJ
Ratio of energy produced to energy used up	= 47 666 742 : 3 094 863 = 15 : 1 (approx)

to feed everybody. The extra food energy is fed to their pigs. It could also be sold or exchanged for other goods. Hunter-gatherers like bushmen spend most of their time gathering food and firewood, or building new camps. There is little time for anything else. People who cultivate crops produce three to four times as much food energy for the same amount of work.

3 Which of these two methods of feeding people: cultivating crops or gathering wild plants do you think is the better? Give reasons for your answer.

4 Which, the cultivators or the gatherers, will have more time for doing other things apart from farming or gathering food? Explain why.

The New Guinea farmer cannot use the same fields for longer than about two years. This is because the crops use up most of the mineral nutrients in the soil. He must therefore clear a new area for the next crop and so on. The old fields are left. Weeds, trees and shrubs grow up again and animals come in from other areas. As these die, their remains gradually rot, releasing minerals which soak into the soil. After about ten to twenty years the land can be cleared again and another crop can be planted. This type of agriculture is still used in many parts of the world especially in tropical countries.

5 What do you think would happen if a New Guinea farmer tried to plant crops on the same field for three or four years running? Give the reasons for your answer.

6 Why does the land have to be left for ten to twenty years before it can be used for growing crops again?

7 In modern agriculture, most land is used successfully year after year for growing crops. What do modern farmers do to the land which makes this possible?

3 Growing some wheat at school

The wheat must be grown outside. An area of at least 1 square metre (m^2) is needed.

Most of the wheat grown in Britain is winter wheat. It is sown in the autumn. However winter wheat varieties might not grow well if they are sown in small plots in schools. This is because of the effects of bad weather, pests such as slugs and neglect during the Christmas holidays. Therefore it is probably better to sow an early spring wheat variety at the beginning of March.

Each year in January, the National Institute of Agricultural Botany in Cambridge publishes a leaflet for farmers called *Recommended varieties of cereals*. This gives the names of suitable spring wheat varieties.

Activity

Sowing

a ▶ Prepare a plot at least 1 m². This is the minimum area needed in order to avoid bad edge effects. The soil should be thoroughly weeded, broken up and raked to get rid of large lumps. For sowing, choose a day early in March when the soil is not too wet. If it runs through the fingers without sticking to them the soil is just right. Avoid sowing on frosty days or when there is snow on the ground.

b ▶ Add a little nitrogen fertiliser when you prepare the soil; any garden nitrogen fertiliser will do. Follow the instructions on the packet about how much to add.

c ▶ Mark out the rows 15 cm apart, and sow the seeds at intervals of about 2.5 cm in a drill 2 cm deep. Farmers roll the soil after sowing so press the soil down firmly and evenly after sowing. Do not water the ground after sowing the seeds.

d ▶ If you have enough space, seeds and time, try comparing two or more plots of wheat; for example, with and without fertiliser.

e ▶ Keep a careful record of what happens to your wheat. For example, you could make a copy of Table 6.4 and fill it in as the weeks go by.

Table 6.4 Record the details of your wheat growth in a table like this one

Date	Details of wheat growth

Care of the crop

In mild weather the seedlings will appear in about a week. They should not need any water unless they are in a place which is sheltered from rain. In very dry weather they may benefit from some watering. Farmers in Britain do not water cereals. Keep the plot free of weeds but be careful not to disturb the seedlings. The sowing density suggested above should give about two to three tillers (shoots) per plant, of which one or two will grow ears of wheat. Farmers aim at a

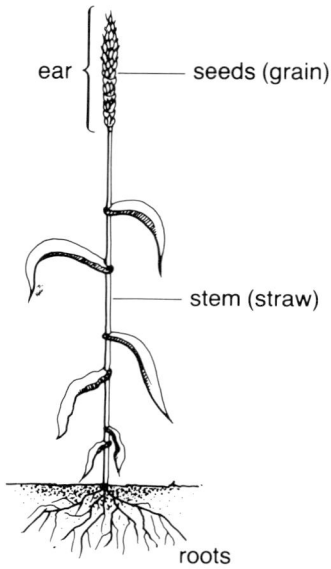

Fig. 6.3 A wheat plant

density of 250 to 300 plants per square metre.

Your wheat will come into ear (flower) in about the third week in June. By the end of the summer term it should be nearly ready for harvesting. This would normally be done in mid to late August. If you leave your crop until the beginning of the autumn term it may get a bit weatherstained.

Harvesting

Harvest your wheat. Separate the grain (seeds) from the straw and chaff and weigh it. If you have grown several plots compare their yields.

Cereals such as wheat are descended from wild grasses. Wild grasses shed their seeds when these are ripe and they usually have a special way of dispersing (scattering) the ripe

Fig. 6.4a A plot of land prepared for sowing the wheat

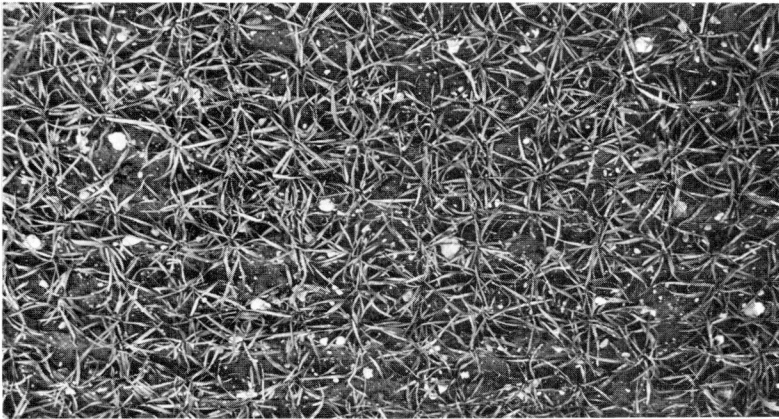
6.4b ▲

6.4c ▶

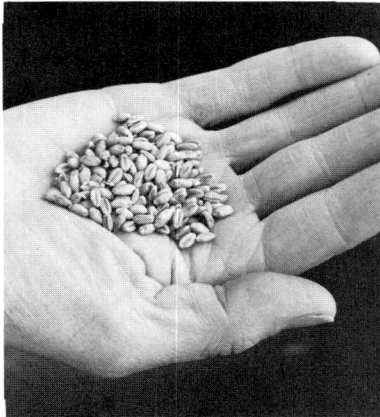
6.4d ▲

6.4e ▲

Fig. 6.4b (top) The wheat seedlings develop

Fig. 6.4c (top right) Fully grown wheat plants

Fig. 6.4d (above) The harvested grain

Fig. 6.4e (above right) When the grain in ground, wholemeal flour is obtained

Fig. 6.4f (right) Flour from the school wheat plot can be used to make scones

6.4f ▲

seeds. Thousands of years ago the ancestors of our modern cereals lost this ability to disperse their ripe seeds.

1 Why is it useful for wild plants to scatter their seeds?
2 Why is it best if our cereal crops do not scatter their seeds when they are ripe?

Grind up the grain which you have harvested into flour. This will be wholemeal flour. You can use it to make bread or biscuits.

4 Britain's wheat

About three quarters of the wheat used today in Britain is home grown. The rest is imported, mainly from EEC countries and from North America.

1 What percentage of the wheat used in Britain in 1962–72 was home grown? (See Table 6.5.)
2 What has happened to the percentage of home grown wheat since 1972?

In Britain wheat is used for three main purposes. Some is milled to make biscuit flour. Some is milled to make bread flour. Some is used to feed farm animals (see Table 6.6).

3 Look at Table 6.6. What was most of the home grown wheat used for in 1978–79?
4 What was most of the imported wheat used for in 1978–79?

Table 6.5 Wheat used in Britain is partly grown at home and partly imported

	1962 –72	1976 –77	1977 –78	1978 –79	1979 –80
% of wheat grown at home	48	58	61	73	76
% of wheat imported	52	42	39	27	24

Table 6.6 In Britain wheat is used either for baking or for animal feed. These figures refer to 1978/79

	Biscuit and bread flour (metric tonnes)	Animal feed (metric tonnes)
Home grown wheat	2 630 160 (52%)	2 947 680 (92%)
Imported wheat	2 427 840 (48%)	256 320 (8%)
Total	5 058 000	3 204 000

You may find it strange that we imported so much bread wheat in 1978–79 and even more in the 60's and 70's. The reason is simple. Some wheat varieties give grain which makes good bread flour and others do not. Many of the best bread flour wheats do not grow well in Britain. The biscuit flour and animal feed wheats do grow well here. However there are some good bread flour wheats which grow well in Britain and it is possible that others may be produced by our plant breeders and that farmers will grow them more. If this happens we could become self sufficient in wheat.

5 The world's major food crops

1 Look at Figure 6.5. Which three crops provided the most food for man in 1979?
2 Which of the eight crops mentioned in Figure 6.5 are cereals?

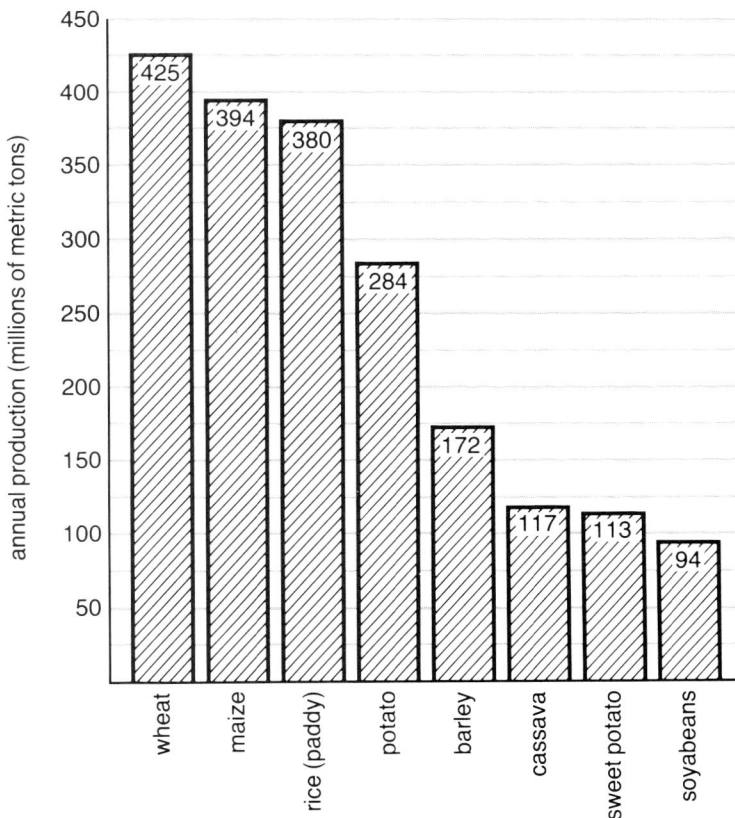

Fig. 6.5 The major food crops for man in 1979

7 Pets

'One for the pigeon, one for the crow; one to rot, and one to grow.'

(Medieval saying about planting seeds)

If the saying above is right, how many seeds must be sown if a farmer wants a hundred to grow?

1 Pests: the size of the problem

From the very beginning of agriculture, pests have always been a problem. In ancient Egypt, the people stored their grain in huge granaries. Rats and mice were serious pests. Cats were allowed to live in the granaries and were looked on as sacred animals.

1 Why do you think that the cat was a sacred animal in ancient Egypt?

Rats and mice are still serious pests of stored food today. The locust has been a pest ever since the first crops were grown. In Egypt, there are carvings of locusts on tombs dating from about 2300 BC. In the Old Testament of the Bible, the Book of Exodus describes the effect of a plague of locusts.

Fig. 7.1a A large swarm of desert locusts which covered 250 square miles in Ethiopia in 1958

Fig. 7.1b Locusts can make things awkward for other fliers!

'They covered the face of the whole earth, so that the land was darkened; and they did eat every herb of the land, and all the fruit of the trees . . . and there remained not any green thing in the trees, or in the herbs of the field, through all the land of Egypt.'

This happened in about 1300 BC. The locust is still a serious pest today (see Figure 7.1).

It is difficult to know exactly how much damage is done to world food production by pests. However, it must be a very large figure indeed. For example, Figure 7.2 shows that even a country which uses modern agricultural methods will suffer large losses of food because of pests.

2 Look at Figure 7.2. For every hundred dollars worth of food grown, how many dollars worth are: **(i)** Destroyed by weeds? **(ii)** Destroyed by diseases? **(iii)** Destroyed by all pests together? **(iv)** Available for sale as food?

The worldwide picture is much worse. The food value of well over half of the crops planted is destroyed by pests. Insect pests alone probably destroy about one quarter of all food grown in the world.

Fig. 7.2 In the USA only 60% of food produced is eventually available for sale. The rest is lost because of different pests

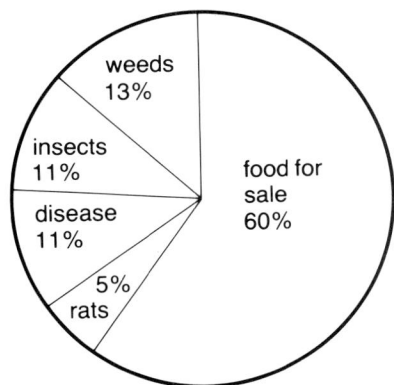

weeds 13%
insects 11%
disease 11%
rats 5%
food for sale 60%

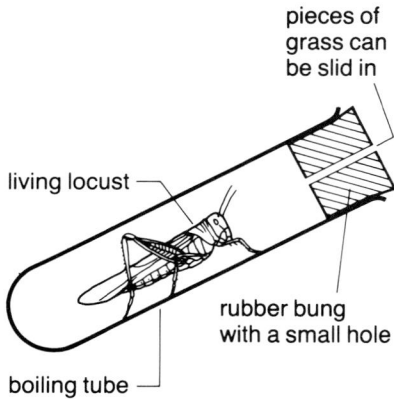

Fig. 7.3 A safe way to take a close look at a living locust

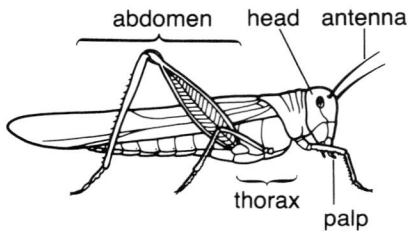

Fig. 7.4 The Desert Locust

Fig. 7.5 A school laboratory locust cage. Notice the tubes of sand at the bottom of the cage with dates on them. These are the dates when the tubes were examined for eggs. If eggs are found, the tubes can be removed and incubated in another cage

2 An insect pest: the locust

When conditions are right, some large grasshoppers gather together in large numbers and start to migrate. Grasshoppers which do this are called locusts. There are about sixteen different kinds of locust. The two types most commonly used in schools are the Desert Locust and the African Migratory Locust. The Desert Locust is larger and more colourful. The African Migratory Locust is easier to breed. The best way to study them is to look at two; a living one in a glass tube (Figure 7.3), and a dead one. A hand lens is useful.

1 How many legs does the locust have? Some may have come off, so look for places where they were attached.
2 Are all the legs the same? If not, say how they differ.
3 How many wings does the locust have?
4 Look at Figure 7.4. The body of a locust is made of three main parts. The front part is the head. What are the middle and back parts called?

human head

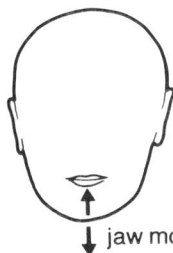

↑ jaw movement ↓

locust head × 3

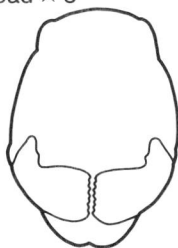

Fig. 7.6 Copy the diagram of the locust head and add arrows to show the direction of jaw movement

5 To which of these three parts are the wings and the legs attached?
6 How many antennae are there?
7 How many palps are there?
8 The locust has a total of five eyes. There are two large compound eyes, easy to see, one on each side at the top of the head. There are also three small simple eyes. One is on the front of the head in the middle. Look for the other two. Where are they? A hand lens will help. Locusts also have a very good sense of smell.
9 Locusts need a cage temperature of about 34 °C during the day. Find out what the temperature is in the laboratory now. Write it down.
10 How much warmer than room temperature does the locust cage need to be?
11 How are locust cages heated? See Figure 7.5.

Locust hoppers and young adult locusts will often feed very readily. Feed your living locust by sliding a piece of grass into the tube through the hole in the cork. Watch the locust carefully as it feeds.

12 What do the palps do while it is feeding?
13 When you feed, your lower jaw moves up and down (Figure 7.6a). What jaw movements can you see in the locust? Copy Figure 7.6b and put arrows on it to show how the locust mouthparts move.

3   Finding out how much a locust eats

Activity

a ▶ Copy Table 7.1.
b ▶ Select a flat blade of fresh grass. Trace carefully round

Table 7.1

Name of group	Time grass was put into tube	Time grass was taken out of tube	Total time grass was in tube (mins)	Area of grass eaten (No. of squares)

outline of grass blade

a

portion of grass eaten by locust

b

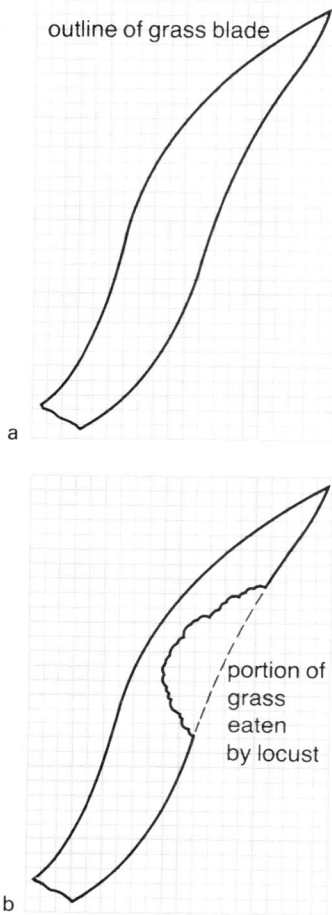

Fig. 7.7 You can use graph paper to measure the amount of grass eaten by a locust

the outside of the grass onto graph paper (see Figure 7.7a). Make sure that you can see a clock or watch.

c ▶ Slide the blade of grass into the glass tube containing a hungry living locust.

d ▶ Record the time. If the locust feeds well, leave the grass in place for several minutes, the longer the better. Do not disturb the locust.

e ▶ After it has fed, remove the grass and record the time.

f ▶ Place the grass on graph paper and mark off the amount eaten (see Figure 7.7b).

g ▶ Count up the number of squares eaten and therefore work out the area of grass eaten.

h ▶ If a locust feeds for six hours each day, work out the amount of grass that it would eat in this time.

i ▶ Weigh a large flat blade of grass on an accurate balance.

j ▶ Trace round the blade of grass onto graph paper and work out its area by counting the squares. This will give you the mass of a certain number of squares. From this you will be able to calculate the mass of grass that the locust can eat in six hours.

Scientists have worked out that the Desert Locust can eat its own weight of food every day. A Desert Locust weighs about two grams. A single, large swarm can contain as many as 40 000 million locusts. If each one ate 2 grams a day, this swarm of locusts would eat 40 000 million × 2 grams each day, or 40 000 million × 0.002 kilograms each day. This

Fig. 7.8 This field of maize has been severely damaged by a locust swarm

72

Fig. 7.9 Areas of the world which are liable to swarms of locusts and grasshoppers

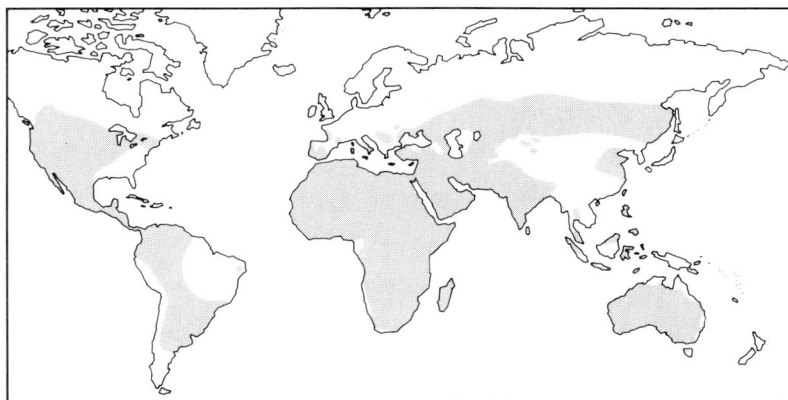

equals 80 million kilograms, which is the mass of 8814 double decker buses. 80 million kilograms of maize is enough to feed 400 000 people for a whole year! A large swarm of locusts consumes the same amount in one day.

Locusts are serious pests (see Figures 7.8 and 7.9). Fortunately they do not often form these large, hungry swarms. Also, careful scientific study of locusts helps to control them. Aircraft are used to kill them with sprays before they have a chance to form large, destructive swarms. There is more information about locusts in the next Section.

4   Fighting the locusts

The African Migratory Locust appears when conditions are just right on the flood plains of the River Niger (see Figure 7.10). This area is called the outbreak area of the African Migratory Locust because it is from this area only that this locust always spreads. The last great plague of this locust occurred between 1928 and 1941 (see Figure 7.10). Since then, scientists have learnt how to control it, and there have been no more plagues.

1 When controlling the African Migratory Locust, which part of Africa do you think that the scientists watch particularly carefully (see Figure 7.10)?
2 If this locust starts to breed rapidly in the outbreak area, what do you think could be done to stop the outbreak becoming a plague?

At one time Britain, France and Belgium used to govern many of the countries affected by plagues of the African Migratory Locust. In 1949, the governments of these three

Fig. 7.10 The invasion area of the African Migratory Locust during recent plagues. Its outbreak area is in the flood plain of the river Niger

countries set up the International African Migratory Locust Control Organisation (OICMA). This organisation is based in the outbreak area on the flood plains of the River Niger. Its job is to keep watch on the area. When the locusts start to multiply, they are killed with sprays.

The OICMA is now run jointly by the governments of seventeen independent African countries. There have been no plagues of the African Migratory Locust since OICMA was set up in 1949.

The Desert Locust is a different problem. Even when conditions are not good for forming swarms, solitary Desert Locusts can inhabit a vast area of Africa, Arabia and India. This is called the recession area (see Figure 7.11). However, when weather and ground conditions are just right, the locust forms the usual huge swarms. These can invade a much larger area called the invasion area (Figure 7.11). The invasion area of the Desert Locust is about 29 million square kilometres. This is about one fifth of the world's land surface. It includes over 50 different countries where several hundred million people live. Many of them depend on local crops for food. A plague of Desert Locusts is therefore very

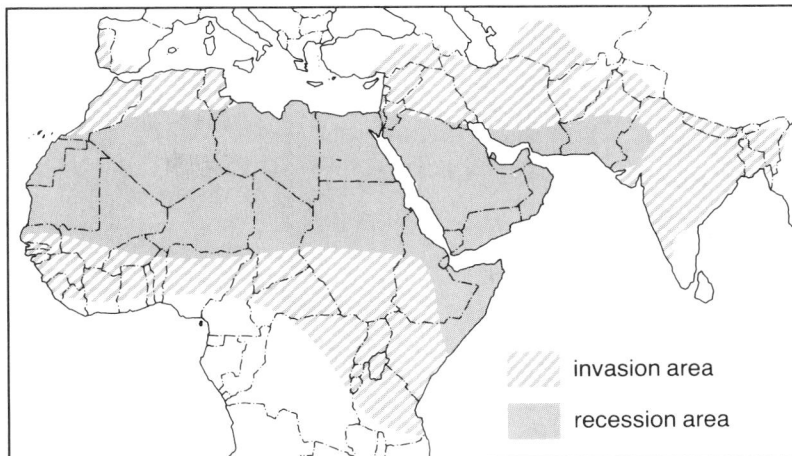

Fig. 7.11 The Desert Locust invasion and recession areas

serious. In the 1940s scientists discovered that the Desert Locust always breeds and migrates in the same way every year (see Figure 7.12).

The shores of the Red Sea must be watched carefully, throughout the year. The Desert Locust Control Organisation for Eastern Africa (DLCOEA) was set up to do this. Aircraft are used as well as teams of people on the ground. As soon as they start to multiply the Desert Locusts are sprayed. This kills most of them and prevents swarm formation. This is very important. If a swarm escapes and spreads into Arabia, East Africa or West Africa, the locusts can breed again. New swarms are formed. The area affected gets larger and larger.

Recently, fighting in Ethiopia and Somalia prevented the survey teams from watching the Red Sea coast, even with aircraft. Late in 1977 heavy rain gave ideal breeding conditions for the Desert Locust. Many swarms formed, and some moved across the Red Sea. About two dozen swarms were reported in Saudi Arabia and Yemen between January and May 1978. By May 1978 there were reports of numerous swarms in Ethiopia and Somalia. Some swarms reached Sudan and five swarms reached India but were controlled.

In July 1978 there was an emergency international meeting at which supplies of aircraft, vehicles, insecticides and equipment were promised for the area. By 1980 the swarms were under control again and the danger was past.

3 What prevented the DLCOEA teams from identifying and destroying the first swarms in late 1977?

Fig. 7.12 These three maps show the spring, summer and winter breeding areas of the Desert Locust. There is a small area where locusts breed all the year round

breeding area

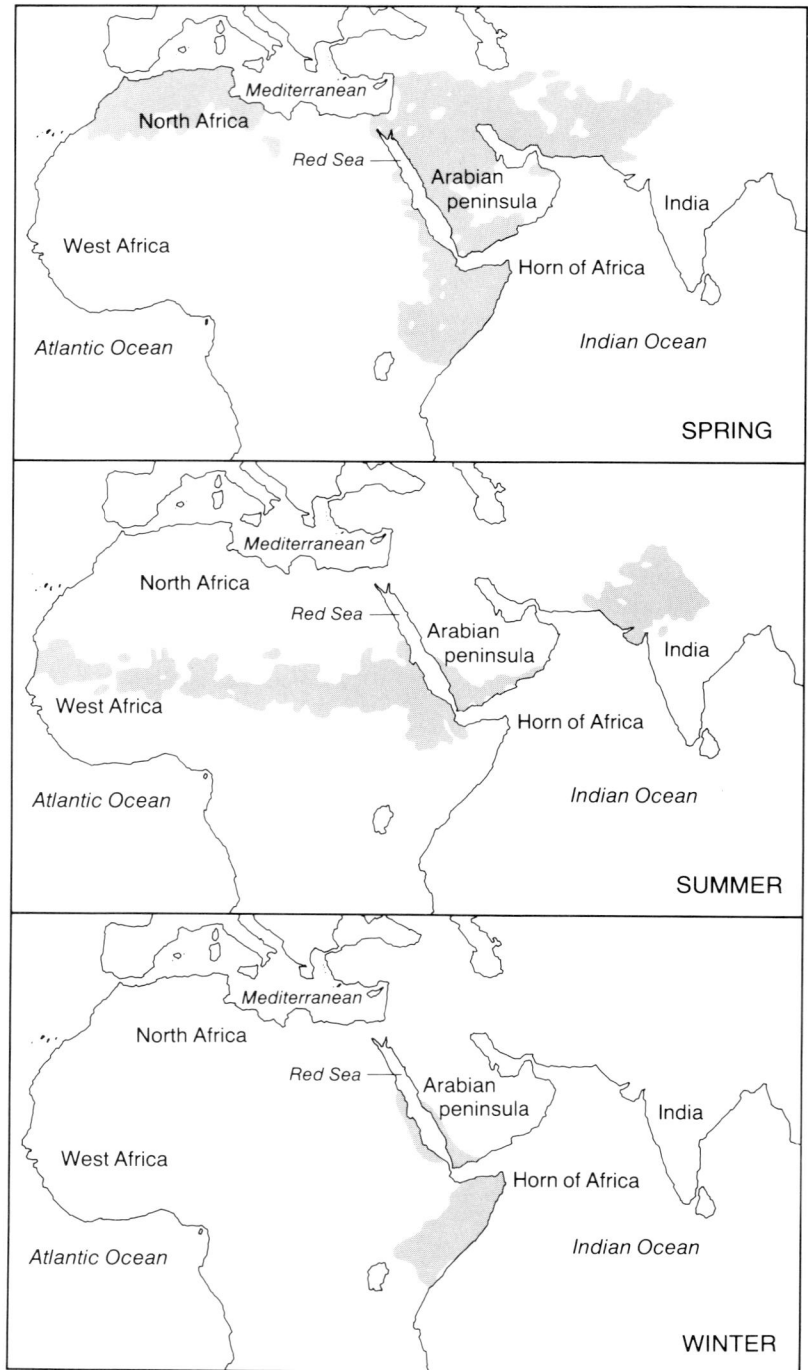

4 Look at Figure 7.12 carefully. There is a small area where the Desert Locust breeds all the year round. Where is it?
5 Where do you think it would be best to concentrate efforts to stop the Desert Locust from forming swarms?

5 Some other pests

A bird: the woodpigeon

Pigeons do most damage in winter and late spring in Britain. Crops on which they feed include clover, brassicas (cabbages, sprouts, etc.), wheat, barley, peas, beans and turnips. They will also damage cherries, currants, gooseberries, lettuces and strawberries. Pigeons are difficult to control. The best way to keep them off valuable crops is to shoot them.

Fig. 7.13 A woodpigeon

A mammal: the wild rabbit

The Ministry of Agriculture has described the wild rabbit as

'the most destructive vertebrate pest of agriculture.'
(*Advisory leaflet number 534, 1978*)

A full-grown rabbit (1.5 to 2 kilograms in weight) may eat about 0.5 kilograms of green food a day. The rabbit disease, myxomatosis, reached Britain in the late summer of 1953, and killed a lot of rabbits. Before 1953, it was estimated that rabbits caused the loss of 45 000 tonnes of winter wheat each year. Since the reduction of numbers in 1953 the rabbit population has increased greatly again, because some of

77

Fig. 7.14 A rabbit

them are immune to myxomatosis. Once again, they are serious pests. Rabbits also damage grassland.

'Experiments have shown that a population of about 20 rabbits to the acre can, after 18 months, reduce sheep-carrying capacity by 27%.'

(*Ministry of Agriculture*)

Rabbits cause great damage to young trees by ring-barking them.

Rabbits are difficult to control. They breed quickly. Shooting at regular intervals will help to keep the numbers down.

Fungus diseases

There are four major fungus diseases which attack wheat in Britain: True Eyespot, Mildew, Yellow Rust, and Septoria. They all cause reduced yields of grain. They are controlled by spraying with a suitable fungicide.

Fig. 7.15 Wild oats can be controlled with special chemicals. Here the area on the right has been treated to prevent growth of wild oats

Fig. 7.16 A wild oat plant growing amongst wheat

6 A serious weed of cereals: wild oats

This weed takes water and food from the soil which would have been used by the crops. Wild oats are very difficult indeed to get rid of. There are several reasons for this. Like cereals, wild oats are members of the grass family. Therefore, the special weedkillers, which kill all broadleaved weeds, are useless. The seeds can remain dormant in the soil for several years. The seeds germinate at the same time as the wheat. Therefore it is difficult to attack them without damaging the wheat as well. Most of the wild oats ripen just before the wheat and scatter their seeds. Some of the wild oat seeds are still not scattered when the cereal is harvested. They are then very hard to separate from the cereal grains because they are the same size. The farmer gets a lower price for grain which contains wild oat seeds. The best time to collect the seeds of wild oats is just before the crop in which they are growing is harvested. For cereals, this is usually some time in August.

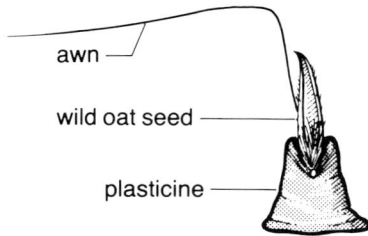

Fig. 7.17 *A wild oat seed held in plasticine*

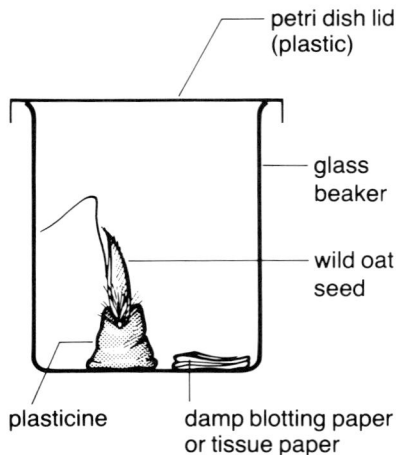

Fig. 7.18

Activity

The seeds of wild oats (see Figure 7.17) behave in a rather interesting way when they are treated to damp and dry air one after the other (see Figure 7.18). You will need a clock or watch, preferably one with a second hand.

a ▶ Put the seed in damp air as shown in Figure 7.18.
b ▶ Record the time and the position of the awn at one minute intervals for a total of about ten minutes.

1 In which direction does the awn rotate when in damp air, clockwise or anti-clockwise?
2 Did other members of the class get the same answer?

c ▶ Then remove the damp paper.
d ▶ Quickly dry the beaker and put a piece of dry paper in it.
e ▶ Record the time and position of the awn at one minute intervals as before.

3 In which direction does the awn rotate in dry air?
4 Did other members of the class get the same answer?

These seeds are shed in August. There are often some showers at this time of year although it is mostly dry and warm. The seeds are most likely to be dry when they are shed.

5 If there is a shower of rain, what will happen to the awns of the wild oat seeds?
6 If a sunny, dry spell follows the shower, what will happen to the awns?
7 What possible advantage to the wild oat seeds do you think the rotating awn could be?

8 Animals

Fig. 8.1 A Honey-guide bird

1 How we use animals

In east and central Africa there is a bird which feeds on the wax and the grubs in the nests of wild bees. The bird is small and finds it difficult to break open the nests. Therefore, it gets man or another animal to help. When the bird sees a suitable bees' nest, it goes to a nearby bush and starts fluttering and calling with an excited, chattering cry. This attracts the attention of other animals. Those which like honey, for example people and honey badgers, have learned to use the bird to show them where the nests of wild bees are. The bird is called a Honey-guide. There is a saying in some parts of Africa that if the Honey-guide shows you a nest you must always leave some of it for the bird. If you don't, the saying goes, next time he will lead you to a snake!

Table 8.1

Animal	Product	Use
Sheep	Wool	Clothing

Table 8.2

Animal	Use
Dog	Sheepdog Guard dog Guide dog for the blind
Horse	

Activity

a ▶ We rely on animals for many things. Some provide us with food, others with wool, feathers, leather and silk. For each of the things listed give the name of the animal which produces it and the use which we make of it, for example, sheep – wool – clothing. Enter the details in a copy of Table 8.1.

b ▶ Animals are also used for other things such as transport, protection, pest control and sport. Make a copy of Table 8.2, and add some more examples.

2   The first domesticated animals

Dogs were probably the first animals to be tamed and used by man. The jaws and teeth of domestic dogs dating from 11 000 to 12 000 BC have been found in caves in the USA and in Iraq. It is possible that dogs were eaten by man in those days. Dogs were also probably used to help man with his hunting. Man still uses dogs to help him hunt wild animals.

1   Give the names of some dogs which are used for hunting. How are these dogs used? In each case, name the animal which is hunted.

Sheep and goats probably followed dogs into domestication. The earliest remains of domestic cattle date from about 6500 BC. They were found in Greece. The wild ancestors of cattle must have wandered about in vast herds in the same way as the wild antelopes of Africa still do today. At first, man must have hunted the wild cattle. Later, the cattle became tame and domesticated. This domestication process must have

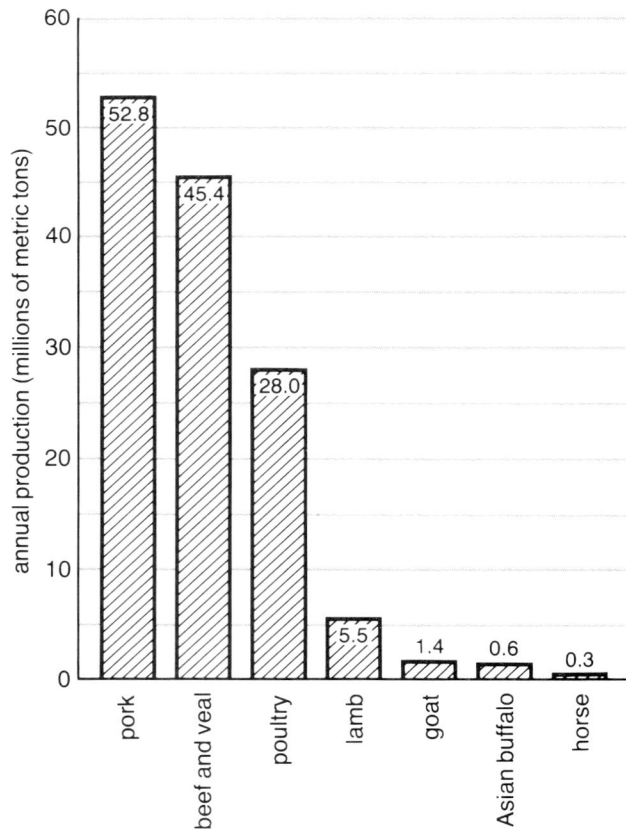

Fig. 8.2 The seven major sources of meat in 1979

taken hundreds of years. It is thought that the horse was first tamed in about 3000 BC. This probably took place in central Asia or southern Russia.

2 Why are tame domestic cattle of more use to man than wild antelopes?
3 What wild animal, living today in tropical Africa, closely resembles the horse?
4 In what ways might horses have been more useful than cattle to man in about 3000 BC?
5 Look at Figure 8.2. Which two types of animal provided the most meat for man in 1979?
6 In Figure 8.2, one of the types of animal is labelled poultry. Name three different poultry animals.

3 Animal behaviour and food production

The important food animals have been carefully studied for many years. We know a great deal about what they eat and how they digest the food. We know what can go wrong with them and how to get the most food from them. However, there is always more to learn. An example of this is a knowledge of animal behaviour. Most of the domesticated animals which provide us with food are social animals. The information below about a group of chickens will help you to understand what this means.

A scientist chose six white chickens for an investigation. They were all the same breed. All of them were hens (females) and they were all the same age. None of them had ever met any of the others before. Each was marked on the wings with a different colour dye.

They were put into a large cage, one pair at a time. They fought, usually for only a few seconds, and stopped when one gave way (see Figure 8.3). The winner was recorded. Both were removed and another pair was tested to find the winner. The investigation continued until each chicken had met each of the other five chickens once. The results are shown in Table 8.3 where the winner is underlined in each case.

Fig. 8.3 The chicken on the left is dominating the one on the right which shows a submissive posture

Table 8.3 Results of the chicken fights

Blue v Yellow	Purple v Green	Pink v Green
Purple v Pink	Pink v Red	Green v Red
Red v Blue	Red v Purple	Green v Blue
Yellow v Pink	Yellow v Purple	Purple v Blue
Yellow v Green	Blue v Pink	Yellow v Red

1 Why were the six chickens marked with different colours?

2 Did one chicken win its fights with all the others; if so which one was it?

3 Did one chicken lose its fights with all the others; if so which one was it?

4 Arrange the chickens in a **peck order** with the most successful one at the top and the least successful one at the bottom.

After these fights, the peck order settled down and remained very stable. For example, whenever purple meets blue, blue will always give way without a fight. This peck order is called a **hierarchy**. Hierarchies are found in many animals, wild and domesticated, such as monkeys, jackdaws, cows and pigs. A stable peck order means less fighting and therefore energy is not wasted. In the case of chickens, they feed better and they produce more eggs.

5 Two different groups of hens have their own stable hierarchies. Would a farmer be wise to mix them up to form one large flock? Give reasons for your answer.

4 Social behaviour in monkeys

Monkeys and apes are social animals. They can be studied in the wild or in captivity. At first they will be frightened of anyone who tries to get near enough to watch them. However, in some cases, groups of monkeys have become

Fig. 8.4 The chimp on the left is trying to threaten the one on the right into giving up the stick. The chimp on the left is dominant

used to being watched closely by the same person. These studies tell us a great deal about the social behaviour of monkeys.

In one study, ten monkeys were watched. The observer recorded the number of times each monkey bit each other monkey. The results are given in Table 8.4. For example, the monkey named 'Peanut' bit the monkey named 'Coffee' 26 times. However, 'Coffee' did not bite 'Peanut' at all.

1 How many times did 'Marmalade' bite 'Mustard'?
2 How many times did 'Mustard' bite 'Marmalade'?
3 Did one monkey bite all the other monkeys? If so, which one was it?
4 Did one monkey get bitten by all the other monkeys? If so, which one was it?
5 Arrange the monkeys in a hierarchy, with the dominant one at the top.
6 Are social hierarchies found among people? If so, give some examples.

monkeys biting

monkeys bitten	Peanut	Crisp	Cornflake	Pepper	Salt	Mustard	Marmalade	Vinegar	Coffee	Tea
Peanut		13	5	0	14	0	25	9	0	0
Crisp	0		8	0	22	0	0	17	0	0
Cornflake	0	0		0	0	0	0	0	0	0
Pepper	14	4	2		1	0	6	3	27	0
Salt	0	0	10	0		0	0	18	0	0
Mustard	8	1	2	32	0		4	2	20	0
Marmalade	0	22	8	0	15	0		15	0	0
Vinegar	0	0	13	0	0	0	0		0	0
Coffee	26	8	4	0	10	0	17	7		0
Tea	7	1	2	24	1	41	2	1	12	

Table 8.4 The table shows the number of times that each monkey bit each other monkey

Breathing

Why do we breathe? What do we need air for?

1 Comparing inhaled air with exhaled air

One way to find out what happens when we breathe is to compare the air which we inhale with the air which we exhale. If there are any differences, these should give us a clue about what happens to the air inside us and why we need it.

Fig. 9.1 *Collecting samples of ordinary air and exhaled air*

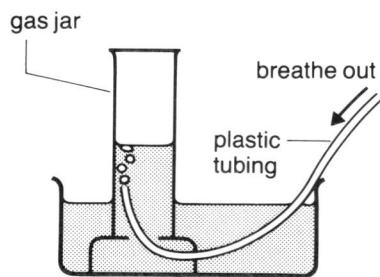

(a)

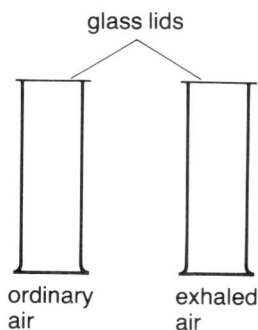

(b)

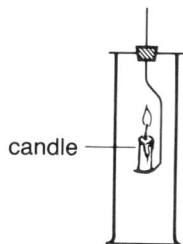

(c)

Activity

a ▶ Move your hand gently backwards and forwards in the air in front of you. This shows you what ordinary inhaled air feels like.

b ▶ Hold your hand a few centimetres in front of your open mouth. Breathe out against it as if trying to whisper the word 'hah'. You should be able to feel two differences between ordinary (inhaled) air and exhaled air. One of these differences is even easier to see if you breathe onto a mirror.

c ▶ Copy down Table 9.1 and fill in these two differences. There is also room in the table to record any other differences when you complete the next part of this work.

d ▶ Collect a sample of exhaled air in a gas jar or similar container (see Figure 9.1).

e ▶ Use an identical container for a sample of ordinary air.

f ▶ Find out how long a candle burns in the jar of ordinary air. Then see how long it burns in exhaled air.

1 What substance, found in ordinary air, does the candle need in order to burn?
2 In which jar did the candle burn for the shorter time? Why did it burn for a shorter time in this jar?
3 Would it be a good idea to do the experiment again several times? Give a reason for your answer.

Table 9.1 Fill in difference 1.
The second difference has been
started for you

	Inhaled air	Exhaled air
1.		
2. Moisture		damper
3. Oxygen		
4. Carbon dioxide		

Fig. 9.2 Apparatus for
examining ordinary air and
exhaled air

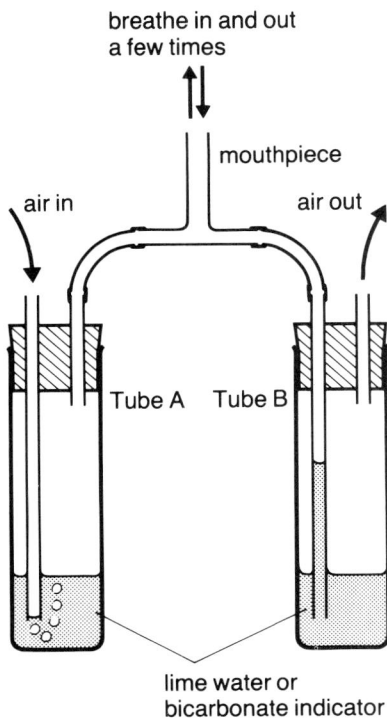

breathe in and out
a few times

mouthpiece

air in   air out

Tube A   Tube B

lime water or
bicarbonate indicator

g ▶ Fill in the third difference between inhaled and exhaled air in your results table.
h ▶ Lime water changes from a clear solution to a milky or
cloudy one if carbon dioxide gas is bubbled through it.
Bicarbonate indicator solution changes from a red to a
yellow colour when carbon dioxide gas is bubbled
through it. Use the apparatus shown in Figure 9.2 to
compare the amount of carbon dioxide in inhaled air
with the amount in exhaled air.

4 Look at Figure 9.2. Through which tube, A or B, does
inhaled air pass?
5 Through which tube does exhaled air pass, A or B?
6 In which of the two tubes does the indicator or lime water
change colour?
7 Which contains more carbon dioxide: inhaled or exhaled
air? Answer this question by filling in the fourth difference in your results table. Your results table should now
contain four differences between inhaled and exhaled air.
Look at these differences and answer questions 8 and 9.
8 What does the body take out of the air which is inhaled?
9 What three things does the body put into the air which is
exhaled?

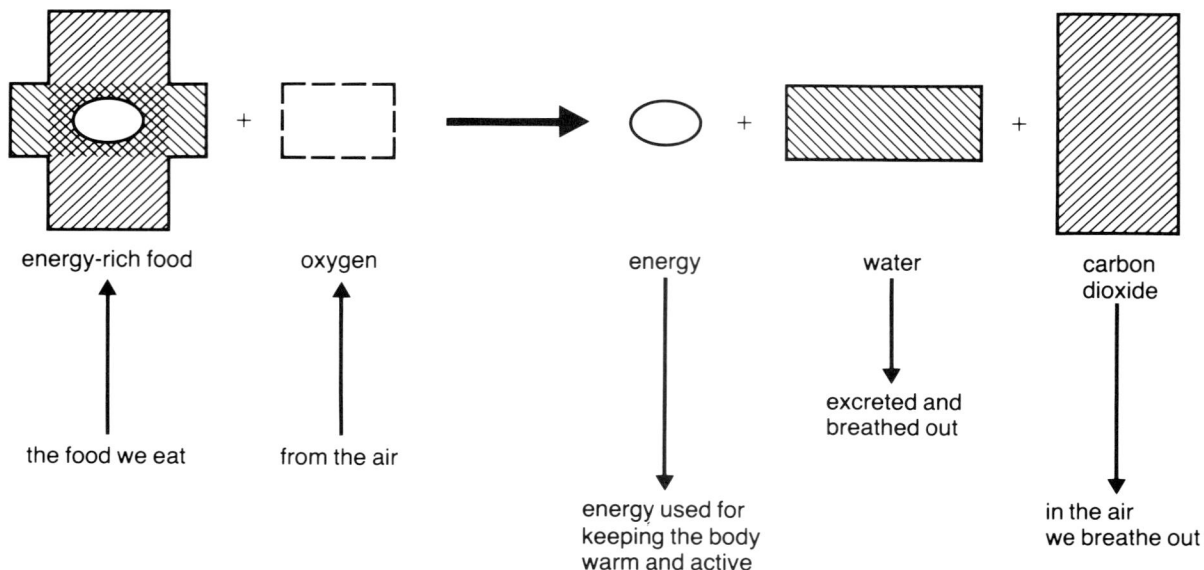

energy-rich food + oxygen → energy + water + carbon dioxide

the food we eat | from the air

energy used for keeping the body warm and active

excreted and breathed out

in the air we breathe out

Fig. 9.3 Energy is released when oxygen breaks down food

When we eat plants (or animals that have eaten plants), the energy they contain passes into us. Oxygen is used by the body to help to break down the energy-containing foods. This releases the energy in them (see Figure 9.3). This energy is used for many things including moving around, keeping the heart beating and the body warm. Without oxygen there is no energy, and these vital processes will stop. The body must get enough oxygen. It must also get rid of carbon dioxide because this is poisonous if too much stays in the body. The next activity follows the route taken by oxygen and carbon dioxide as they pass into or out of the body.

2 The air passages and the lungs

1 Look at Figures 9.4 and 9.5. Arrange the following in the correct order to show the route taken by the air as it travels from the nose to the alveoli in the lungs:

alveoli, bronchi, bronchioles, larynx, nose, trachea.

Activity

Movements of the diaphragm and ribs cause air to enter and leave the lungs.

a ▶ Watch someone who is sitting down at rest. Count the number of times that they inhale in one minute.

Fig. 9.4 ▶

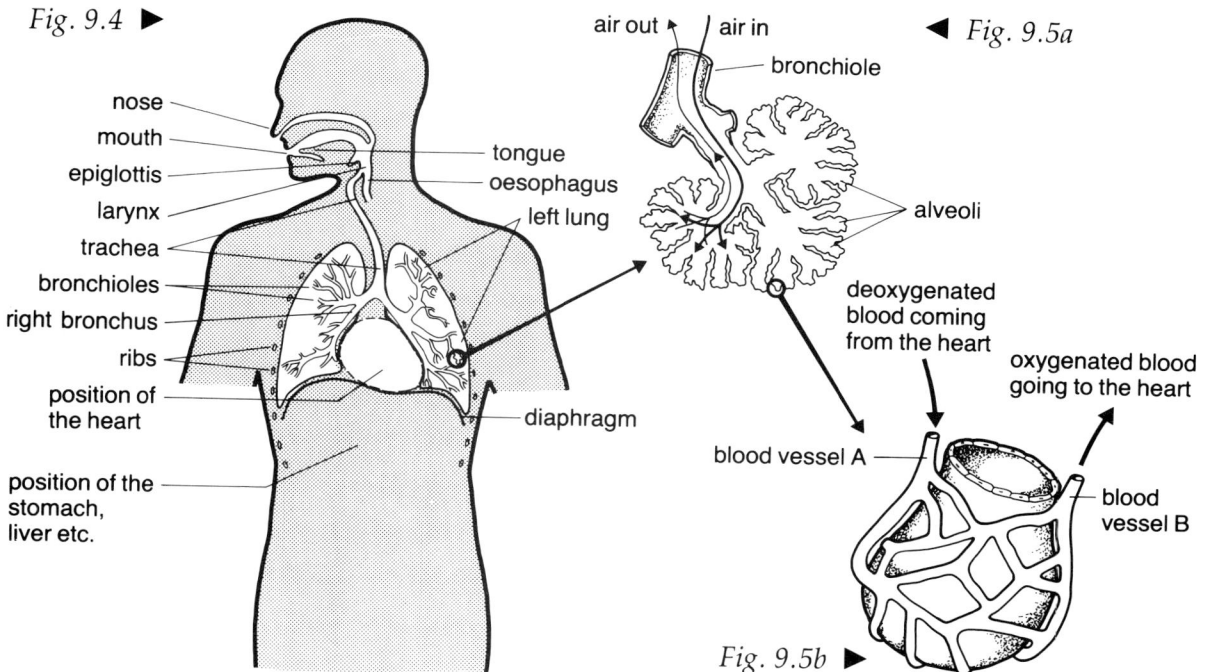

nose
mouth
epiglottis
larynx
trachea
bronchioles
right bronchus
ribs
position of the heart
position of the stomach, liver etc.

tongue
oesophagus
left lung
diaphragm

air out ◄ / air in
bronchiole

◄ *Fig. 9.5a*

alveoli

deoxygenated blood coming from the heart

oxygenated blood going to the heart

blood vessel A

blood vessel B

Fig. 9.5b ▶

Fig. 9.4 The air passages and breathing system in humans

Fig. 9.5a A small section of the lung

Fig. 9.5b A single alveolus

b ▶ Ask the same person to do some hard exercise for a few minutes. Step-ups or squat jumps are good exercises. Then count the number of times they inhale in one minute.

c ▶ Compare your results with those taken by other members of the class.

d ▶ Look up normal breathing rates in the Reference Section at the back of this book.

2 How do your results compare with the figures given in the Reference Section?

3 Look at Figure 9.5. Whereabouts in the lungs does oxygen pass from the air into the blood?

4 Where does carbon dioxide leave the blood and pass into the air?

5 Which do you think has more oxygen in it, blood vessel A, or blood vessel B in Figure 9.5? Give a reason for your answer.

6 Which blood vessel contains more carbon dioxide, A or B? Give a reason for your answer.

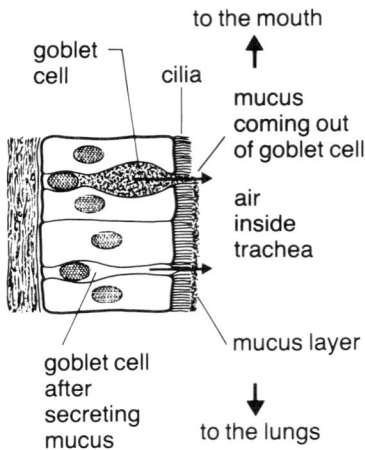

Fig. 9.6 The cells lining the trachea

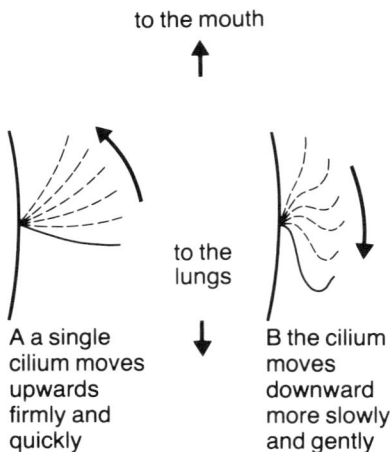

Fig. 9.7 Movements of a cilium on the lining of the trachea

3 How the walls of our air passages help to keep us healthy

Air contains the oxygen which we need. It also holds a lot of other things. Some of these can be dangerous, for example, dust, smoke and harmful bacteria. The amount and type of dust in the air varies a great deal. Some types of dust are more harmful than others. In healthy people the bacteria and larger dust particles all get trapped in the upper air passages. They are therefore prevented from reaching the lungs where they might cause infection, irritation or inflammation. The inner surface of all the air passages (nose, trachea, bronchi etc) is covered by special cells of two main types. These are goblet cells, which produce **mucus**, and ciliated cells, which have tiny hairs called **cilia** on them. Both of these cells are shown in Figure 9.6.

Mucus is a thick sticky liquid. The cilia move up and down all the time as shown in Figure 9.7. Dust particles in the air are trapped by the sticky mucus. The cilia carry the mucus up towards the mouth. Coughing also helps. When the mucus gets to the mouth it is swallowed and eventually passes out of the body.

Good health depends partly on a healthy breathing system. The goblet cells and cilia have a very important part to play in making sure that the breathing system stays healthy.

1 What is it that traps dust particles in the air passages?
2 How is unwanted material removed from the air passages?
3 What do you think would happen, in your air passages, if the cilia stopped moving?

4 Some diseases of the airways and lungs

Lung cancer kills more men in Britain today than any other type of cancer. The disease starts quietly and you may feel nothing at first. Often, by the time lung cancer is discovered, it is too late to treat it. People with this disease may suffer great pain before it finally kills them. Lung cancer is much more common in smokers than in non-smokers. **Bronchitis** is a disease of the air passages. **Emphysema** is a disease of the alveoli. These two diseases cause the loss of about 30 million working days each year in Britain. Smoking is now the main cause of bronchitis in Britain. More information about diseases of the breathing system is given below.

Chronic bronchitis

In this disease, too much mucus is produced in the air passages, and the walls become inflamed. The ciliated cells are gradually destroyed, and so the only way to move the mucus up to the mouth is by coughing. The extra mucus and the inflamed walls both make the air passages narrower. This obviously makes breathing more difficult. Common symptoms of bronchitis are wheezing and a tight feeling in the chest, especially in the morning. This causes great discomfort and distress. Chronic bronchitis seems to be caused by breathing air containing dust, smoke of various kinds or other fumes for several years. The disease is more common in towns than it is in country districts. It is also more common in smokers than in non-smokers. About 95 people out of every 100 with chronic bronchitis are smokers.

Emphysema of the lungs

This disease often affects people who already suffer from chronic bronchitis. The walls of many of the alveoli break down or become overstretched. Therefore movement of oxygen into the blood is slower because there are fewer alveoli. People with chronic bronchitis and emphysema of the lungs usually have a cough which carries large amounts of mucus (phlegm) up to the mouth. They find breathing difficult, and they wheeze all the time as they breathe. They move slowly. They find it difficult to climb even a few steps because they quickly become exhausted. People who suffer from bronchitis and emphysema are much more likely to get pneumonia than are healthy people. Pneumonia is very dangerous for people with emphysema. If someone with emphysema gets pneumonia as well, this usually kills them.

Each year about 25 000 men and women die from bronchitis and emphysema in Britain, many of them having suffered years of disability. The number of people actually suffering from these diseases is far greater. It is thought that about 30 million working days are lost each year in Britain due entirely to sickness caused by these two diseases.

The proportion of people who die from chronic bronchitis and emphysema has been falling steadily in recent years. There are probably several reasons for this. Various clean air laws have provided smokeless zones in towns and cities. These laws have reduced the amount of coal smoke and other fumes in the air. Conditions in factories are better than

Fig. 9.8 London in 1951.
Smoke was a serious hazard in
London until recently

they were. There are better ways of protecting workers from
dusts and smoke. These include dust extractors and special
protective clothing, especially face masks. There have been
several improvements in the treatment of patients with
bronchitis. They can be made to feel more comfortable and
they probably live a little longer. Fewer people now smoke
cigarettes. (See Table 10.3 in Chapter 10.) Those who do
smoke, may be smoking less. The tar and nicotine content of
cigarettes sold in Britain have both been reduced steadily in
recent years. Tar and nicotine are both harmful.

1 Which of the points listed above help to prevent bronchitis?
2 What advice would you give to someone who wants to
avoid getting bronchitis?

Asthma

Attacks of asthma can be caused by a temporary narrowing
of the air passages. This may be due to swelling of the walls,
or to the production of too much mucus. It may also be
caused by the contraction of muscles in the walls of the air
passages. Breathing becomes more difficult as in bronchitis.
Asthmatic attacks occur in people who are especially sensitive to certain things, such as pollen carried in the air by

Fig. 9.9 London in 1980. Notice how much cleaner the air is now

wind currents. Some asthmatic people are sensitive to other things. Dusts, feathers, the fur of certain animals, some cosmetics or certain foods can all cause asthma. Excitement or worry can also bring on an attack of asthma in some people. Many asthmatic people feel wheezy and short of breath in a smoky atmosphere.

Pneumonia

In this disease the lungs become inflamed. It is usually caused by certain bacteria, or by other microbes called viruses. These get into the lungs and multiply so that the walls of the alveoli become swollen and inflamed. The alveoli become filled with fluid and blood cells. Movement of oxygen into the blood therefore slows down. In a healthy person there are few microbes which can cause pneumonia. However in someone with, for example, chronic bronchitis, some of the bacteria which normally live harmlessly in the upper air passages, can get into the lungs and cause pneumonia. It is pneumonia which often finally kills those who suffer from bronchitis.

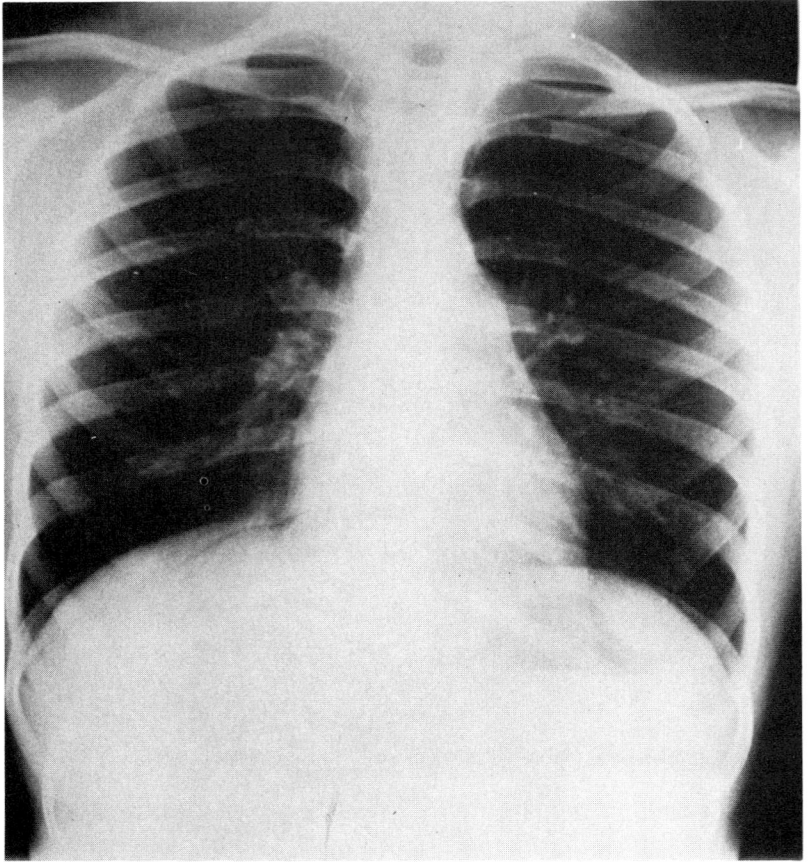

Fig. 9.10 An x-ray photograph of a normal chest. The white area just right of centre is the shadow of the heart

Lung cancer

In this disease, cells in the lungs or in the air passages suddenly stop behaving normally. Instead they start to multiply rapidly. They form a lump or **tumour**. Doctors call this a carcinoma. The lump grows slowly at first and gradually blocks some of the air passages. It slowly invades the healthy parts of the lungs. One of the most dangerous things about lung cancer is that it starts quietly and secretly. The victim often feels nothing at first. Later a cough may start. Then breathing becomes more difficult. The cancerous lump is often widespread by the time it is discovered. By then it may be too late to save the patient. Lung cancer kills more men in Britain than any other type of cancer. No one knows yet exactly why the lung cells suddenly become cancerous. However, there are some clues. Lung cancer is rare in people who do not smoke.

Fig. 9.11 An x-ray photograph
of a chest with severe lung
cancer; notice the abnormal
white shadow above the heart
caused by the cancer tumour

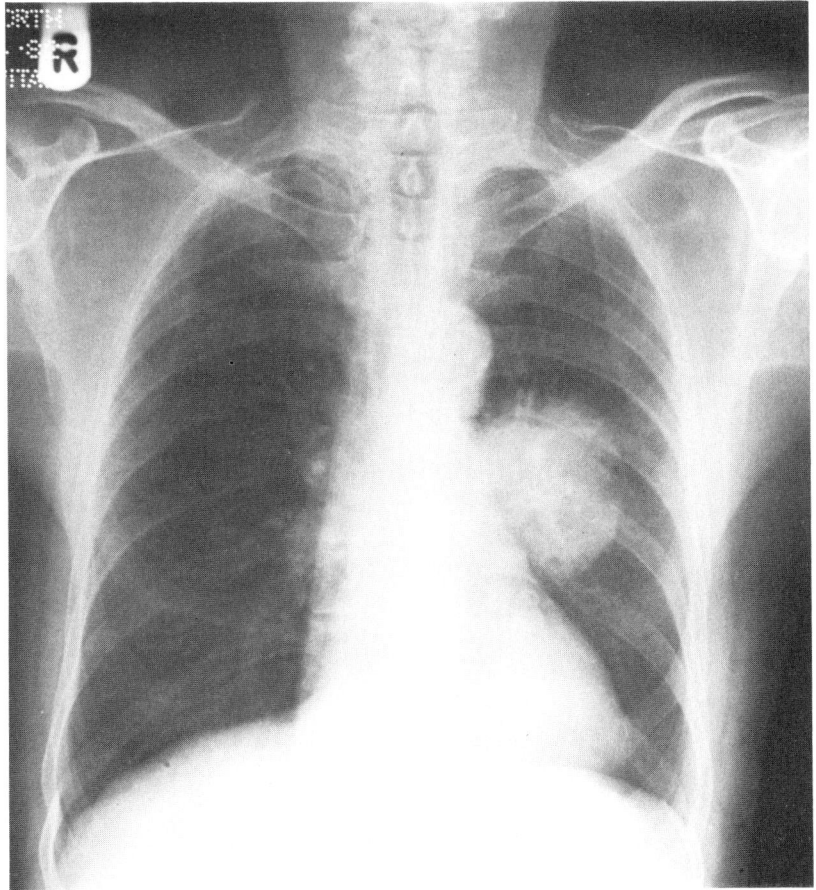

Fig. 9.12 Sand blasting was
widely used for cleaning
surfaces, and removing paint.
This created a lot of abrasive
dust. Sand blasting is now
carefully controlled by law.

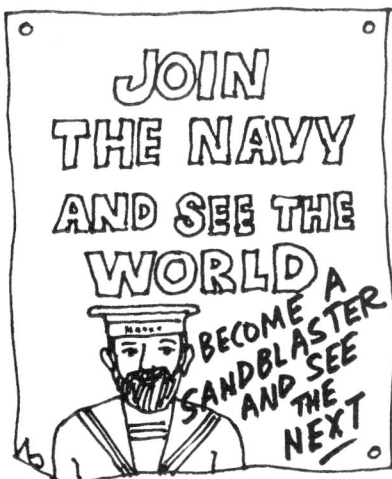

Industrial lung diseases

Some industrial processes produce dusts. These processes
include drilling, polishing, crushing and sawing. Industrial
dusts are often much smaller than the ordinary dust in the
air. This means that they can avoid being trapped by the
mucus in the air passages. Therefore these dusts can get into
the lungs. This can cause serious diseases such as silicosis or
pneumoconiosis of coal miners. It is because of diseases such
as these that there are strict regulations about the conditions
under which men and women work in industry. These
regulations are being brought up to date all the time as our
knowledge of industrial diseases grows.

(Smoking or Health *was the title of a report by the Royal College of Physicians, London, 1977.)*

Fig. 10.1a *Tobacco growing is a major agricultural industry in many countries*

Fig. 10.1b *The leaves are collected, dried and cured*

In Britain it is against the law to sell cigarettes to people under the age of sixteen. However, in one recent survey of shops which sell them, 43 out of 50 shops sold cigarettes to people who were under sixteen.

The tobacco plant is widely grown in warm countries such as the USA, Cuba, Sumatra, Egypt, Brazil and in the countries of tropical Africa. The leaves of the plant are gathered, hung up, and dried slowly. This is called curing. Some tobacco varieties and curing methods make the tobacco which is used to make cigarettes. Other varieties and methods produce pipe or cigar tobacco. Snuff is made from powdered tobacco.

Fig. 10.2 *Apparatus for collecting the tar in cigarette smoke*

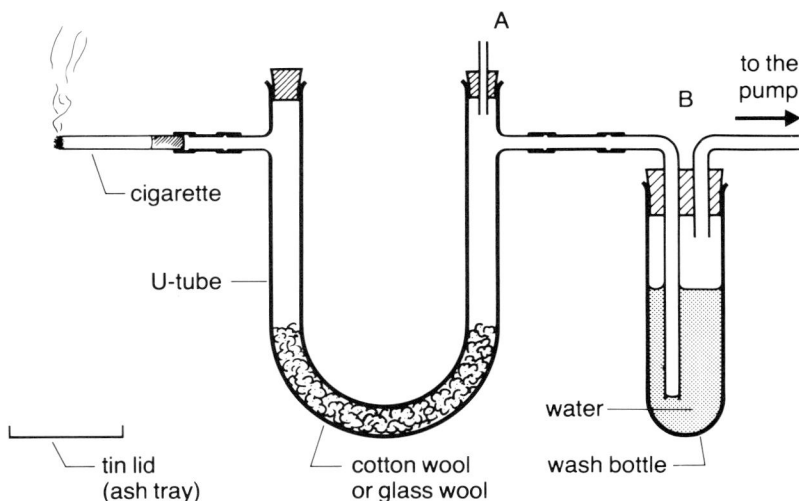

1 What's in the smoke?

Cigarette smoke, cigar smoke and pipe smoke all contain four main types of substance:

cancer-producing substances called **carcinogens**,
irritant substances which cause coughing,
poisonous gases such as **carbon monoxide**,
and **nicotine**, which is a poisonous drug that makes people become addicted to smoking.

The cancer-producing substances are found in the dark brown tar which collects on the cotton wool in the smoking machine (see Figure 10.2). This tar gathers in the lungs and airways of smokers. Experiments show that tar can cause cancer in animals. Lung cancer is common in smokers, but very rare in non-smokers. This does not *prove* that lung cancer in humans is caused by something in cigarette smoke. However, many experts believe that smoking does cause lung cancer. It is a painful and dangerous disease.

Activity

a ▶ Set up the apparatus shown in Figure 10.2.
b ▶ Use a non-tipped cigarette first. Start the pump. Then put your finger over the tube at A when you are ready to light up. The wash-bottle at B will show you how fast the smoke is being sucked through the machine. This will help you to make the speed of the pump suitably slow.

97

c ▶ The cigarette will burn slowly. Put your finger over the tube at A when you want the machine to suck in some smoke.

d ▶ Remove the cotton wool when the cigarette is finished.

1 What colour does the cotton wool go?
2 What does the cotton wool smell like?
3 Describe a suitable control for this experiment.

e ▶ Clean the U-tube. Put in some fresh cotton wool. Repeat the experiment using a tipped cigarette.

f ▶ Remove the cotton wool and examine it. Look at it and smell it.

4 Does the filter tip remove all the tar?
5 Do you think that tipped cigarettes are harmless? Give a reason for your answer.

Smokers often cough much more than non-smokers. This is because the smoke contains various irritant substances such as acrolein. These irritants have three effects on the air passages of the lungs. They make the passages narrower because the muscles in the walls contract. The irritants cause more mucus than normal to be produced. Finally, they paralyse the cilia (tiny hairs) on the walls of the air passages.

6 If the air passages become narrower, will this increase or decrease the amount of air that can pass into the lungs with each breath?
7 What does the mucus do? (Look at Chapter 9 if you need help with this question.)
8 What do the cilia do in the air passages of a healthy person?
9 If the cilia are paralysed, what will happen to the mucus?
10 If the cilia are paralysed, how will the mucus be carried up the air passages to the mouth?
11 Is tobacco smoke good or bad for the air passages? Give a reason.
12 Is smoking good or bad for your health?

Blood carries oxygen to all parts of the body. The body dies if there is not enough oxygen being carried in the blood. Carbon monoxide reduces the amount of oxygen that the blood can carry. Cigarette smoke contains carbon monoxide, and so does the smoke from cigars and pipes. Carbon monoxide may increase the risk of heart disease.

13 Look at Table 10.1. Which mothers give birth to babies with the lowest birth weight?

Table 10.1 Birth weight of babies born to mothers who smoke when they are pregnant

	Number of cigarettes smoked per day by mothers after the 4th month of pregnancy	Mean weight of their babies at birth, in kg
Non-smoker during pregnancy	0	3.39 (7.47 lbs)
Light smoker during pregnancy	5–9	3.20 (7.05 lbs)
Heavy smoker during pregnancy	20–30	3.18 (7.0 lbs)

14 What effect does smoking during pregnancy have on the birth weight of babies?

15 How much lighter are babies born to pregnant women who smoke heavily compared with babies born to women who do not smoke during pregnancy?

16 Now look at Table 10.2. This shows what happens when mothers give up smoking early in pregnancy. What is the average weight at birth of babies born to women smoking 20–30 cigarettes per day who give up smoking early in pregnancy?

17 How does this compare with the average weight at birth of babies born to women who continue to smoke heavily during pregnancy?

Table 10.2 Birth weight of babies born to mothers who do not smoke when they are pregnant

	Number of cigarettes smoked per day *before* pregnancy by mothers who gave up smoking by the 4th month of pregnancy	Mean weight of their babies at birth, in kg
Non-smoker before and during pregnancy	0	3.39 (7.47 lbs)
Light smoker before pregnancy	5–9	3.39 (7.47 lbs)
Heavy smoker before pregnancy	20–30	3.36 (7.40 lbs)

The lower birth weight of babies born to mothers who smoke during pregnancy is probably caused by the carbon monoxide in cigarette smoke. This passes from the mother's blood into the baby's blood. The carbon monoxide makes the baby grow more slowly because of the oxygen shortage. Babies with a lower than normal birth weight are more likely to die or to suffer set-backs.

18 What advice should be given, when they become pregnant, to women who smoke?

The British Government publishes tables which give the tar and nicotine content of cigarettes. Some people think that these tables should include some idea of the carbon monoxide content as well.

Nicotine is a very poisonous drug. It is nicotine which makes people become addicted to smoking. The Royal College of Physicians has this to say about nicotine:

> 'Inhalation of tobacco smoke is an efficient way of transferring nicotine from the (tobacco) leaf into the bloodstream.'
> (*Smoking* or *Health, page 44*)

There is enough nicotine in one small cigar to kill a man. However, to do this the nicotine would have to be extracted from the cigar and injected into his bloodstream. A smoker can absorb up to 10% of the total amount of nicotine from a cigar. The effect of the nicotine will, however, be spread over about 30 minutes. This is long enough for some of the drug to be destroyed. When tobacco is swallowed, the nicotine causes vomiting. This empties the stomach and prevents poisoning. Children have been known to eat cigarettes and to survive because they vomit before the nicotine is absorbed.

2 The cost of smoking

The report by the Royal College of Physicians says that a smoker shortens his life span by about five minutes every time he smokes a cigarette.

1 If a person smokes twelve cigarettes each day, how many hours or days of life would they lose when smoking for one day, one week, one year or ten years?

Fig. 10.3 It does not take long
to burn away the chances of
having your own sports moped

Many people smoke much more than twelve cigarettes each
day. For someone who smokes 24 cigarettes each day, you
can double all the figures which you got above.

In October 1981 a packet of twenty tipped cigarettes cost
about £1. At the same time the cheapest new sports mopeds
were about £430 including tax and insurance for one year.

2 If you smoke 20 cigarettes each day, for how long would
you need to give up smoking in order to save up enough
money to buy a new moped?

It is difficult to estimate precisely how much money smoking
costs the country. People who suffer from diseases caused by
smoking need special medical treatment. This costs a lot of
money. One estimate puts the figure at £2 million each week
in 1979. These people miss more working days than non-
smokers do. This costs money. They need social security
payments when they are off sick. They need sickness benefits when they become too ill to work. A recent report says
that in Britain as many as 50 million working days may be
lost in industry every year because of cigarette smoking. This
is greater than the number of days lost through strikes.

Smoking also causes accidents. For example, it is dangerous to light a cigarette when driving a car. Fires at home, in
factories, and in woodlands can all be caused by careless
smokers. The cost of all these smoking-related problems is
enormous.

Fig. 10.4 Smoking and
smoking related diseases
probably cause more days off
work each year than industrial
disputes

	Women(%)	Men (%)
1972	41	52
1974	41	51
1976	38	46
1978	37	45
1980	37	42

Table 10.3 The proportions of adults who smoke in Britain since 1972

The Government expected to get about £3350 million from tobacco duty and VAT in 1980–81.

3   Fewer smokers

Table 10.3 shows that the proportion of smokers in the British population has fallen steadily in recent years.

1 In 1972, what percentage of the male population were smokers?
2 In 1972, what percentage of men were non-smokers?
3 How had these figures for the male population changed by 1980?
4 Among which group, men or women, has the proportion of smokers fallen most?
5 Why do you think that the smoking habit is declining?

4   The tobacco companies

The tobacco companies manufacture and sell cigarettes, cigars and pipe tobacco. They employ people whose job is to try and sell more of their products. They spend about £80 million each year on the advertising and promotion of tobacco products. Recent reports on the tobacco industry refer to the effect of health campaigns on cigarette sales. They say that these campaigns have helped to reduce sales in countries such as Britain and the USA.

In 1971, the tobacco companies agreed to print this warning on the side of every pack of cigarettes sold in Britain:

'Warning by H.M. Government: Smoking Can Damage Your Health.'

Most smokers already knew this, and in one survey most of them said that this warning had no effect on their smoking. Later the warning was changed to read:

'Warning by H.M. Government: Smoking Can *Seriously* Damage Your Health.'

The tobacco companies were then asked to alter the warning again to:

'Danger: Cigarettes Cause Lung Cancer, Bronchitis and Heart Disease.'

So far, they have refused to do this.

1 What do the tobacco companies stand to lose by admitting that smoking causes ill health?
2 In what ways would the country benefit if more people stopped smoking?

In many developing countries there are no health warnings on cigarette packets, and cigarette advertising is not restricted as it is in Britain. In these countries cigarette sales are increasing and so are the smoking related diseases.

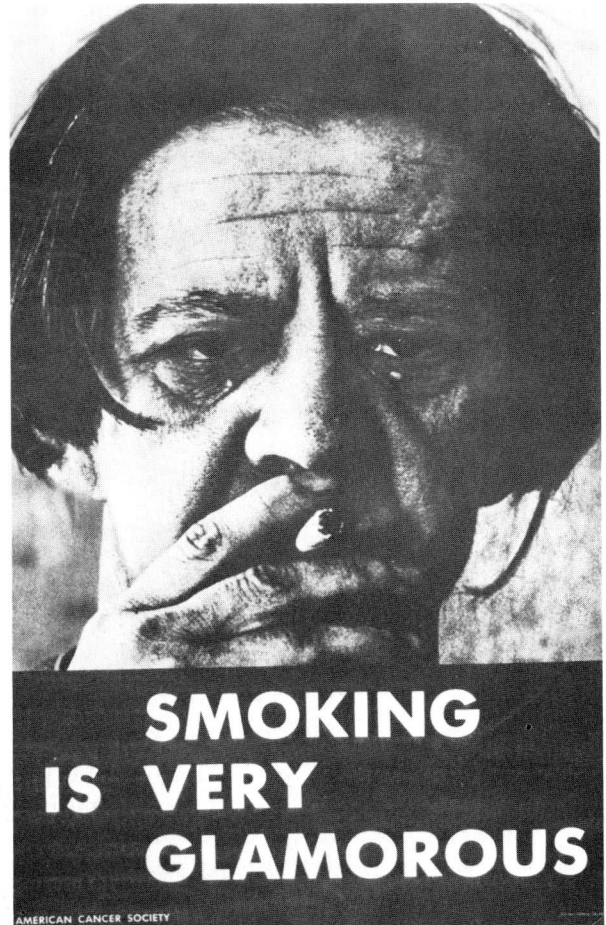

Fig. 10.5 W.H.O. and other health organisations have started campaigns to try and reduce the number of smokers. Can you explain the message in these photographs?

11   The heart

Why do we have a heart? What does it do?

1   The pulse

There are blood vessels all over the body. Some are easy to see, because they are close to the skin surface. Most blood vessels cannot be seen because they are buried deep among the muscles and other tissues. If you press your fingertips against some blood vessels you will feel a regular throbbing movement. This is called the pulse. Blood vessels which have a pulse are called arteries. They carry blood away from the heart. There are various places on the body where the pulse can be felt.

Activity

a ▶ Try to find some of these pulse points on yourself. Use the tips of your fingers only. Figure 11.1 shows how to find the pulse point on the wrist. The head and the neck are other good places on which to find pulse points.

 1 Name three places on your body where you can feel a pulse.

Fig. 11.1 How to take your pulse

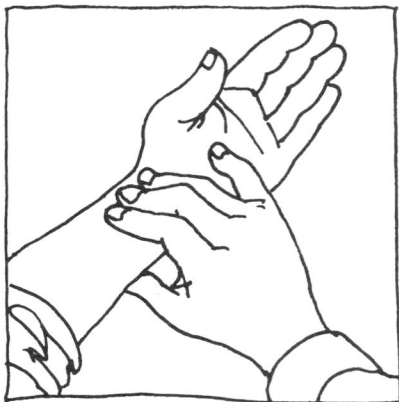

2   Heartbeat and pulse

Activity

a ▶ Work in pairs. First look at Figure 11.2 and decide who will be pupil A and who will be pupil B. Later you can change over.
b ▶ Pupil A: use your right hand to find the place on your chest where you can feel the heart beating. Just to the left of centre is best.
c ▶ Pupil B: find the pulse on pupil A's left wrist.
d ▶ Pupil A: start counting your heartbeat throbs out loud, speaking just loud enough for pupil B to hear.

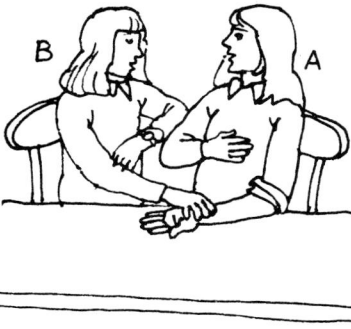

Fig. 11.2 *Pupil B is taking Pupil A's pulse and listening to Pupil A counting her heartbeats*

e ▶ Pupil B: listen to pupil A counting. Compare this with the pulse you can feel on pupil A's wrist.

1 A question for pupil B to answer. Is pupil A's pulse rate faster, slower or the same as pupil A's heartbeat rate?

f ▶ Now change over and see if you get the same answer.

2 Each pulse throb is caused by a sudden rise in the pressure of the blood in the artery. What do you think causes this sudden rise in pressure of the blood in the artery? The exercise that you have just done on heartbeat and pulse rate should help you to answer this question.

3 What makes the hot water move through the pipes and radiators of a modern central heating system?

Blood vessels are like pipes. The blood is like water. A pump is needed to move the blood through the blood vessels. This pump is the heart. Every time it beats, the heart forces blood out through the arteries. With each heartbeat there is a rise in pressure. This causes the arteries to swell, which is what you can feel at the pulse points. This explains why pulse rate is the same as heartbeat rate.

Fig. 11.3 *During the course of your lifetime your heart will probably pump about 60 million gallons of blood. That is enough to fill a small reservoir*

g ▶ Write down your own pulse rate (number of beats in one minute) after sitting down, then after walking around, and finally after running.

h ▶ Compare your results with the results of other people in the class.

4 Does your pulse rate stay the same? What happens to it when you move about?

5 Do all people have the same pulse rate when they are doing the same thing?

6 If a girl's heart beats, on average, 70 times each minute, how many times will her heart beat in one hour, in one day, in one year, and in 75 years (a lifetime)? You will find a calculator useful for this question, and you may need help, especially with the last part, because it is such a large number.

Your heart is the best pump ever made. In most people, the heart works all the time, without repair or servicing, for the whole of their lives. The speed at which it beats can be changed, in a few seconds, from about 70 to 140 beats per minute or more. Rates of 200 or more occur during violent exercise. Most important of all, the heart does not damage the blood as this passes through it. Blood is a delicate thing. No man has ever built a pump which is so gentle, so strong and so reliable. But the heart can go wrong if it is not looked after properly.

3 Finding out how fit you are

Activity

a ▶ Copy out Table 11.1.
b ▶ Work in pairs. Decide who will do the exercise first. Make sure you can see a clock with a second hand.

Total exercise time = 4 mins (240 secs)

1st pulse reading =..........beats in 30 secs
2nd pulse reading =..........beats in 30 secs
3rd pulse reading =..........beats in 30 secs

Total pulse reading =..........beats
(add up your 3 readings)

Multiply your total pulse reading by 2 to get your Grand pulse reading

Grand pulse reading = ...

Fitness score = $\dfrac{\text{Total exercise time (secs)}}{\text{Grand pulse reading}} \times 100$

= ....

Fitness scores:
over 90 — very fit indeed
81 – 90 — very good
71 – 80 — good
61 – 70 — quite good
51 – 60 — poor
under 51 — very poor

Table 11.1 Use a table like this to work out your fitness score

Fig. 11.4 Sebastian Coe slicing 1·07 seconds off the world Mile Record on 28 August 1981

Fig. 11.5 Red and white blood cells and platelets. There are more white blood cells than normal in this photograph. Normally there are about 600 red blood cells for every 1 white blood cell

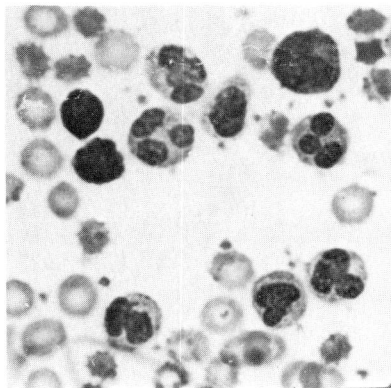

c ▶ Use a box, chair or stool which is about 40–50 cm high for the physical exercise. Carry out the exercise like this. First, step up onto the box and stand on it with both legs straight. Then step down and stand on the floor with both legs straight. Step up and down like this for a total of four minutes. Do not try to go too fast. You should keep going at a steady rate of about one step up every two seconds. Step up and down, without stopping, for four minutes. Then sit down and rest.

d ▶ Rest for exactly one minute. Then get your partner to take your pulse for 30 seconds. This is your first pulse reading. Write it down in your results table.

e ▶ Rest for a further 30 seconds. Then get your partner to take your pulse for another 30 seconds. This is your second pulse reading. Write it down.

f ▶ Repeat the previous stage. This gives you a third pulse reading.

g ▶ Work out your fitness score (see Table 11.1).

h ▶ Change over and let your partner do the fitness test.

1 How fit are you (see Table 11.1)?
2 Who are the fittest people in the class? Why are they fitter than other people?
3 In 1981, Sebastian Coe held three world track records. What sort of fitness score do you think he had?

4 Blood

Look at Figures 11.5 and 11.6. Your teacher may be able to show you some preserved blood on a microscope slide, a film or filmstrip about blood, or even some fresh blood.

Blood is a liquid with some small solid objects in it.

1 Look at Figure 11.5. Name three of the solid objects in blood.

The red blood cells carry oxygen. The white blood cells help the body to fight against infection and diseases. When the skin is cut, the platelets help to form a clot. This stops further bleeding. The liquid part of the blood is called **plasma**. Plasma is water with lots of things dissolved in it, for example glucose. One of the most important things that blood does is to carry things around the body. For example, it carries oxygen and glucose to the parts where they are

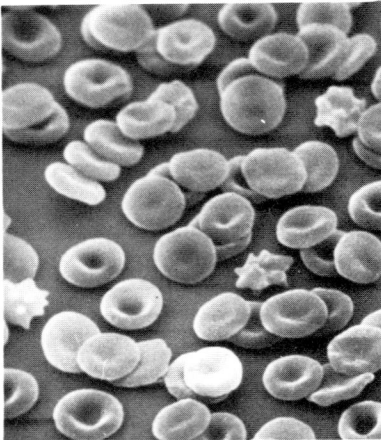

Fig. 11.6 A scanning electronmicrograph of red blood cells. Notice the doughnut shape, and notice also that some have lost this shape and are becoming ragged. The cells are magnified 1200 times

Fig. 11.7 The blood circulation system as described by William Harvey

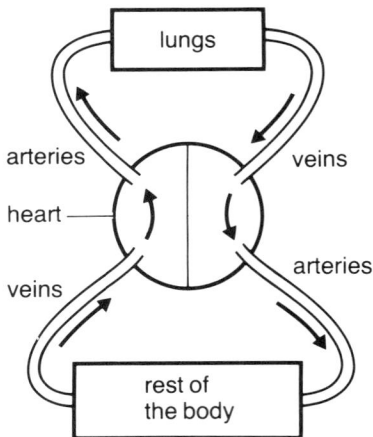

needed. Blood also carries waste products away from the places where they are produced. This is why the blood and the blood vessels are called a transport system.

2 Make a list of important things which the blood does. These have been mentioned in the passage above.

5 The blood circulation

Two thousand years ago, the Greeks thought that blood moved backwards and forwards in the blood vessels rather like waves on a beach. They also believed that blood was gradually used up by the body, and that new blood was made from food, water and air. In 1628, William Harvey, an English doctor who worked at St Bartholomew's Hospital in London, published a famous book about the heart.

Doctors in Harvey's day were taught the Greek ideas about blood. They were not expected to study the heart and blood vessels for themselves. It was enough to hear about the Greek ideas and to glance at a few dissected bodies. Harvey was the first doctor to make a really careful study of the heart and blood vessels for himself. He was able to show that the Greeks were wrong. The blood moves in one direction only through the heart and blood vessels. The heart acts as a pump to keep the blood moving.

Harvey discovered the circulation of the blood (see Figure 11.7). He worked out how much blood was pumped out of the heart each minute. He also showed that this was far more than could be made from the food and water taken in. This helped to support his idea that blood moves round the body continuously, and that it is not used up. Harvey was unable to see the smallest blood vessels, which we now call capillaries, but he knew that they must be there. However, soon afterwards in 1661, an Italian scientist named Malpighi used a microscope to examine the lungs of a frog. He was able to see the capillaries. Blood passes from the arteries through the capillaries to the veins. The last link in Harvey's discoveries about blood circulation was now in place.

1 In which direction do arteries carry blood, towards or away from the heart? (See Figures 11.7 and 11.8.)
2 In which direction do veins carry blood?
3 Look at Figure 11.7. Pretend that you are a red blood cell in a blood vessel in the lungs. How many times will you pass through the heart before you get back to the lungs?

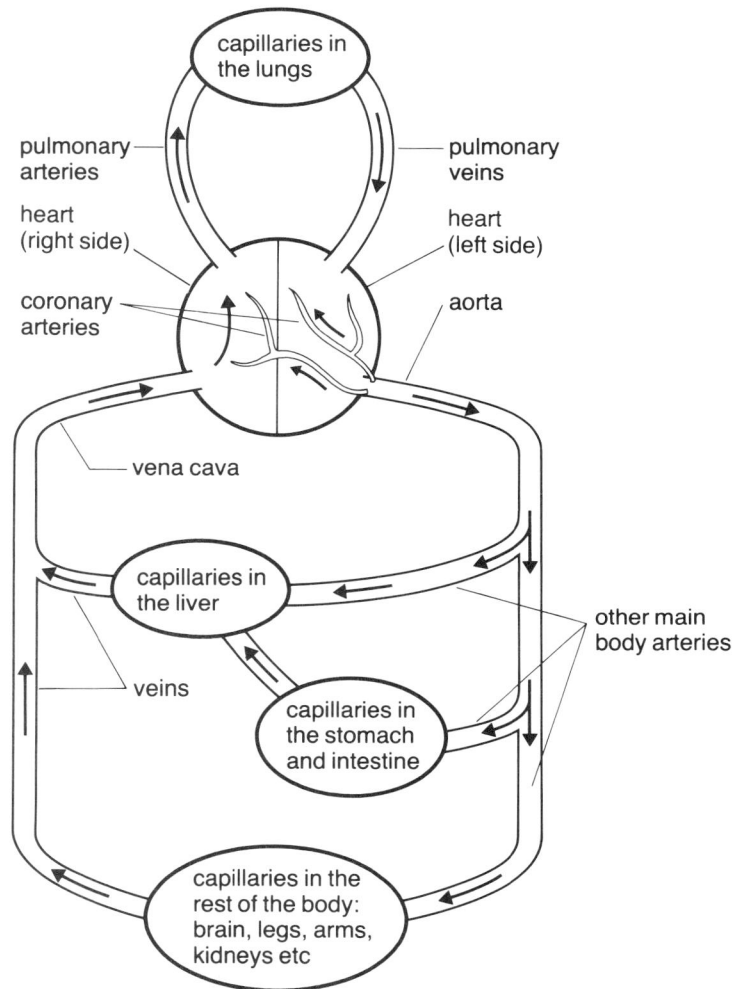

Fig. 11.8 *The blood circulation system including the capillaries which were discovered by Malpighi*

4 Whereabouts on the route which you follow in question 3 will you pick up oxygen, and where will you lose it?

5 Harvey showed that some Greek ideas about blood were wrong. Which ideas were wrong?

6 Use Figure 11.8 to help you to arrange the following in the correct order to show the path followed by blood as it travels from the liver capillaries to the main body arteries. Start your list with 'liver capillaries' and end it with 'main body arteries'.

aorta	liver capillaries	pulmonary vein
lung capillary	main body arteries	right side of heart
left side of heart	pulmonary artery	vena cava

7 In which of these two arteries is there more oxygen, the aorta or the pulmonary artery? Explain your answer.

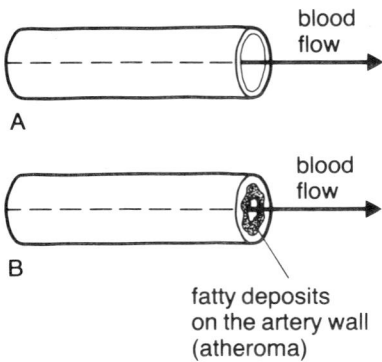

A

blood flow

B

blood flow

fatty deposits
on the artery wall
(atheroma)

Fig. 11.9

*Fig. 11.10 The main causes of
death in Britain in 1978*

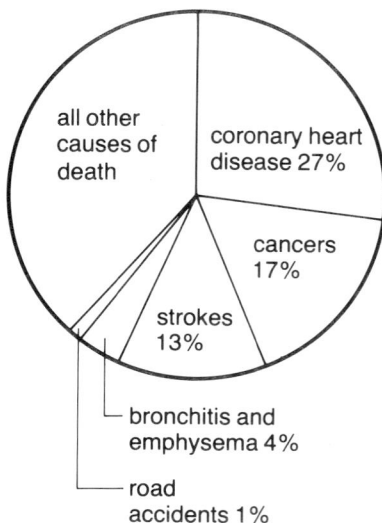

all other causes of death

coronary heart disease 27%

cancers 17%

strokes 13%

bronchitis and emphysema 4%

road accidents 1%

6 Diseases of the blood circulation

Many things can go wrong with the blood circulation. By far the most common disorder occurs when a fatty substance collects in the walls of the arteries making them narrower (see Figure 11.9).

1 Which of the two arteries shown in Figure 11.9 will allow the most blood to pass through in a given time? Assume that the blood is at the same pressure in both vessels.

2 The blood carries food, oxygen and other important things to all parts of the body. Imagine that artery B in Figure 11.9 is carrying blood to the leg. How will the amount of food and oxygen reaching the leg be affected?

This kind of arterial disease is very serious if it occurs in the arteries leading to the brain. In this case it can cause a **stroke** because the brain gets insufficient oxygen. The person collapses. They might recover, but if they do the brain is often permanently damaged. Arterial disease in the coronary arteries is also serious.

3 Where are the coronary arteries (see Figure 11.8)?

The coronary arteries carry blood to the muscles in the walls of the heart. If these arteries become narrower, it may lead to a **heart attack**. When the coronary arteries become narrower this is called coronary heart disease or ischaemic heart disease. Coronary heart disease kills more people than anything else in Britain today (see Figure 11.10). Death is caused, in this case, when the heart stops beating properly (a heart attack) and the blood supply to the brain stops. It is often very sudden and very unexpected. Some people survive one heart attack only to be killed later by another one.

Coronary heart disease is much more common in smokers than in non-smokers. Smokers who give up smoking after surviving a heart attack are less likely to have another heart attack than those who continue to smoke. Nearly all people with arterial disease of the legs are smokers. For these people, walking becomes painful and many of them get **gangrene** so that one or both legs have to be **amputated** (cut off). Gangrene is caused by lack of food and oxygen. In this case it is caused by the blocked leg arteries.

No one knows why the fatty material collects in the walls of the arteries. There seem to be several things which

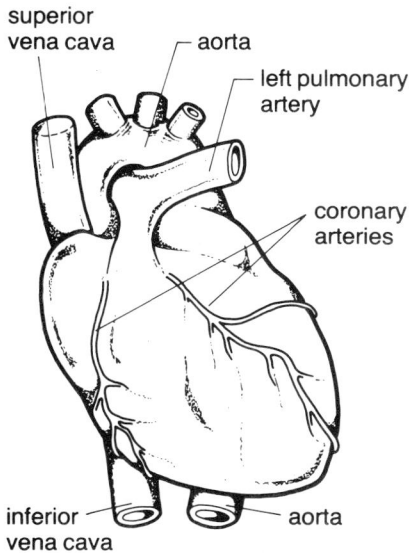

Fig. 11.11 The human heart

Fig. 11.12a The coronary arteries can become blocked

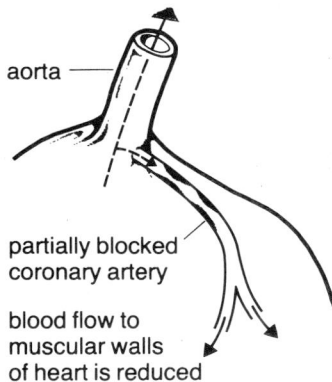

aorta

partially blocked coronary artery

blood flow to muscular walls of heart is reduced

Fig. 11.12b The blocked area can be by-passed by stitching a second vessel into place

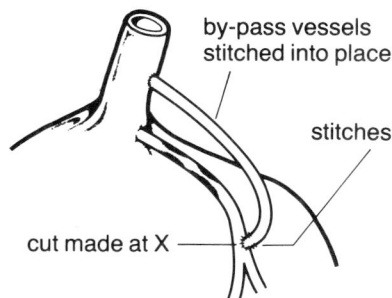

by-pass vessels stitched into place

stitches

cut made at X

increase the risk of this type of arterial disease. They are: smoking, high blood pressure, obesity, high levels of a fatty substance (cholesterol) in the blood, lack of exercise, stress (worry), and old age. The disease is also more common in some families than it is in others. It is more common in men than in women up to the age of 50. After this age, it is equally common in men and women.

7 Repairing the heart

A healthy heart gives the body a good blood supply so that all parts get enough food and oxygen. However, several things can go wrong with the heart. For example, a few people are born with a faulty heart. Many more people start their lives with a healthy heart, but later it becomes diseased. Some heart disease is caused by infections which may be treated with modern drugs and recovery can be quick. An example is rheumatic heart disease.

By far the most common type of heart disease occurs when one (or more) of the coronary arteries becomes partly or almost completely blocked. This is called coronary heart disease and more information about it is given in Section 6. The main coronary arteries are shown in Figure 11.11. A good way to treat coronary heart disease is to by-pass the blocked bit of coronary artery. Usually, pieces of one of the veins in the leg are used to make the by-pass. The leg does not suffer, because there are plenty of other veins there to share the job of carrying the blood.

1 Which will allow more blood to pass through it, the old partly blocked bit of coronary artery or the new by-pass vessel?
2 How will this make the heart more healthy?

Putting the by-pass vessel in place is obviously a difficult operation. Questions 3 and 4 will help you to work out why it is difficult. There are several reasons.

3 What will happen to the blood in it when the coronary artery is cut at point X in Figure 11.12b?
4 Many small stitches are needed to put the by-pass vessel into exactly the right position. Normally the heart beats at about 70 beats to the minute. What problem do these two pieces of information provide for the surgeon?

For this operation to be successful, the heart must be stopped and by-passed completely. However, the heart is really two pumps. One delivers blood to the lungs. The other delivers blood to the rest of the body. Therefore, in order to make the operation simpler, the lungs are by-passed as well. This means that only one artificial pump is needed, and an artificial oxygenator is used instead of the lungs. The circulation diagram shown in Figure 11.7 can be modified to show what is needed. (See Figure 11.13.) Normal body temperature is 37 °C. Cooling the body to about 30 °C reduces the activity in all parts. Therefore less oxygen is needed. The heart is kept much cooler and treated with various chemicals which stop its muscular activity. Therefore it is not damaged when its blood supply is cut off. This means that the problems mentioned in questions 3 and 4 are solved. There is no great leakage of blood when the coronary artery is cut, because there is very little blood in it. Also, the heart has stopped beating and is perfectly still. This enables the surgeon to put the stitches in exactly the right places.

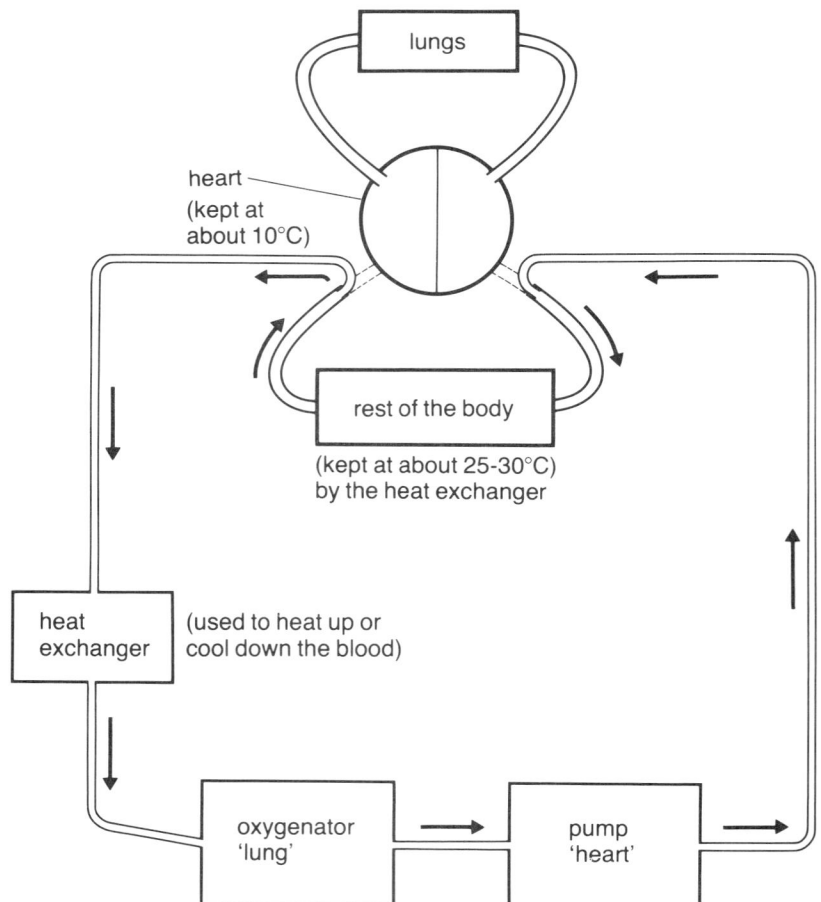

Fig. 11.13 During a major heart operation the blood system is kept going by machines

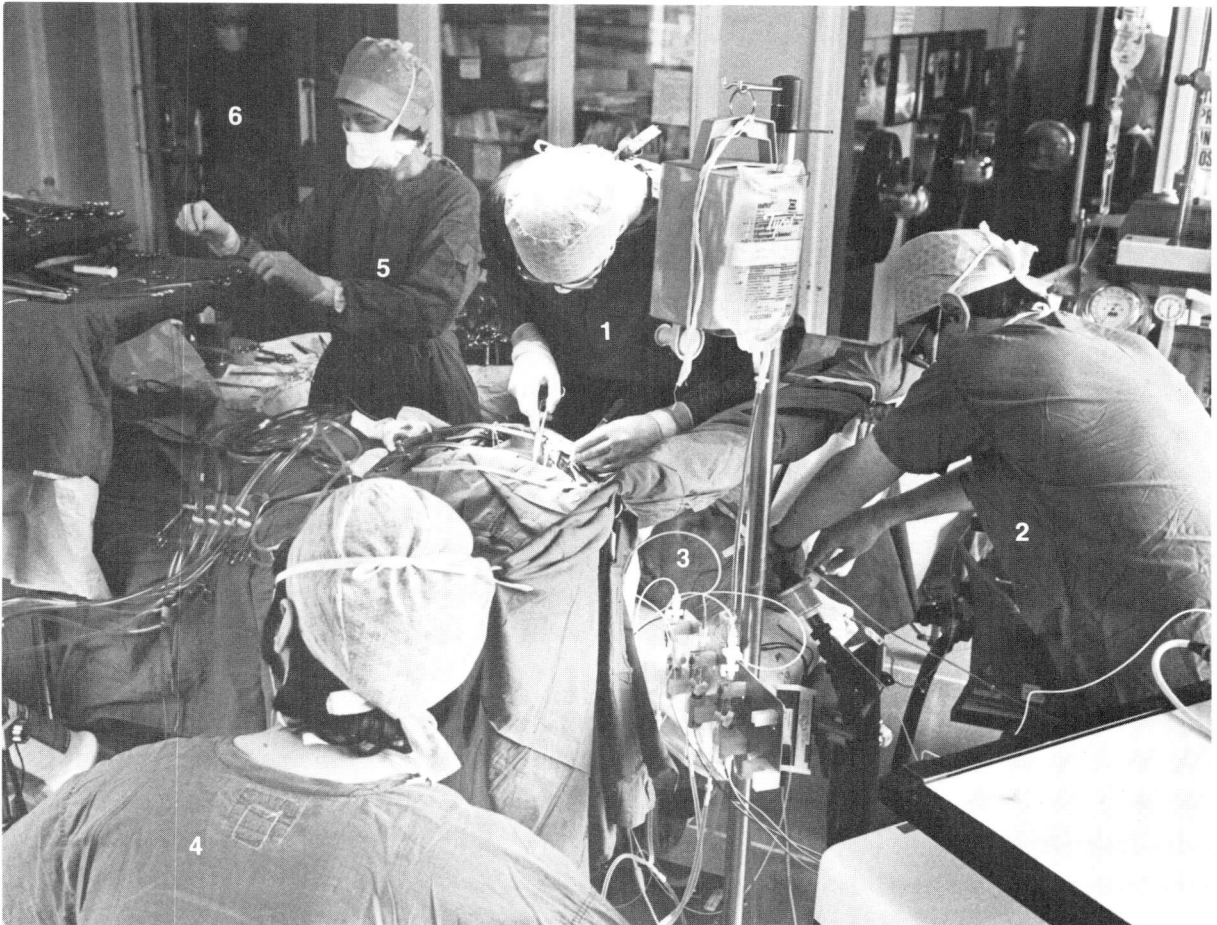

1 surgeon
2 anaesthetist
3 patient
4 technician
5 theatre sister
6 nurse

Fig. 11.14 An operating theatre at Papworth hospital, Cambridgeshire during a heart operation

5 How many differently trained people are shown in Figure 11.14?

8 Cardiac arrest!

All parts of the body need a continuous supply of blood. For example, if the blood supply to the brain stops for longer than three minutes it becomes damaged. Other parts of the body can go without a blood supply for longer without being damaged. However, the muscular walls of the heart itself are quickly damaged if their blood supply is stopped.

1 Which blood vessels supply blood to the walls of the heart (see Figure 11.8)?
2 When the heart stops beating, what happens to the movement of blood around the body?

113

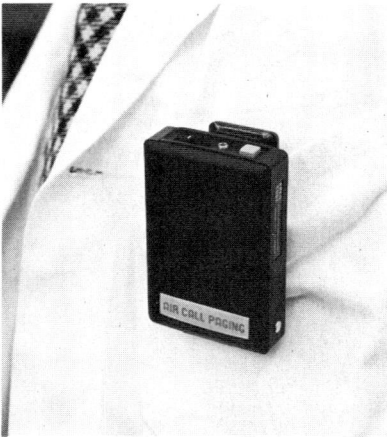

Fig. 11.15 *A bleep is a small radio receiver which the doctor can carry in his pocket*

3 Which part of the body will suffer damage first if the blood circulation does not start up again quickly?
4 If a person's heart stops beating, it is very important to get it going again as quickly as possible. When the heart stops beating, doctors and nurses call this a **cardiac arrest**. What do you think the word 'cardiac' means?

Hospitals are always prepared for cardiac arrests. In a large hospital, there will usually be three or four doctors called the **crash team**. Their job is to get to any patient with a cardiac arrest as soon as possible. The problem is that hospitals are large, busy places. These doctors may be a long way from the patient. To overcome this, each member of the crash team carries a special **bleep** for emergencies (see Figure 11.15). The bleeps are small radios which are tuned to a special transmitter at the hospital switchboard. There are telephones all over the hospital. If a patient has a cardiac arrest someone, usually a nurse, calls the switchboard. The switchboard operator presses a button and all the emergency bleeps make a loud bleeping noise. This noise can easily be heard by those who carry the bleeps. At the same time, the operator can tell the doctors, over the radio, where the patient is. The members of the crash team stop what they are doing. They go as quickly as possible to the cardiac arrest patient. When they arrive, they try to get the heart beating again. They may use drugs or a special electric shock machine. If these fail, an operation may be needed.

Fig. 11.16a *Nurses at Newmarket General Hospital discover a patient with a cardiac arrest. One immediately rings the switchboard while the other starts to ventilate the lungs. They will then start cardiac massage*

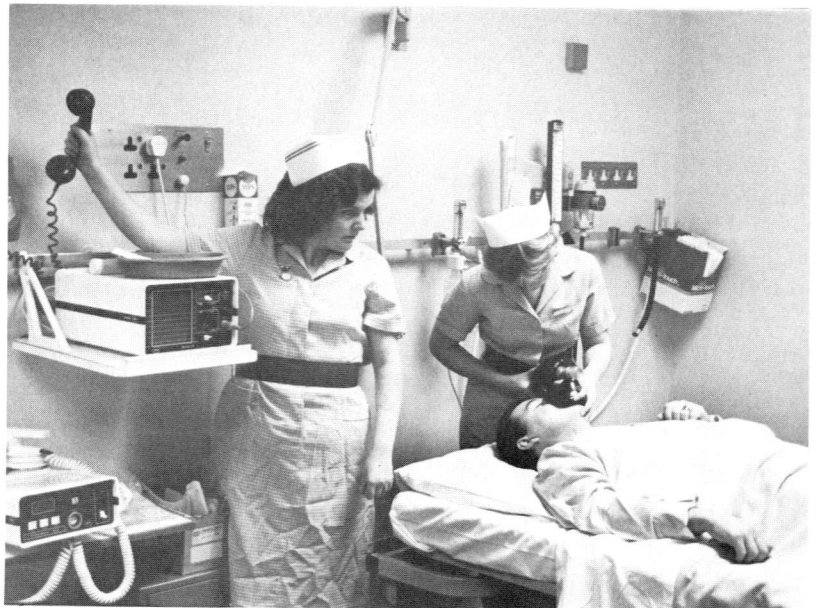

114

11.16b ▲

Fig. 11.16b (above) The switchboard immediately broadcasts a message which tells the doctor where the patient is

11.16c ▲

11.16d ▲

Fig. 11.16c (above right) The doctor receives the message . . .

Fig. 11.16d (far right) . . . and comes running

Fig. 11.16e (right) The chest is being massaged to keep the blood moving. A tube is put into the trachea to help the breathing, and drugs to stimulate the heart are being given. Notice that one of the nurses is recording everything that happens

Fig. 11.16f (right) If he still does not recover the patient may be given an electric shock to try and start his heart again. Everyone stands back

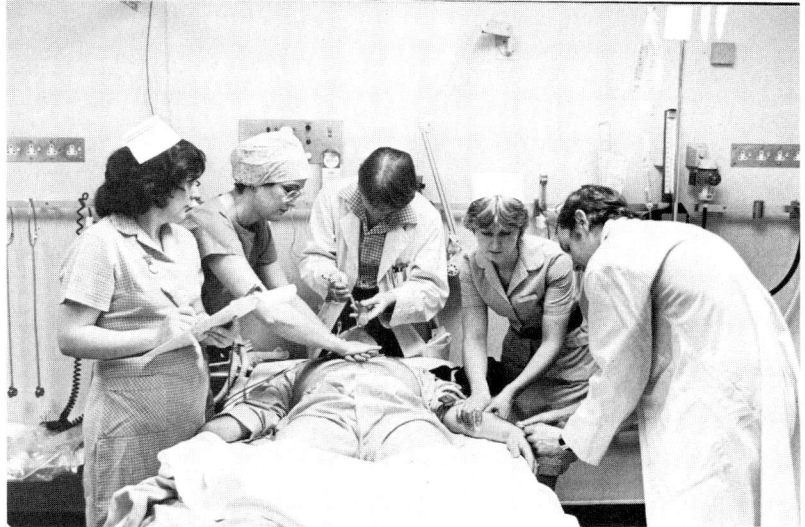

11.16e ▲

11.16f ▼

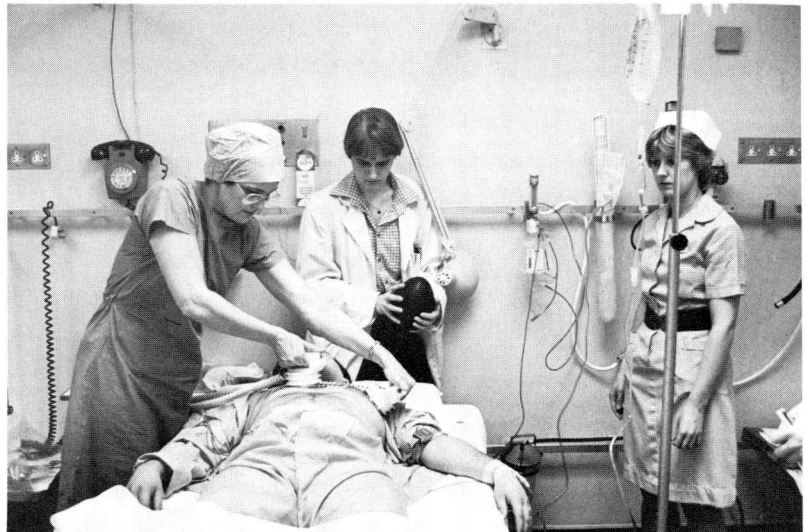

Human population

1 Introduction

Today the world population increases by about one million people every four days. This means that, by this time tomorrow there will be a quarter of a million more people on earth than there are now. For many people life today is very hard and miserable. They do not get enough food. They suffer from diseases. They lack clothing and proper housing. In addition to this, many of them are unemployed and they receive no unemployment pay. Do you think their life is worth living?

Throughout this chapter, all figures for world population are given in billions. One billon equals one thousand million, or 1 000 000 000.

Fig. 12.1a *Many towns and cities are becoming very crowded*

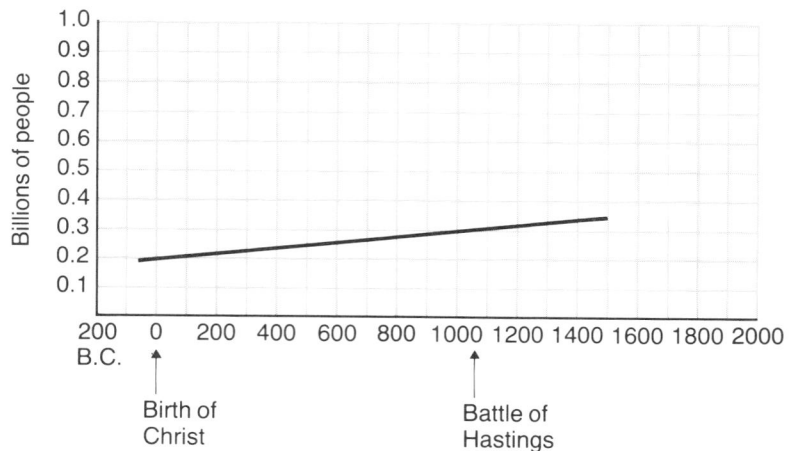

Fig. 12.1b *Estimates of human population for the years from 200 BC to 1500 AD*

Year when estimate was made	Estimated figure for world population in 1980 (billions)
1951	3.277
1954	3.628
1958	4.220
1963	4.330
1968	4.457
1973	4.374
1980	4.415

Table 12.1 Estimates for the 1980 world population

2 The size of the problem: estimating world population

1 Look at Figure 12.1b. What happened to the world population between the birth of Christ and the year 1500 AD? Did it increase, decrease or stay the same?

2 Imagine that you are living in the year 1500 AD. Someone shows you Figure 12.1b on the previous page. They ask you to guess what the world population will be in the year 2000 AD. What would your answer be? This is your estimate for world population in the year 2000 AD.

3 What information did you use in order to make this estimate?

For many years, experts have been making estimates of the world population and trying to guess what it will be in the future. For example, Table 12.1 shows the estimates made, in the past, for the year 1980.

4 Which estimate for the population in 1980 is likely to be the most accurate? Give reasons.

5 Do most of the past estimates for world population in 1980 seem to be too high or too low?

6 Figure 12.2 shows world population estimates for the years 1400 to 2000. These are based on recent population studies by the United Nations. What has happened to world population between the years 1500 and 2000?

7 The dotted line in Figure 12.2 shows the estimated future world population up to the year 2000. Use this line to give you an estimate of world population in the year 2000.

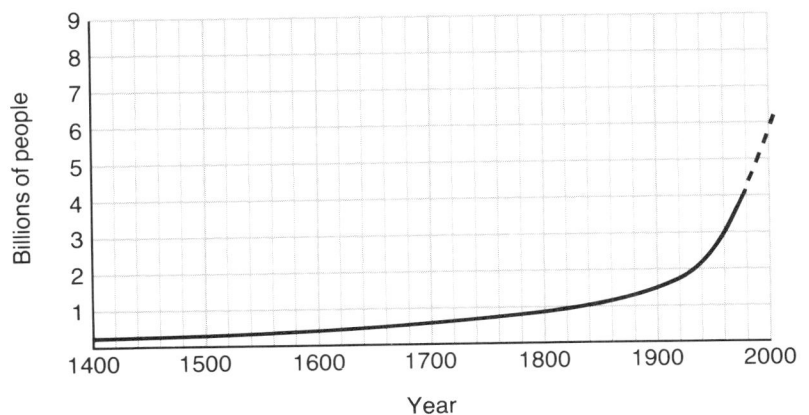

Fig. 12.2 World population estimates and a projection for the year 2000

117

8 Compare this estimate (your answer to question 7) with your earlier estimate for the year 2000 (question 2). What is the difference between the two estimates?

9 Which of these two estimates is likely to be the better? Give reasons.

Scientists and other experts often have to make estimates. As you can see, it is not an easy task. It depends very much on the information which you already have. For example, in 1945 some experts said that the world's grain supply would never be enough to feed a population of more than 2.8 billion people.

10 Was the estimated world population in 1980 more or less than 2.8 billion?

11 Were the experts right?

The population experts have often been wrong, but they have a very difficult job. One of the main reasons for mistakes in the past was a lack of accurate information about the population of one country. That country is China. One recent United Nations report said that China's population growth rate in the 1950s and 1960s was higher than generally believed. About one quarter of all the people on Earth live in China. Therefore any error in estimates for China will affect estimates for the whole world.

When speaking about the human population, it is convenient to divide countries into two types. These are the developed countries and the developing countries. The developed countries are industrialised countries. They include those of North America, Europe, the USSR, Australia, New Zealand and Japan. Some developing countries have very little industry. They include many countries in Africa. In other developing countries, such as India and Brazil, industrial development is well under way. However, this division is an artificial one. Some countries would rather not be included under either of these labels.

Recently, there has been a slight fall in the birth rate in many developing countries. For example, China's population is not growing as fast as it was. This information leads some experts to say that the period of most rapid increase in world population is over. This period was between 1951 and 1975. During this short time, the world population rose from about 2.5 billion to nearly 4 billion.

The huge human population sets us many problems. For example, how can we feed and house a population of 6 billion people in the year 2000? How can we safely get rid of all the waste that they and their activities produce? These are important questions for everyone. They must be tackled by politicians, scientists and other experts throughout the world.

3 A closer look at human population growth

The study of populations is complicated. Figure 12.3 shows that the world population is not growing at the same rate in all parts of the world. In Figure 12.3 one centimetre (cm) on the vertical scale is equal to one billion people. Therefore, if a bar is 3.1 cm high, this represents 3.1 billion people.

1 If a bar is 2.8 cm high, how many people does this represent?
2 What was the estimated population of south Asia in 1970?
3 What was the estimated population of south Asia in 1980?
4 Look at the bar for the year 1990 in Figure 12.3. Which area has a future estimated population of about 0.6 billion people?
5 Which area of the world had the largest estimated population in 1980?
6 Which area has the largest estimated population in the year 2000?
7 The estimates in Figure 12.3 show that between 1980 and 2000 the population of several areas will almost double. Which areas are they?
8 Where will the greatest efforts to increase food production have to be made?
9 One country makes up most of the population of east Asia. Which one do you think it is?

4 Factors affecting populations

A population increases if the number of births in one year is greater than the number of deaths. Factors which might affect the survival of plants or animals are listed below.

Good food supply	Only a few natural
Diseases	enemies (predators)
Not enough food	Little disease
	Many predators

1 Which of these might make it possible for a population of plants or animals to increase?

Fig. 12.3 Populations grow at different rates in different parts of the world

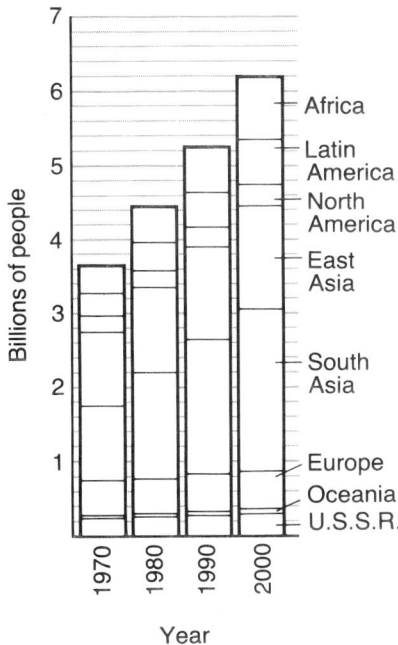

119

2 Which might cause a population to decrease?

3 Which of the factors listed above might also reduce survival in a human population?

4 What other factor or factors might reduce survival in human populations?

Food is obviously important. The factors listed below might affect human food production.

Good weather, especially the right amount of rain

Pests of growing crops, for example locusts
   and fungus diseases

Strong healthy farmers

Pests of stored food, for example rats and insect pests

Land which is well looked after

Farmers weakened by hunger and disease

War

Pest-proof food stores

Peace

Natural disasters, for example floods,
   earthquakes or drought

Soil erosion

Pest control on growing crops

5 Which of the factors listed above might help to provide enough food for the world's population?

6 Which of these factors might reduce food production?

Few people think that the world's population problem can be solved merely by providing more food. There seems likely to be a limit to the amount of food which can be produced even with advanced food technology. The problem is this. The human population cannot go on increasing as it is at the moment (Figure 12.2). Some factor or factors must act to stop this huge increase. There are many different ideas about how this might happen. A nuclear war could do it. The human population could be limited by starvation. People might start to limit the size of their families, for example, to two or three children only. New, highly infectious diseases could appear and spread so quickly through the human population that many people would die before medical science could act to stop the disease from spreading. Pollution could interfere with food production causing starvation. Pollution might kill people directly. There are many unknown factors. For example, we do not know how man would behave in really over-crowded conditions throughout the world. We might become even more selfish and aggressive. No one knows.

5 Rich and poor nations – do they need one another?

The Food and Agriculture Organisation (FAO) of the United Nations has a worldwide network of staff. Their job is to collect information about food and agriculture. They offer advice to governments. They also raise money and give financial help and food aid to countries in need. The number of countries helped by the FAO is increasing every year and there is never enough money to give all the help that is needed.

From time to time reports of hunger, starvation and famine appear in the news. The causes of these disasters include poor harvests, floods, earthquakes and war. The rich countries have been criticised for making this situation worse. If the rich countries helped the poor countries to reduce poverty, then people would be well fed. They would also have more money to spend. They will want to buy the sort of things that the developed countries manufacture. These include cars and other machines, refrigerators, clothes, tape recorders, computers, machine tools and other factory equipment. This would give more jobs in the developed countries. The rich and poor nations need each other. The rich nations need people to buy their manufactured goods. If the poor nations were not so poor, they could buy these manufactured goods. The poor nations need help that only the rich nations can provide. Without it they remain poor.

No one says that the problems are simple or that there are simple answers. The fact remains that the world population seems likely to reach at least 6 billion by the year 2000. These

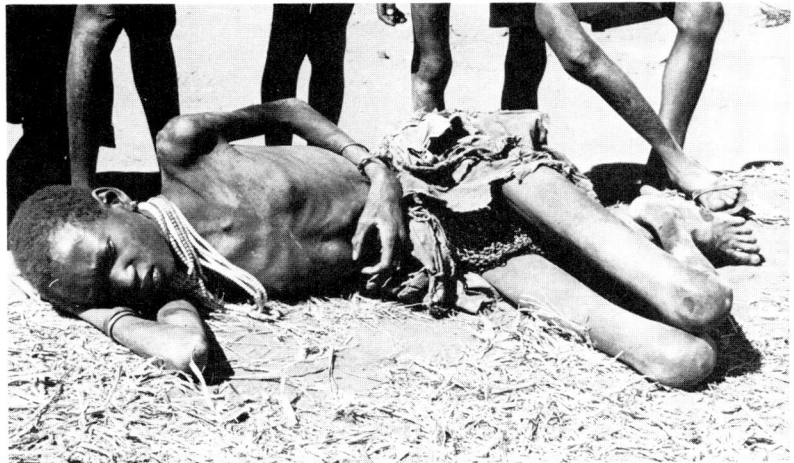

Fig. 12.4 One of the victims of the severe famine in Uganda in 1980 and 1981. Millions of people are badly underfed in many parts of the world

people will need food. Present world agricultural trade is unable to feed today's population properly. There is probably enough food, but it doesn't get to all the people who need it.

From time to time the richer nations have made real efforts to help those in need. For example, at the end of the Second World War (1939–45), famine threatened much of Europe and India. The British Prime Minister at the time said that Britain would have to go without in order to help. In July 1946, bread rationing began in Britain. Bread was never rationed during the war. The decision to ration bread was a very unpopular one. However, the Prime Minister believed that it was the right thing to do. The USA, Australia and Canada also helped and the threat of famine was avoided.

It may now be time that the rich nations again went without in order to help the poor nations.

1 What do you think?

Many aid programmes are financed by charities. These programmes now aim to help poor people to help themselves. Fishing nets or a pest-proof food store may be provided instead of food. Efforts are also made to get people together to help each other. In this way local self-help schemes are set up and the local people benefit directly from their own efforts. However, the needs of each group of poor people are different. The best solution in one place may not be the best solution in another place. It will depend on local conditions. Efforts to find the right solutions to local problems must always involve the local people.

Human reproduction

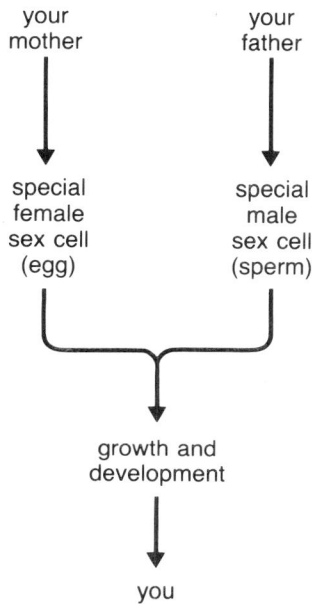

Fig. 13.1 *How you began*

Fig. 13.2 *A human ovum with three or four sperm cells around it. Magnification:* ×12,000

1 Introduction

How did you begin? Where did you come from?

You began life when a male sex cell from your father joined together with a female sex cell from your mother. Before finding out how these cells actually got together, you need to know something about where they are made.

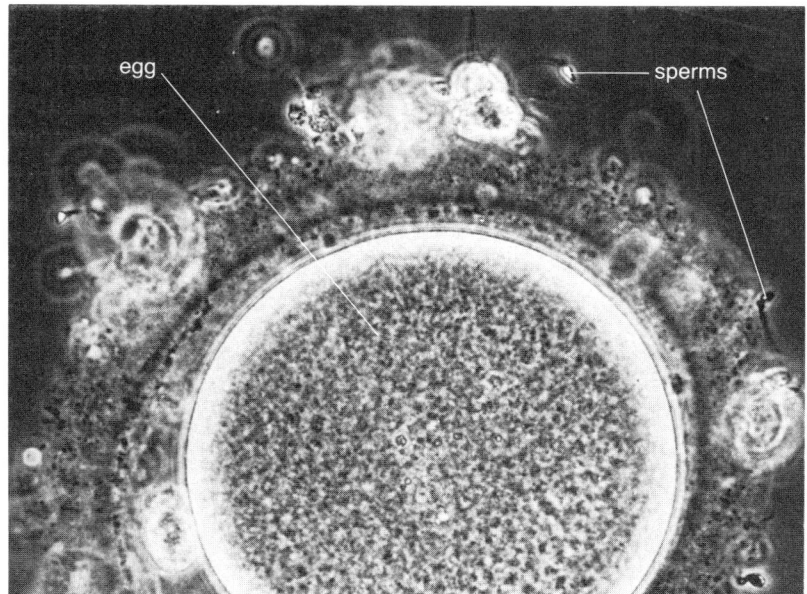

2 The female system

The female sex cells are called **eggs**. They are about the size of a pin head, so they are much larger than **sperms** (see Figure 13.2). Eggs are made and stored in the **ovaries** of a woman (see Figure 13.3). Each **ovary** contains thousands of eggs. Usually, one egg ripens and is released from an ovary every month. There are two ovaries. They usually take it in turns to release the monthly egg.

1 How many eggs would you expect to be released by a woman in one year?
2 How many of these would you expect to have come from the left ovary?

Fig. 13.3 Human female
reproductive organs

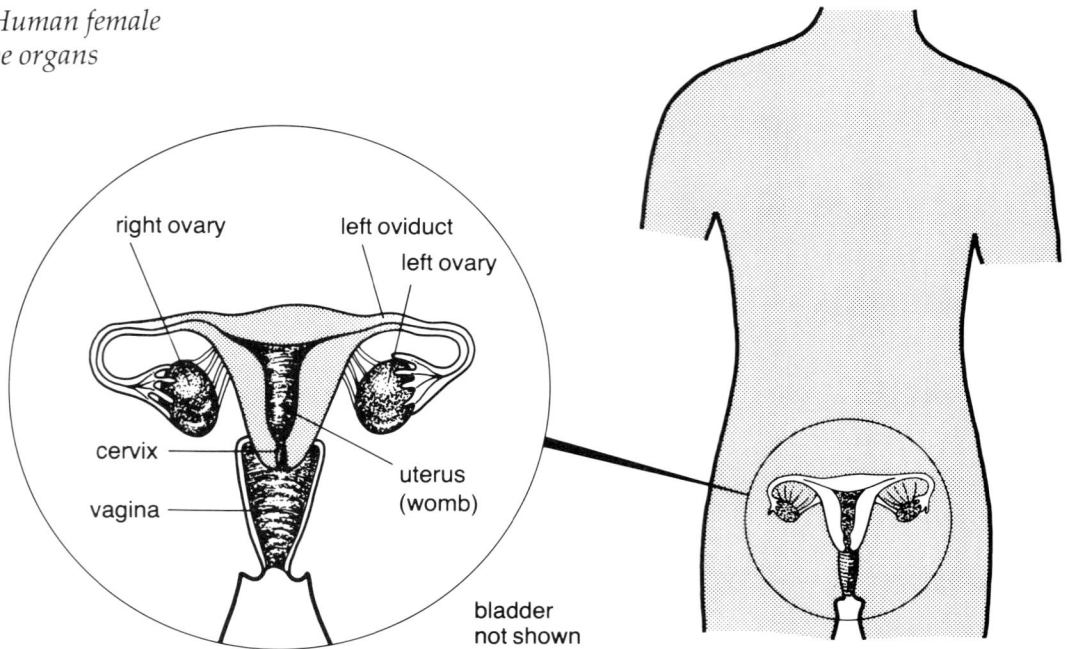

right ovary

left oviduct
left ovary

cervix

uterus
(womb)

vagina

bladder
not shown

Fig. 13.4 The human female
menstrual cycle. In this example
the complete cycle is 30 days

time from
egg release
to start of
period is
always 14 days

menstrual
period

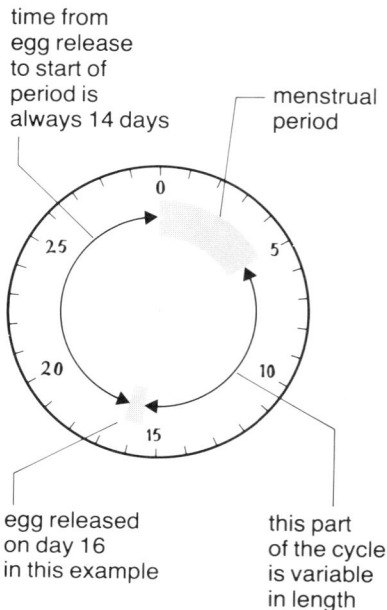

egg released
on day 16
in this example

this part
of the cycle
is variable
in length

Sometimes, more than one egg is released at the same time. After escaping from an ovary, the egg travels down the **oviduct**. It may take about three days to reach the uterus. Once in the uterus, the egg is lost. It either disintegrates here or passes out, unnoticed, through the vagina. Later, the lining of the uterus breaks down. This causes the monthly bleeding, or 'period', which all women experience. Its proper name is **menstruation**. It normally lasts for about four to seven days. Figure 13.4 shows when egg release and the period usually occur in the human female menstrual cycle.

The time between the release of an egg and the beginning of the period is always (as far as we know) exactly fourteen days. On the other hand, the time between the start of the period and the release of an egg varies. In Figure 13.4 it is shown as sixteen days. This makes the total length of the cycle 30 days in this example.

The menstrual cycles often vary in length from one woman to another. They also vary from month to month in the same woman. For example, a woman may find, during the course of the year, that her longest cycle is 31 days and her shortest 25 days. Sometimes, the cycles are very irregular. This is especially true in girls who are just starting to menstruate. Cycles shorter than 25 days, or longer than 31 days can occur in all women.

3 If the interval between the start of the period and the release of the egg is twelve days, how long will the whole cycle be? Use Figure 13.4 to help you get the answer.

4 If a woman's period began on the 3rd March, and the next period began on 29th March, how long was her cycle that month?

5 On what date was the egg released from her ovary during that cycle?

6 If the next cycle in this woman is the same length, on what date would you expect the next egg to be released?

Girls start to have periods at **puberty**. This is normally somewhere between the ages of eleven and fifteen years. This is one of the signs that their ovaries have started to release eggs. At first the cycles may be very irregular. At this time various other changes take place. Their breasts and hips grow larger. Hair grows under their armpits and in the pubic region. They begin to show more interest in boys.

Women go on having periods and releasing eggs until about the age of 45. At this age, called the **menopause**, or 'change of life', the periods gradually stop. The release of eggs from the ovaries also stops.

7 A woman began having periods at the age of 15 and stopped at the age of 45. Her menstrual cycles are about 30 days long. How many eggs could she release in her life?

3 The male system

The special male cells are called sperms. They look rather like tadpoles. However, they are so small that you need a good microscope to see them (see Figure 13.2). They are made in the testes of a man (see Figure 13.5). When they are released, the sperms are mixed with various liquids from special glands. This mixture of liquid and sperm is called the **semen** or seminal fluid. Sperm release in a man is called ejaculation. The total volume of semen produced during ejaculation is, on average, about 3.4 cm^3. There are about 100 million sperms in each cm^3 of semen. However this figure is very variable.

1 If the volume of semen produced is 4 cm^3, about how many sperms will it contain altogether?

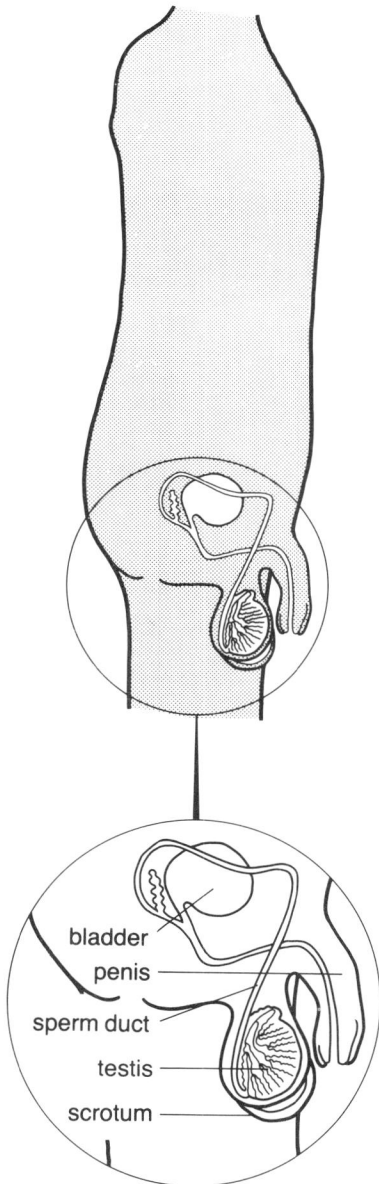

Fig. 13.5 Human male reproductive organs

bladder
penis
sperm duct
testis
scrotum

125

Boys start to produce sperm at puberty. This is normally somewhere between the ages of twelve and sixteen years. Various other changes take place at the same time. Their testicles now hang between the legs instead of being held up against the body as in young boys. Their bodies become more muscular. Hair grows on the face, legs, arms and chest, in the pubic region, and under the armpits. They begin to show more interest in girls. Their voices break and become deeper.

Men go on producing sperms for the rest of their lives. At puberty, boys sometimes find that they release sperms when they are asleep. This is called a 'wet dream' and is quite normal.

4 Getting the sperm and eggs together: courtship and fertilisation

The word fertilisation is used to describe the moment when a sperm enters and joins with an egg. Figure 13.1 shows that you began life when a sperm from your father fertilised an egg from your mother. There are three ways in which the sperm and egg might get together:

A   The egg could leave the female and enter the male.
B   The sperm could leave the male and enter the female.
C   Both sperm and egg could leave the male and female and join up outside.

Fig. 13.6a Ospreys mating

Fig. 13.6b Stag beetles mating

Animals use either method B or method C. Method A is not used.

For the sex cells to join together successfully, it is best if the male and female are close together. When animals get close together for this purpose, they are said to be mating. In Figure 13.6 various animals are shown mating. Some of them are using method B and others are using method C.

1 Which animals are using method B?
2 Which animals are using method C?

In method B, the sperms are pumped into the female by the male. The sperm joins with the egg inside the body of the female. This is called internal fertilisation.

In method C the sperms and eggs are released together into the water. The sperm joins with the egg outside the body of the female (in the water). This is called external fertilisation.

3 Which method is used by most land animals?
4 Which method is used by most animals that live in water?
5 Which method is used in human beings?

In man, mating is called **sexual intercourse** or making love. In all animals, including man, courtship usually takes place before mating. Courtship is very important. Animals do not usually get very close together except to fight. They normally keep their distance from other animals, even of the same

Fig. 13.6c Foxes mating

Fig. 13.6d Frogs mating

Fig. 13.7 A courtship display between a male and a female crane

type. The purpose of courtship is to get a male and female animal to overcome their natural fear and aggression. They can then get close enough together to mate. The sperm can fertilise the egg. Following this, baby animals are born. Some animals seem to behave in a very strange way during courtship. Many male birds have brightly coloured feathers which they display to the female. Scorpions have a special courtship dance.

Human courtship

Courtship starts when a couple, meeting for the first time, begin to like each other. Courtship is not the same as making love.

6 Describe some of the things which are done by the couple during courtship.

If you find this difficult, ask yourself how a girl can tell if a boy likes her, or how a boy can tell if a girl likes him.

Human sexual behaviour is very complicated. There is a great deal that we do not yet understand about it. However, men and women fall in love with one another. They often remain together for the rest of their lives. Biologists call this **pair-bonding**. Several other types of animals form pair-bonds for life. For example, many birds such as the Arctic Tern, and some mammals, such as the gerbil, pair for life.

It is interesting to ask why pair-bonding, often for life, has developed in man. Probably the most important reason is connected with the rearing of children. Human children take very much longer to become adults than the young of other animals. During this time they must be fed, protected, and taught. One of the main differences between man and all other animals is the amount that children learn from their parents. They also learn from other adults and from each other. This learning extends over a very long period of time. During this time, children are also completely dependent on adults for food and protection. Many male animals leave the rearing of young completely to the females and play little or no part in it. However, feeding, protecting and teaching human children is a difficult and demanding task. It is easier if there are two people to share the job.

Sometimes there is only one parent to look after the children. This may be because the other parent has become very ill or died, or the parents may have separated. In some human societies, the rest of the family will help the single parent to bring up the children. For example, this is true in many traditional African societies. In other societies, single parents can find it very difficult to bring up children. Whatever happens, the way in which children are brought up and educated is very important. This is because the children of today are the adults and leaders of tomorrow. Today's children make tomorrow's decisions.

5   Fertilisation in humans

The terms 'in season' and 'on heat' are used to describe a female mammal that is ready to mate. The male can tell by the behaviour, smell or appearance of a female whether or not she is in season. The females of most mammals such as cats, dogs, cattle, and sheep, will only allow a male to mate with them if they are in season.

The human female is not like other female animals. She does not need to come into season in order to make love (mate). Instead, she may be prepared to make love at any time during the menstrual cycle (Figure 13.4). Some couples may decide not to make love during menstruation.

Sexual intercourse usually takes place between a man and a woman who love each other. The penis becomes filled with blood so that it is stiff and erect. If it remained limp it would not enter the vagina. Once inside the vagina, movements of the penis eventually cause the ejaculation of the semen. This

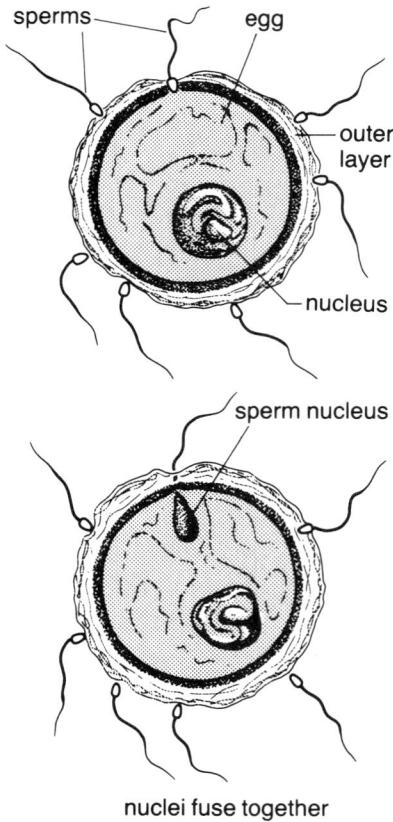

Fig. 13.8 *The ovum is fertilised by the penetration of a sperm*

Fig. 13.9 *The X and Y chromosomes in a male and the X chromosomes in a female*

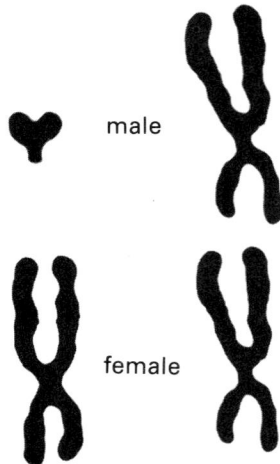

takes place when the walls of the parts in which the sperm and liquids are stored suddenly contract. This forces the semen along so that it spurts out of the end of the penis, and into the vagina. The sperms swim up into the uterus and then into the oviducts. They can be helped by movements of the walls of the vagina and uterus. If there is no egg in either of the oviducts all of the sperm die. However, if an egg, travelling down an oviduct, meets the sperms coming up, fertilisation may take place (Figure 13.8).

There may be several thousand sperms around the egg but only one of them will enter it. Other sperms are prevented from entering by changes which take place on the surface of the egg. These changes take place after the first sperm has entered. The other sperms will all now die.

Inside the egg, the sperm nucleus joins together with the egg nucleus to form a single new nucleus. This is the moment of fertilisation. It is the moment when a new person starts life. About nine months later, if all goes well, a baby will be born. We are all therefore about nine months older than the date shown on our birth certificate. The first nine months of life are spent inside our mothers.

6 What makes a baby grow into a girl or a boy?

The sperm nucleus brings information from the father. The egg nucleus provides information from the mother. This information is carried on long, thin threads called **chromosomes**. The chromosomes are found in the nucleus. The information carried on the chromosomes is arranged in a special code. Every time the nucleus and cell divides, this code is copied so that all the body cells eventually have a copy of the same code.

A normal egg contains a total of 23 chromosomes. These are numbered 1–22 and the last one is called an X chromosome.

Each normal sperm contains a total of 23 chromosomes just like an egg. However, there are two types of sperm. Half the sperms produced by a man contain chromosomes 1–22 and an X, exactly like the eggs. The other half contain chromosomes 1–22 and a Y chromosome. The Y chromosome is always smaller than the X chromosome. Fertilisation brings the sperm and egg chromosomes together (see Figure 13.10).

Fig. 13.10 The X and Y chromosomes determine whether the fertilised egg will grow into a boy or a girl

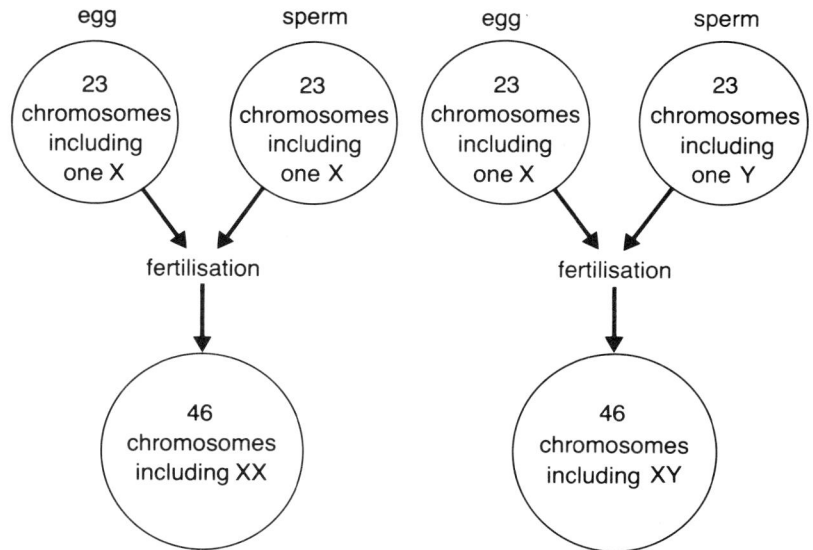

This fertilised egg will grow into a girl   This fertilised egg will grow into a boy

Fig. 13.11 Division of a fertilised egg

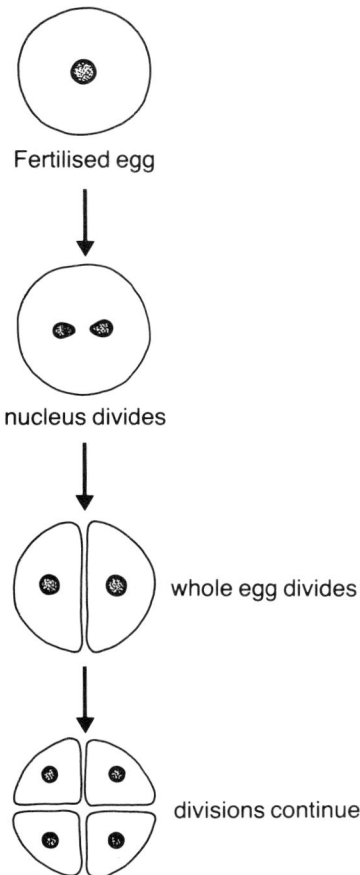

Fertilised egg

nucleus divides

whole egg divides

divisions continue

1 Whereabouts in the sperm and egg would you expect to find the chromosomes?
2 What do the chromosomes carry?
3 How many chromosomes are there in a sperm?
4 How many chromosomes are there in an unfertilised egg?
5 How many chromosomes are there in a fertilised egg?

This X and Y chromosomes are called the sex chromosomes, because they combine to decide what sex a child will be.

6 What will be the sex of a child with sex chromosomes XY? (See Figure 13.10.)
7 What will be the sex of a child with sex chromosomes XX?

7 Development

The fertilised egg continues to move slowly down the oviduct towards the uterus. After a few hours, it starts to divide. First the new nucleus divides into two. Then the whole cell divides into two smaller cells (see Figure 13.11). The two cells usually stay joined together. If they separate from one another, identical twins will be formed (see Section 9). A few hours later, each of these smaller cells divides again. This gives four cells. These divisions go on, forming a ball of more and more cells. The ball of cells is called an **embryo**. It continues to travel down the oviduct. Three or four days after fertilisation it will contain about 40 cells.

131

About five days after fertilisation the ball of cells reaches the uterus. It now contains over 100 cells.

About seven days after fertilisation, the ball of cells burrows into the wall of the uterus. Up until this moment the cells have been using up food which was stored in the original egg. This is one of the reasons why the egg was so large. The wall of the uterus is thick and is full of blood vessels. At this stage, the ball of cells starts to take in food from the cells in the mother's uterus.

Nine days after fertilisation, the ball of cells is about 1 millimetre (mm) in diameter (the size of the letter 'o' printed here). However, it is growing larger and is now made of several hundred cells. The cells inside the ball are those which form the baby. The cells on the outside will form the **placenta**. They also form the membranes which will surround and protect the baby until it is born.

The placenta takes three months to complete its growth and development. Its function is described later.

Three weeks after fertilisation, the embryo is still only about 2 mm long. It hangs in a bag of liquid called the **amnion**, within the lining of the uterus (see Figure 13.12).

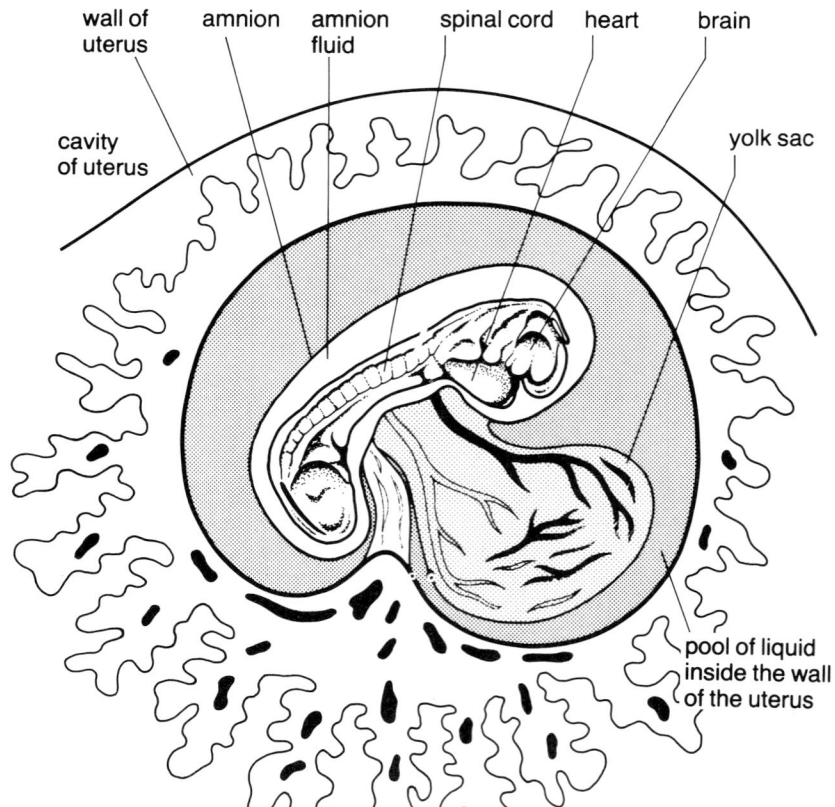

Fig. 13.12 The embryo is now about three weeks old. It is embedded in the wall of the uterus and is beginning to develop

Fig. 13.13 The embryo is about five weeks old and growth and development are continuing

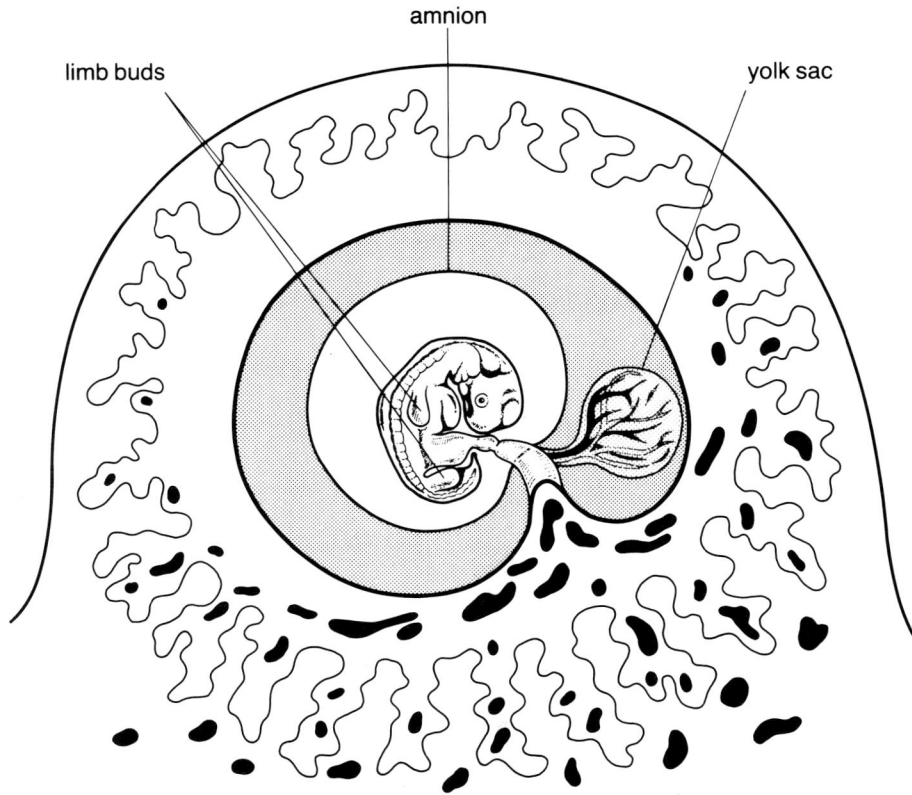

position and size of the foetus at this stage

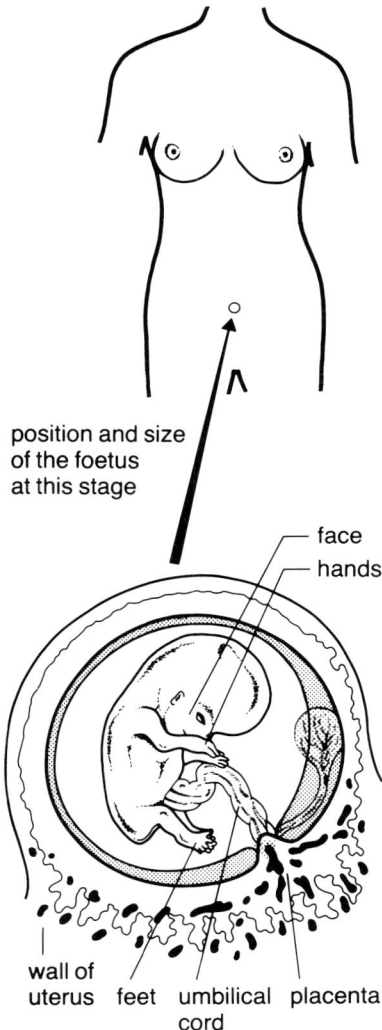

face
hands

wall of
uterus   feet   umbilical   placenta
                cord

Fig. 13.14 The foetus is about eight weeks old. The face, hands and feet are now clearly visible

This bag of liquid acts as a shock absorber and protects the embryo, and later the baby, from sudden jolts.

Five weeks after fertilisation, the embryo is about 8 mm long. Arms and legs are starting to appear (Figure 13.13).

Eight weeks after fertilisation the embryo looks like a human baby. It is now called a **foetus**. All the main parts of the body have formed (see Figure 13.14). It is about 23 mm long from head to rump.

No scale has been given for Figure 13.14. The human foetus is 23 mm long at this age.

1 Measure and record the length of the foetus in Figure 13.14.
2 Work out what the scale should be. (If the diagram is four times larger than real life, the scale is $\times 4$. If it is the same size, the scale is $\times 1$. If the diagram is half the real life size, the scale is $\times \frac{1}{2}$.)

During the first three months the placenta develops. It is formed partly from some of the cells on the outside of the very young embryo, and partly from cells in the wall of the

133

uterus. The placenta allows vital substances such as dissolved food and oxygen to pass from the mother's blood into the blood of the foetus. The blood of the foetus carries these along the umbilical cord into the foetus. Waste substances are carried in the reverse direction from the foetus to the mother.

Sixteen weeks after fertilisation, the foetus or baby is about 11.2 cm from head to rump (about 15.7 cm from head to heel). It weighs about 105 grams. It is growing rapidly. It completely fills the uterus which therefore starts to stretch. At this time, the mother's abdomen starts to swell and she feels the baby moving about (see Figure 13.15).

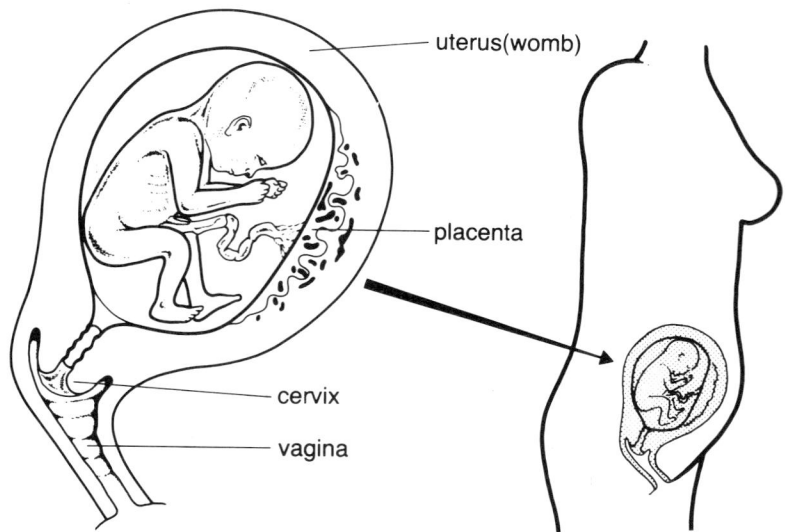

Fig. 13.15 The foetus is now about sixteen weeks old and is beginning to look more human. The mother's abdomen is beginning to swell

Twenty-six to thirty weeks after fertilisation, the foetus turns and rests head downwards in the uterus. At twenty-eight weeks it is about 24.2 cm from head to rump (33.5 cm from head to heel) and weighs 1.08 kilograms (2.2 lbs). Thirty-eight weeks after fertilisation, the baby is ready to be born. It is about 35 cm from head to rump (50 cm from head to heel) and weighs about 3.4 kilograms (see Figure 13.16).

Fig. 13.16 The foetus is now fully developed and ready to be born. It is about nine months since fertilisation

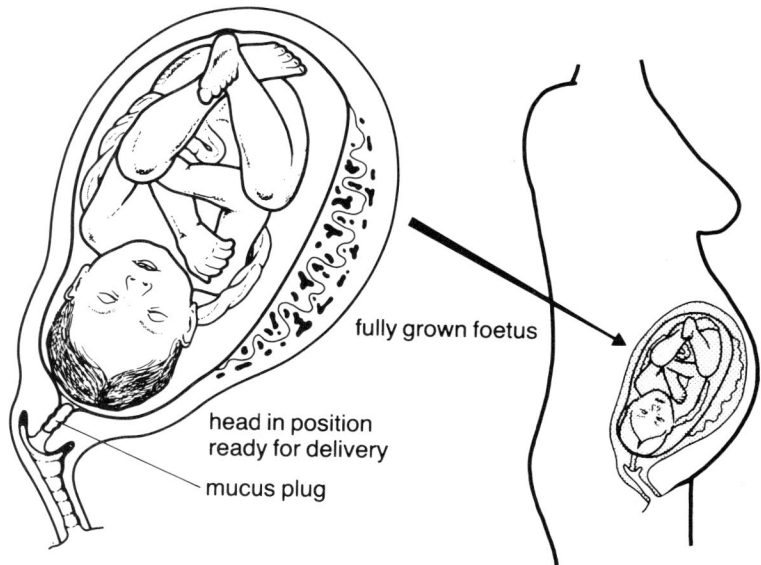

fully grown foetus

head in position
ready for delivery

mucus plug

8 Birth

One of the most important moments in the life of a couple is the birth of the child. In British society, the father used to be kept well out of the way. Nowadays, many fathers are present when their children are born. However, most of the attention must fall on the mother. It is she who has carried the child for the last nine months. It is she who will give birth to the child.

Many women have been taught to believe that childbirth is always a painful and unpleasant experience. Because they believe this, they find that it is painful. Other women have been taught how to control the pain. For them, the birth of their children is a happy experience. Many women say that the presence of their husband was a great help to them.

Labour is the word used to describe the events of child-birth. When a woman is giving birth she is said to be in labour.

1 Look at Figure 13.15. What is the name of the narrow passage, through which the baby has to pass, between the uterus and the vagina?

The walls of the uterus are made of muscle. The opening which leads from the uterus to the vagina is called the **cervix**. Throughout pregnancy, right up to the beginning of labour, the cervix is narrow (see Figure 13.15). The main purpose of the first stage of labour is to make the cervix wider.

2 Why does the cervix need to be wider?

135

Fig. 13.17a *The first stage of labour. The cervix becomes fully dilated to allow the baby to pass through*

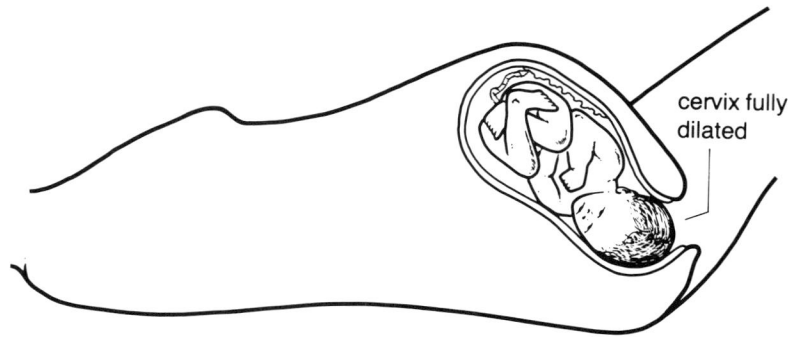

cervix fully dilated

Fig. 13.17b *Once the baby's head has been born, the rest of its body will follow quickly*

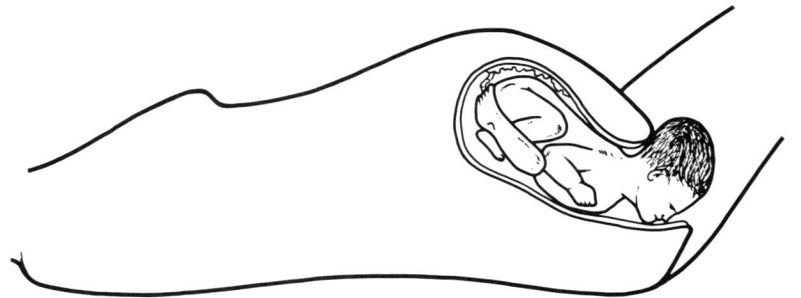

Fig. 13.18 *A baby is born*

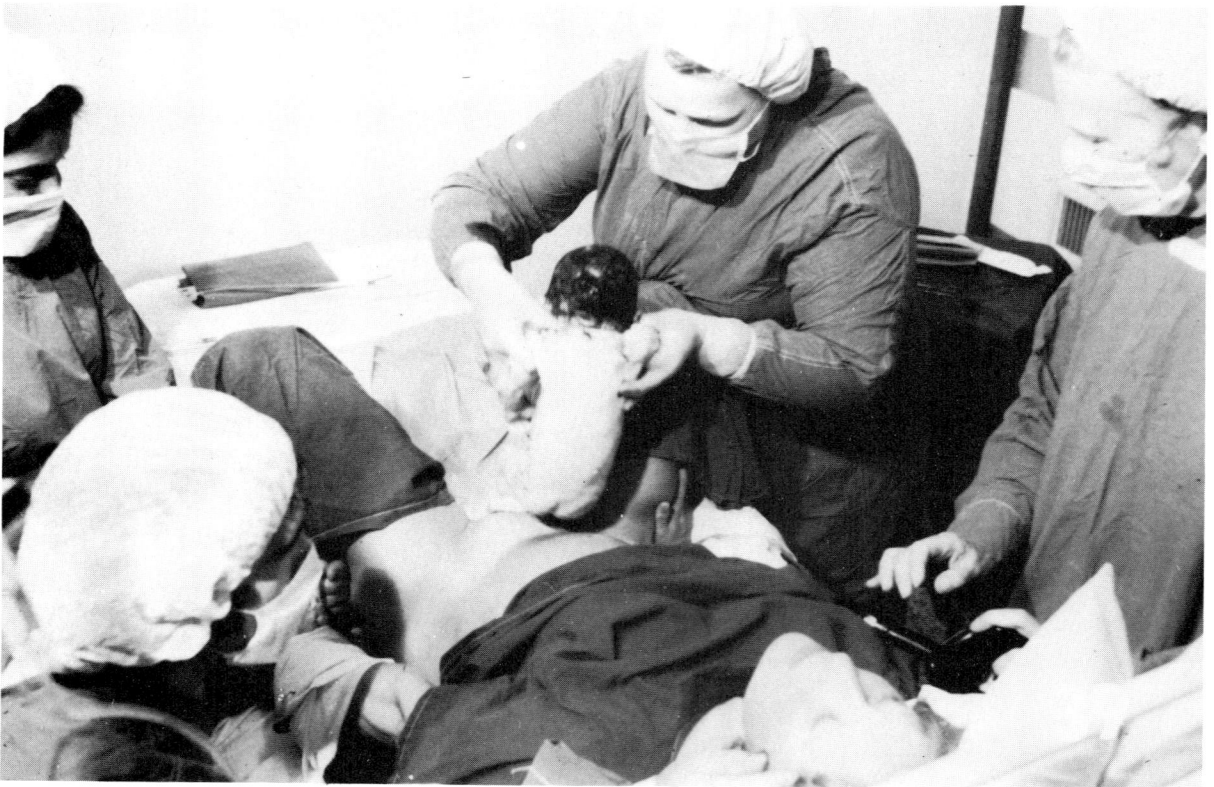

The muscular walls of the uterus start to contract occasionally during the last few weeks of pregnancy. These contractions are the preparation for labour. They can be painful if a woman becomes tense and frightened. They are not so painful if a woman learns how to relax. The purpose of these contractions is to make the cervix slowly open up. Labour begins properly when these contractions occur regularly and frequently. At the same time, two other things happen. First, the plug of mucus, which filled the cervix throughout pregnancy, will gradually come out. This is called a 'show'. Secondly, the membrane which formed a fluid-filled bag around the baby may start to leak. Eventually it bursts and the liquid escapes through the vagina. This is sometimes called 'the breaking of the waters'. At the end of the first stage of labour the contractions of the uterus will have opened up the cervix. It will be wide enough for the top of the baby's head to be visible from outside (see Figure 13.17a). In the second stage of labour the baby is born (Figure 13.17b). Shortly after birth, the baby takes his or her first breath. At this moment the baby makes a kind of crying sound as the lungs fill with air for the first time. Two clips are put onto the umbilical cord (Figure 13.19). The cord is then cut between the clips. The baby is now on its own, separated from the mother.

In the third stage of labour, the uterus contracts again, pushing out the placenta ('after birth') and the rest of the cord.

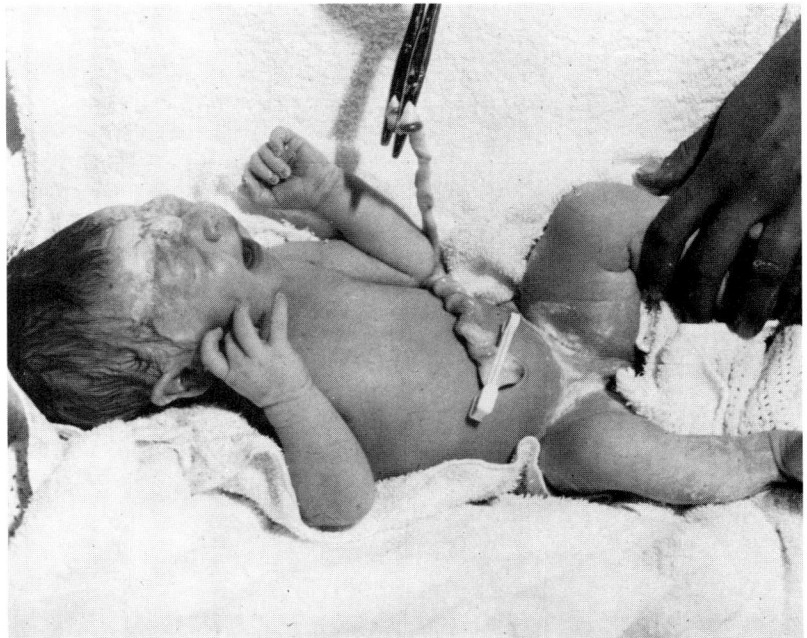

Fig. 13.19 A newborn baby

9 Twins

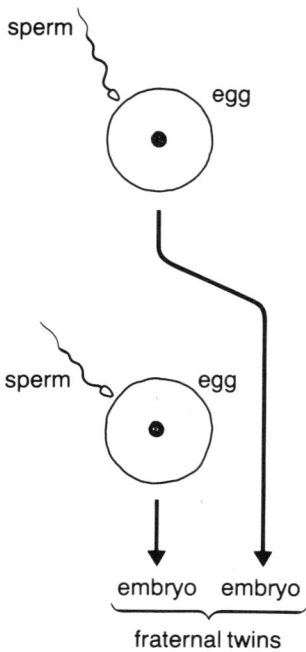

Fig. 13.20a Two separate fertilisations occurring at the same time can give rise to non-identical twins

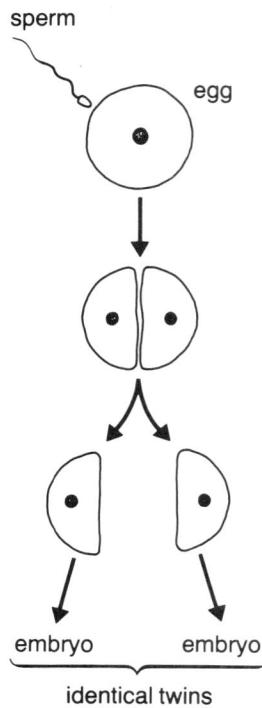

Fig. 13.20b After a single fertilisation, if the egg divides in half and separates then two identical twins may be born

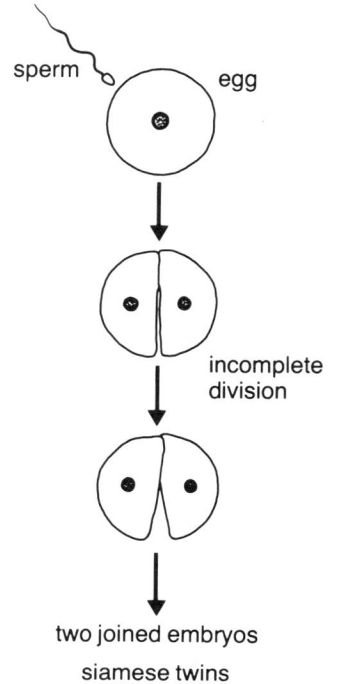

Fig. 13.20c After fertilisation if the egg divides in two and partially separates it is possible for Siamese twins to be born. Siamese twins remain joined together even after they are born. Only a few survive to become adults

Fig. 13.21a Non-identical twins often look quite different from each other

Fig. 13.21b Identical twins are always the same sex

1   Introduction

Common diseases in Britain today include coronary heart disease, bronchitis, dental caries, lung cancer, breast cancer, other types of cancer, pneumonia, common cold, various venereal diseases and influenza. There are some diseases which are particularly common in childhood.

Table 14.1 Some common diseases which can occur in childhood

chicken pox
common cold
diphtheria
influenza
measles
mumps
polio
rubella (German measles)
whooping cough

1 Look at Table 14.1. Then write down the names of any of the diseases in the table which you have had.
2 Which of these diseases can a person get several times?
3 Which of these diseases does a person usually get only once?

Heart disease and cancers are the leading killers in Britain. However, these are not the leading killers in the world. There are many other serious diseases which kill or disable millions of people every year. They include malaria, cholera, plague, tuberculosis (TB), and leprosy. These diseases are not usually a problem in Britain today. Many of them were widespread here in the past. Scientists are studying these diseases all the time in order to try to control them. Sometimes this is successful and the disease is wiped out. An example of this is smallpox. In 1980 the World Health Organisation (WHO) declared that smallpox had been completely wiped out from the planet Earth. Smallpox provides an interesting disease study.

2   The history of smallpox

Smallpox was a terrible disease which disfigured, blinded or killed millions of people (Figure 14.1). It is one of the most unpleasant diseases known to man. It is caused by a tiny microbe, the *Variola* virus. The disease is highly infectious. It is passed from person to person by direct contact or by contact with contaminated clothing. It can also be passed on by inhaling tiny moisture droplets in the air, breathed out by the smallpox victims. Many who recover from the disease have badly scarred skin and may also be blind. There is no cure for smallpox. Some people are killed by it, others recover naturally. The only way to stop it from spreading is

139

Fig. 14.1 Smallpox was a painful, ugly and often fatal disease

Fig. 14.2 Dr Edward Jenner vaccinating James Phipps in 1796

to isolate the sufferers and to vaccinate all those who have not yet caught it. Vaccination provides the body with resistance to the disease. However, vaccination will not cure those who already have smallpox. Smallpox was once a common disease in Britain. For example, there was a serious outbreak in 1561–1562 when Queen Elizabeth I got the disease. She recovered, but many others died.

In 1694, Queen Mary II of England, wife of William of Orange, died of smallpox. She was 32 years old. King Louis XV of France died of the disease in 1774 at the age of 64.

At this time, late in the 18th century, some people began to realise that there was a way of protecting people from smallpox. Dairymaids frequently caught a mild disease from the cows which they milked. This disease is called cowpox. It is caused by the *Vaccinia* virus. Cowpox caused mild sores and spots on the skin of people who caught it. Many dairymaids, after recovering from cowpox, said that they were safe from smallpox.

There was a smallpox outbreak in England in the year 1774. A Dorset farmer called Benjamin Jesty decided to test the dairymaids' claim. With a needle, he collected some material from a cowpox sore and scratched it into the skin of his wife and two children. They did not get smallpox during the outbreak.

1 This did not prove that cowpox protected people from smallpox. Why not?

Unfortunately, Jesty did not keep a record of what he did. But he is probably the first person to have carried out a smallpox vaccination.

Edward Jenner was a country doctor who worked in Gloucester. When he was a medical student, Jenner had heard a milkmaid say:

'I cannot take smallpox, I have had cowpox'.

We assume that he did not know about Jesty's experiment. On the 14th May 1796, Jenner took some material from a cowpox sore from the hand of a dairymaid. Using a needle, he scratched this into the skin of an eight year old boy (see Figure 14.2). The boy got cowpox and recovered.

Two months later, Jenner took some material from a true smallpox sore. He scratched this into the skin of the boy. The boy did not get smallpox. Jenner also tried to give smallpox to ten other people, all of whom had suffered from cowpox. None of them caught smallpox.

2 Whereabouts on the eight year old boy did Jenner vaccinate him? (See Figure 14.2.)
3 In what way did Jenner's experiment go further than Jesty's experiment?

In 1800, the first smallpox vaccination in America was carried out. A famous experiment was done in Boston in 1802. It showed clearly that vaccination protected people from smallpox. On 16th August, 119 boys were vaccinated. Later, they were all infected with smallpox, together with two boys who had not been vaccinated. Not one of the 119 vaccinated boys got smallpox. Both of the non-vaccinated boys got the disease.

4 Which group of boys, the 119 or the two, was the control experiment?
5 In what ways did the Boston experiment go beyond Jenner's experiment.

Jenner published several books and articles. The first page of an article about vaccination is shown in Figure 14.3.

6 When was this article published?
7 Read what Jenner wrote. Notice that in those days a small 's' was sometimes printed as an 'f'. What forecast is Jenner making here?

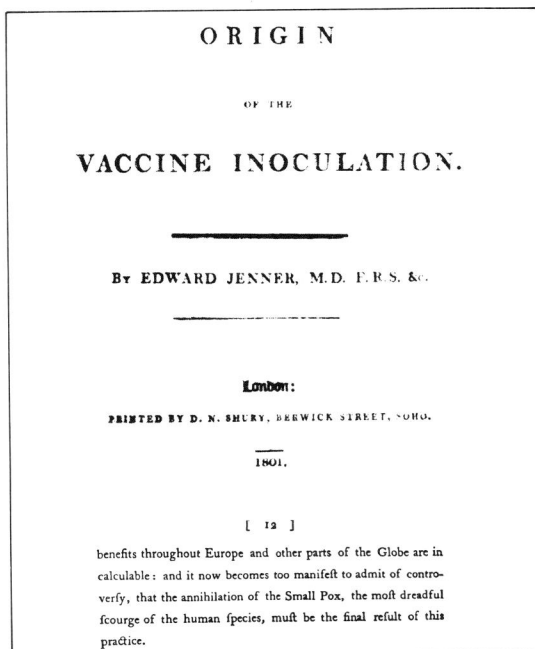

ORIGIN

OF THE

VACCINE INOCULATION.

By EDWARD JENNER, M.D. F.R.S. &c.

London:

PRINTED BY D. N. SHURY, BERWICK STREET, SOHO.

1801.

[12]

benefits throughout Europe and other parts of the Globe are incalculable: and it now becomes too manifeſt to admit of controverfy, that the annihilation of the Small Pox, the moſt dreadful fcourge of the human fpecies, muſt be the final refult of this practice.

Fig. 14.3 The first page of an article by Dr Jenner

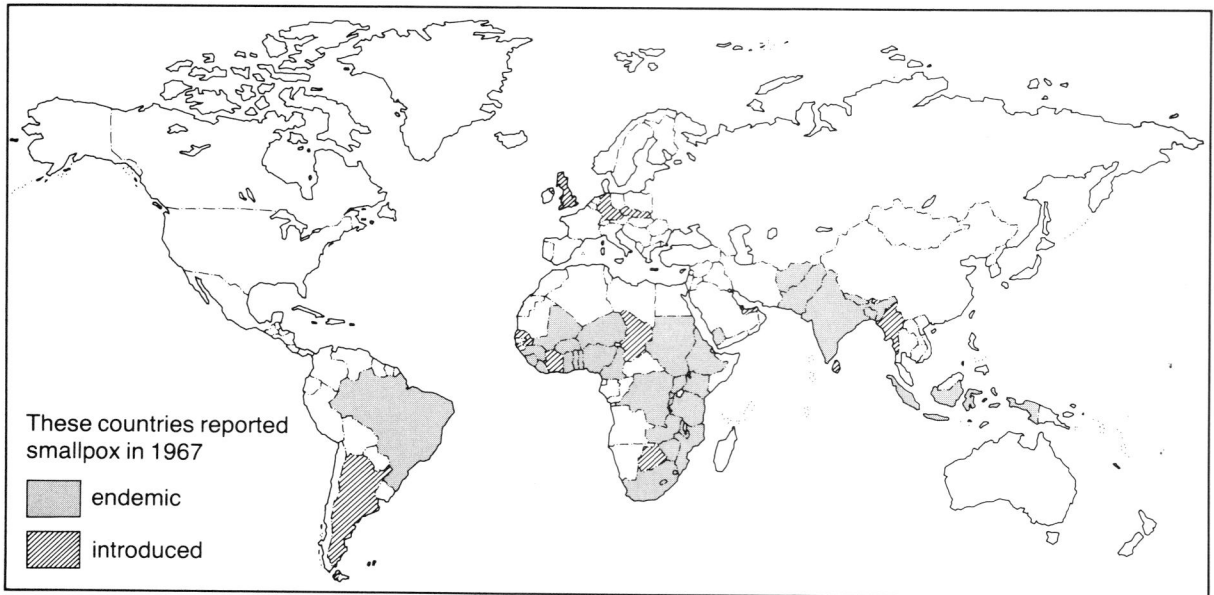

Fig. 14.4 Map to show countries which reported smallpox in 1967

Outbreaks of smallpox in Britain decreased during the 19th century. The last large outbreak occurred between 1900 and 1905. Since then, there have been small outbreaks. These were traced to people who had arrived from other parts of the world, where smallpox was still a common disease.

3 'Smallpox is dead!'

In 1959, the World Health Organisation (WHO) decided to try and wipe out smallpox altogether. It was not an easy task and Figure 14.4 shows that plenty of countries were still reporting cases of smallpox in 1967. The world map in the Reference Section will help you to name these countries.

1 On which continent in 1967 was smallpox reported in the most countries?
2 In which countries in South America was smallpox reported?
3 In which countries in the Indian sub-continent was smallpox reported?

It is estimated that there were over 10 million cases of smallpox in 1967 and that about 2 million died of the disease in the same year.

Fig. 14.5 In Ivory Coast, the hanged bird was used as a warning to travellers to keep away because of smallpox

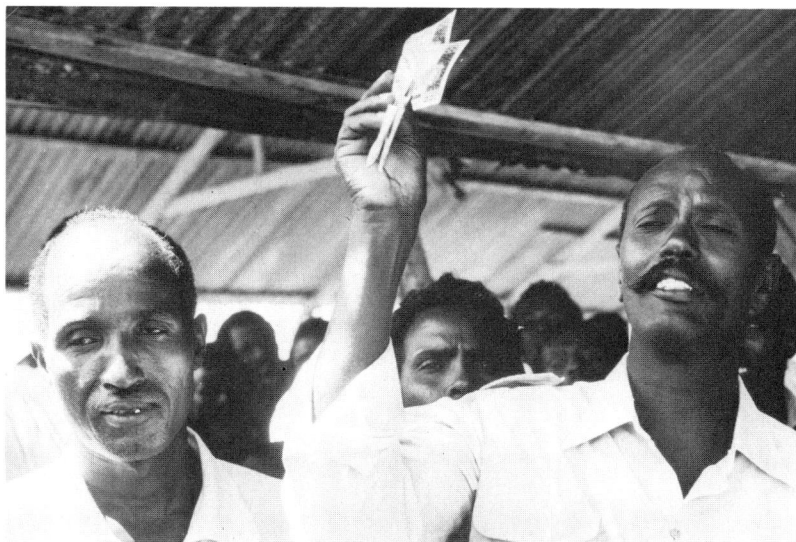

Fig. 14.6 During the campaign to wipe out smallpox, villagers were paid for information about smallpox victims

Table 14.2 The dates of the last naturally occurring cases of smallpox in different countries

Date	Country or area
1959	China
1970	West Africa
1971	Brazil
1971	Central Africa
August 1973	Afghanistan
March 1974	Bhutan
October 1974	Pakistan
6th April 1975	Nepal
24th May 1975	India
16th October 1975	Bangladesh
9th August 1976	Ethiopia
February 1977	Kenya
22 October 1977	Somalia

There are three things about smallpox that made health workers confident that they could wipe it out altogether.

Firstly, it affects human beings only. As far as we know, there is no animal which can suffer from smallpox, or carry the smallpox virus.

Secondly, a person who gets smallpox either dies or recovers completely. With certain diseases e.g. typhoid, some people get the disease and appear to return to normal health whilst still carrying the disease microbe. These carriers can infect others.

Thirdly, the smallpox vaccination leaves a very small scar on the arm. It is therefore very difficult for anyone who has not been vaccinated to say that they have.

Efforts to wipe out smallpox were stepped up in 1967 (see Figure 14.6). Between 1967 and 1980, 300 million US dollars were spent on the smallpox programme.

Table 14.2 shows how the smallpox campaign slowly won the battle against this terrible disease.

4 Which country reported its last case of smallpox in the year 1973?
5 On what date was the last case of smallpox in Nepal recorded?
6 Where and when was the last case of smallpox in Asia?
7 Where and when was the last case of smallpox in the world recorded?
8 Whereabouts is Somalia? (See world map in the Reference Section.)

In August and September 1978, there were two artificial cases of smallpox in Birmingham, England. Mrs Janet Parker was a medical photographer. She worked in a building where research on the smallpox virus was still being carried out. Some virus particles were accidentally released and they affected her. Mrs Parker caught smallpox and died. Her mother, who nursed her during her illness, suffered mildly from the disease and later recovered. This confirmed the warning already issued by the WHO on several occasions. It said the greatest risk of smallpox infection today comes from stocks of smallpox virus maintained in laboratories.

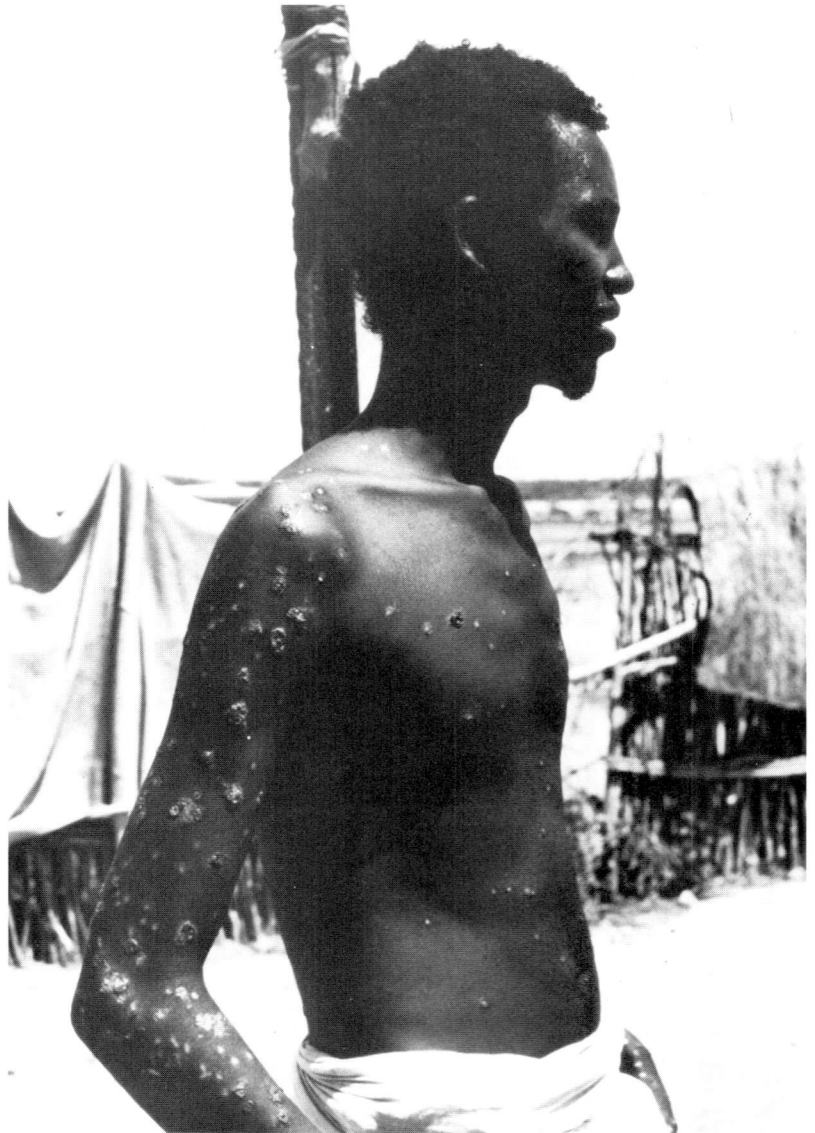

Fig. 14.7 The last man to suffer from smallpox worked in a hospital in Somalia. His name was Ali Maow Maalin

144

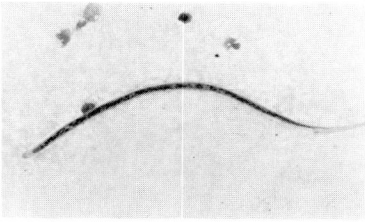

Fig. 14.8a The filaria worm which causes elephantiasis

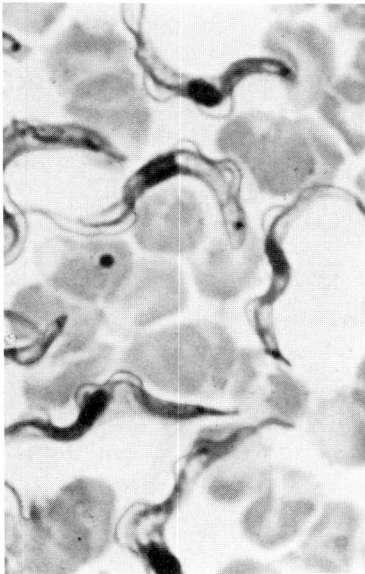

Fig. 14.8b Trypanosomes in human blood. They cause sleeping sickness

In 1980 the World Health Organisation officially declared that smallpox had been completely eradicated from the planet Earth. Between 1967 and 1980, the intensified fight against smallpox involved a total of 700 international staff and about 200 000 locally trained people. 2400 million doses of smallpox vaccine were used. 200 million of these were produced in the countries involved in the campaign.

9 When did Jenner suggest that smallpox could be eradicated? (See Figure 14.3.)
10 How many years passed until Jenner's dream came true?

The last case of smallpox in the world (outside a laboratory) was seen on 26th October 1977. The patient was 23 year old Ali Maow Maalin (see Figure 14.7). He was a hospital cook who lived in Mogadishu in Somalia. He recovered, and this time it was smallpox that died.

4 Uninvited guests: parasites and the diseases they cause

A **parasite** is a living thing which lives on or inside another living thing, called the **host**. The parasite gets its food from the host. The health of the host often suffers. So we say that the parasite causes a disease in the host.

Figure 14.8 shows some of the important disease-causing parasites. Some important parasitic diseases are shown in Figure 14.9. One of the reasons that smallpox was fairly easy to eradicate (see Section 14.3) is the fact that the smallpox virus is carried only by man.

Fig. 14.9a A man with elephantiasis of his leg and foot

Fig. 14.9b A woman with sleeping sickness

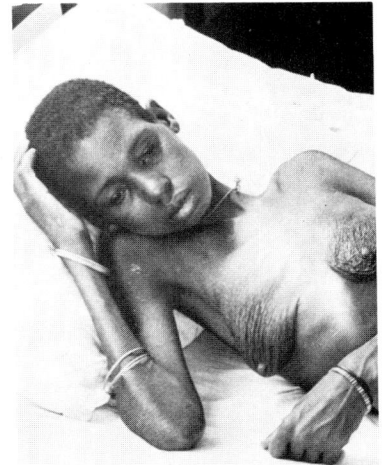

Fig. 14.10 The Tsetse fly which spreads the trypanosomes which cause sleeping sickness

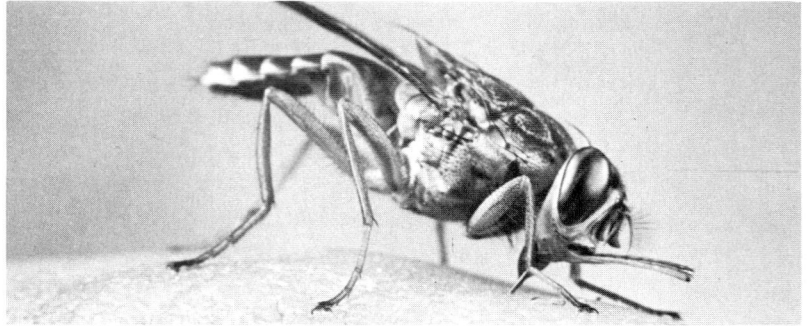

Many of today's serious human diseases are carried and spread by other animals (Figure 14.10). This makes these diseases much more difficult to control. The animals which carry the diseases do not seem to be affected by them. They appear to live healthy, normal lives.

5 Malaria

Many animals which carry diseases are insects. One of the most serious diseases in the world today is **malaria**. Malaria is caused by a tiny, single-celled animal which lives in the liver and the blood of man. The malaria parasite is carried and spread by the female *Anopheles* mosquito (see Figure 14.11). You cannot get malaria by touching an infected person. The only way you get this disease is by being bitten by an infected female *Anopheles* mosquito.

Malaria has been a serious disease for hundreds of years. We know this because in the past, various writers have described the symptoms. There are three stages (Figure 14.12

Fig. 14.11 The transmission of malaria

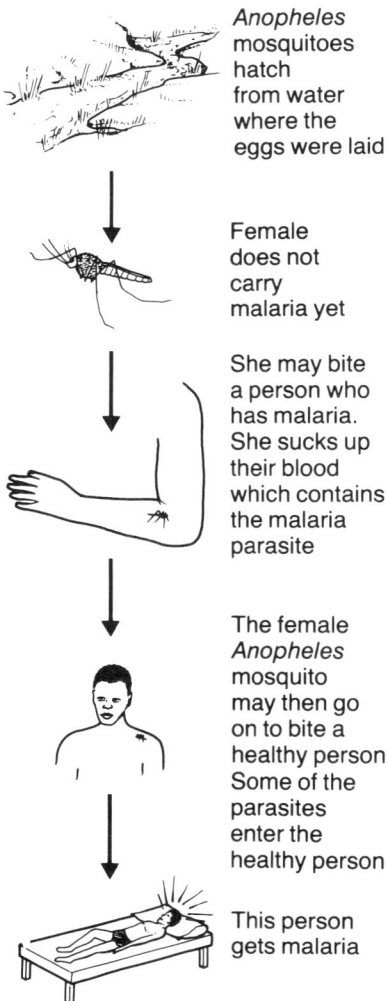

Anopheles mosquitoes hatch from water where the eggs were laid

Female does not carry malaria yet

She may bite a person who has malaria. She sucks up their blood which contains the malaria parasite

The female *Anopheles* mosquito may then go on to bite a healthy person. Some of the parasites enter the healthy person

This person gets malaria

Fig. 14.12 Temperature chart of a patient suffering from malaria

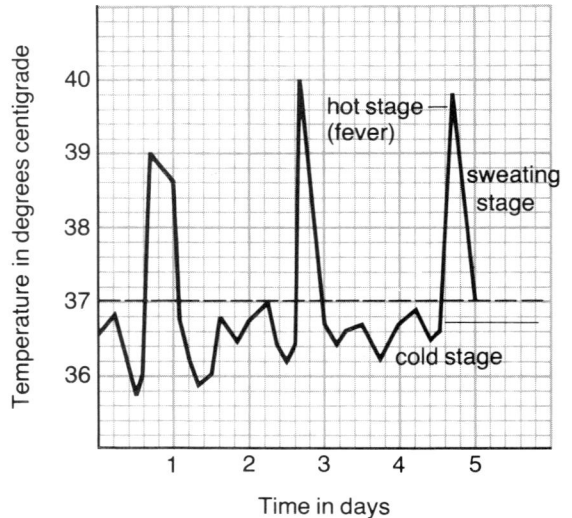

146

Fig. 14.13 A cartoon by Rowlandson showing a sufferer from malaria

and Figure 14.13). In the first stage, the person feels very cold and shivers violently. The body temperature starts to rise and there is a very bad headache and vomiting.

The second stage is the hot stage. The patient has a very high temperature (39–40 °C). In the third stage, the patient starts sweating, which brings the temperature down. These three stages are then repeated at regular intervals for several days. If the patient survives, the disease may seem to die away. However, sooner or later the malarial attacks return.

Malaria has probably killed more people in the world than any other single disease. In 1978, the WHO estimated that malaria still killed more than 1 million children every year in Africa alone.

People either die or recover completely when they get smallpox. Malaria is different. Many die, but many more survive with the disease. They are often weakened for life. It is estimated that there were about 150 million suffering from malaria in 1978. Table 14.3 shows that only 13.7 million cases were actually reported in 1978.

Table 14.3 The number of cases of malaria reported by W.H.O. between 1972 and 1979

	Numbers of cases reported (millions)							
	1972	1973	1974	1975	1976	1977	1978	1979
Africa	3.995	6.662	5.120	4.136	5.212	4.353	5.330	2.451
Americas	0.285	0.280	0.269	0.357	0.379	0.399	0.465	0.432
S E Asia	1.816	2.686	4.162	6.059	7.296	5.552	4.264	3.192
Europe	0.013	0.009	0.007	0.013	0.041	0.119	0.093	0.033
E Mediterranean	0.830	0.746	0.480	0.424	0.347	0.227	0.126	0.133
W Pacific	0.171	0.201	0.179	0.188	0.211	4.464	3.422	2.690
Totals	7.110	10.584	10.217	11.357	13.486	15.114	13.700	8.931

1 Why do you think that there is such a big difference between the number of cases that are officially reported and the actual number of cases?

2 In which year was there a total of just over 7 million cases of malaria?

3 In which year was the highest total of malaria cases reported.

4 What happened to the total number of malaria cases reported between 1972 and 1977?

5 Which three areas have reported the highest malaria totals?

6 Look at Figure 14.11. What carries malaria from a person with the disease to a healthy person?

7 If there were no *Anopheles* mosquitoes, would malaria be able to spread from person to person?

Millions of pounds have been spent on trying to control malaria. Part of the money is spent trying to kill the *Anopheles* mosquito. The rest is spent trying to cure those who have the disease. There are many difficulties. A major problem is that many rural areas of tropical countries have no health services. These areas are also difficult to get to.

However, the biggest problem is the *Anopheles* mosquito. An area can be cleared of malaria completely. It just needs one malaria carrying mosquito to reinfect the whole area. For example, in India, control of the *Anopheles* mosquito reduced malaria from 75 million cases in 1935 to just 60 000 (0.06 million) cases in 1962. However, there was not enough money to continue mosquito control. By 1974 the figure had risen to 2.5 million cases.

Travellers can also infect malaria-free areas. The *Anopheles* mosquito is found in parts of Britain, but this country has been free of local malaria since 1911. However, British people returning home after staying in malarial areas have carried the disease back to Britain. In Britain, there were 111 cases in 1967, 363 in 1972 and 1909 in 1978, including ten deaths. Most of these cases were quickly identified and treated. There is always the fear that one of these people will be bitten by a British *Anopheles* mosquito. If this happened, the disease could spread rapidly to other people.

British travellers who go abroad are therefore advised to take anti-malarial tablets to protect them from the disease.

Fig. 14.15 *Stages in the life cycle of mosquito* Anopheles

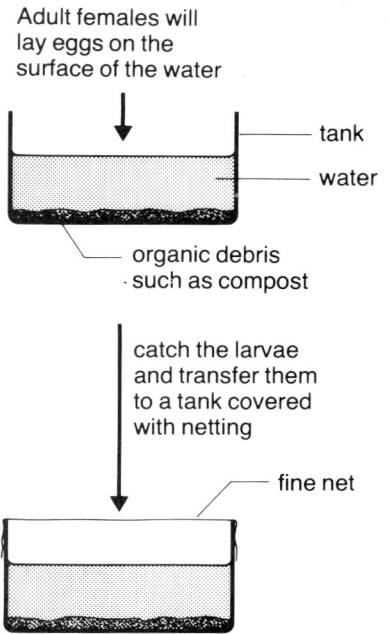

Adult females will lay eggs on the surface of the water

tank
water

organic debris such as compost

catch the larvae and transfer them to a tank covered with netting

fine net

Fig. 14.14

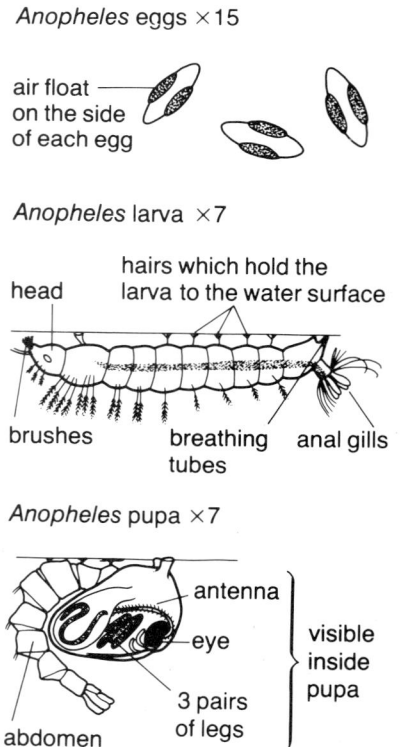

Anopheles eggs ×15

air float on the side of each egg

Anopheles larva ×7

head
hairs which hold the larva to the water surface
brushes
breathing tubes
anal gills

Anopheles pupa ×7

antenna
eye
3 pairs of legs
abdomen
visible inside pupa

6 Mosquitoes: a practical problem

About 60 different types of *Anopheles* mosquito can carry malaria. There are hundreds of other types of mosquito. Some carry other diseases such as Yellow Fever.

All these mosquitoes have one thing in common. They must breed in water. Mosquitoes are easy to breed in Britain. They will lay their eggs in suitable water in the spring, summer and early autumn. See Figures 14.14 and 14.15.

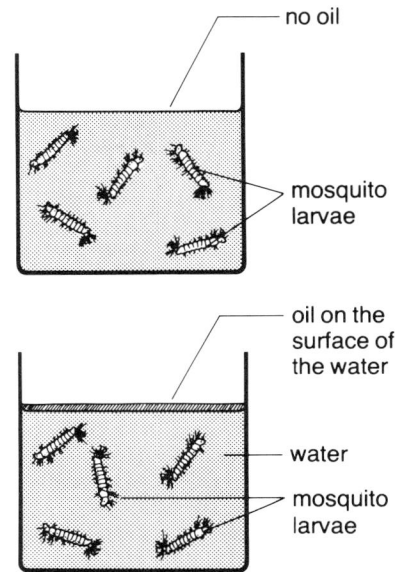

Fig. 14.16 Experiment with mosquito larve

Activity

a ▶ Place a mosquito larva in a 250 cm³ beaker full of tank water.

b ▶ Watch its behaviour for a few minutes.

1 How often does it come to the surface? The next part of this investigation will help you to find out why it comes to the surface.

c ▶ Set up two similar beakers. Each should have a similar mosquito larva in.

d ▶ Pour a little oil onto the surface of the water in one beaker (Figure 14.16). Leave the other beaker as it is. Watch the larvae for some time.

2 What happens to the larva in the beaker with oil? Try to explain why this has happened.

3 Fish, water shrimps and water lice die quickly if they are put into water which has been boiled and cooled. Mosquito larvae do not. Explain why.

4 Use what you have discovered in this investigation to suggest one way in which mosquitoes could be controlled.

5 Look at Figure 14.17. What do you think these men are doing? Why do you think they are doing this?

Fig. 14.17 These men are trying to control the spread of malaria

Pollution

1 Introduction

Pollution is a very complicated subject. It is difficult even to say what pollution is. We would all agree that dense, black smoke escaping from a factory chimney is an example of pollution. But how 'clean' does the smoke have to be before we stop calling it pollution? The smoke may contain harmful, invisible gases.

DDT is an insecticide which is widely used in many parts of the world. Its use in Britain is now restricted. Water containing 1 gram (g) of DDT in a thousand million cubic centimetres (cm^3) of water is harmless to man, but would kill some fish. Should this water be described as polluted? A water authority would describe it as pure water. A fisherman would call it polluted!

1 Look at the photographs in Figure 15.1. Which ones show examples of pollution?

Fig. 15.1a The eruption of the volcano Mount St. Helens in Washington USA in 1980

Fig. 15.1b Foam covering a river running through an industrial region

You may find that you disagree with the opinions of other people. This is to be expected. There is disagreement, even among experts, about what is and what is not pollution.

Pollution is often in the news. Some newspaper articles and TV programmes tell horrifying stories of pollution. On other occasions we are told that there is nothing much to worry about. Whom should we believe? Often, it is difficult to know. Some people like to make a fuss about pollution. They want publicity in order to make their views known to other people. They may paint a rather one sided picture of the damage done by pollution.

Other people may try to hide the effects of pollution. This might be true of some industrial firms. They fear that they might be forced to reduce the amount of waste materials escaping from a factory. This would make their product more expensive. It might reduce sales and profits.

We should always try to take a balanced view; to look for the dangers of pollution and try to balance these against the benefits of whatever is producing the pollution.

Fig. 15.1c A car dump

Fig. 15.1d Many factories produce large amounts of smoke

Fig. 15.1e Dead leaves on a pond

151

2 Measuring water pollution

The amount of oxygen dissolved in water is a good guide to the amount of pollution. Untreated sewage and industrial waste both use up oxygen very rapidly. Badly polluted water therefore contains very little oxygen.

A few animals are able to live in water containing only a little oxygen. Other animals require much higher oxygen levels. We can therefore use the animals which we find in water to tell us how polluted the water is (Figure 15.2).

Use Figure 15.2 to help you to identify animals collected from streams and rivers, and to decide how polluted the water is.

Plants can be used to study pollution. One plant is easy to use. It is called duckweed. Duckweed (see Figure 15.3) will grow well in tanks in a school laboratory. Set up a tank as shown in Figure 15.4. Put a single duckweed frond in the tank. In the summer, leave the tank outside in a sunny place. In cold weather, bring the tank in and shine a bench lamp on it day and night. The duckweed will grow and multiply fast. In several weeks, it will cover a small tank. When this

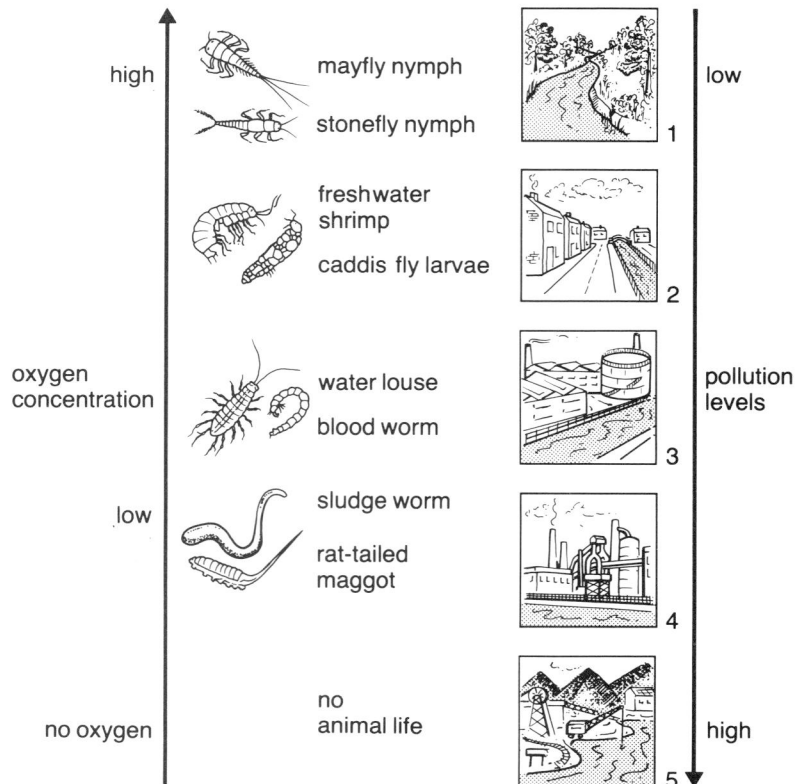

Fig. 15.2 This chart can be used to investigate stream and river pollution

152

Fig. 15.3a A tank of duckweed

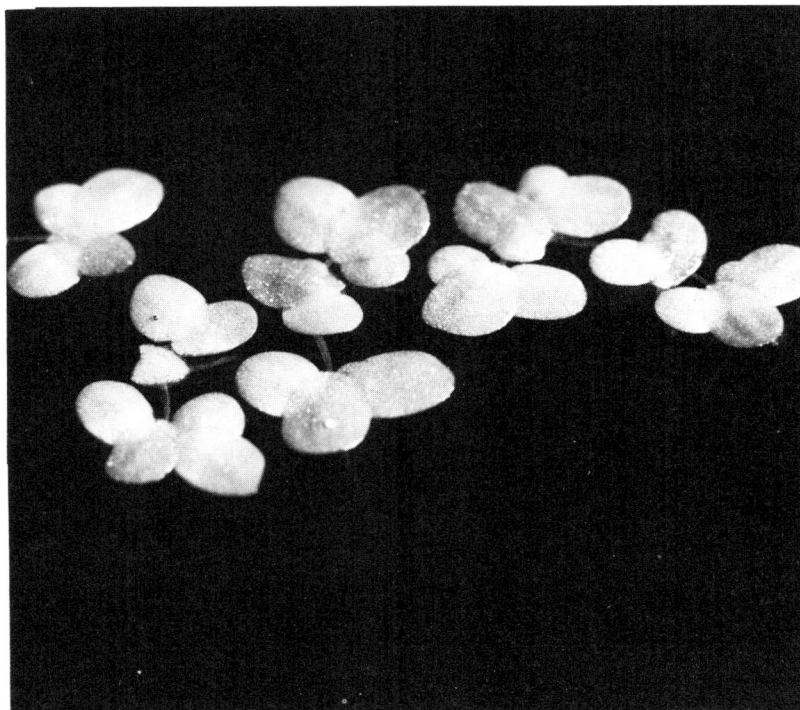

Fig. 15.3b Close up of the duckweed floating on water

Fig. 15.4 How to grow duckweed

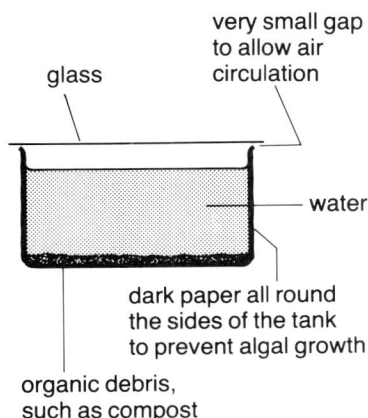

glass

very small gap to allow air circulation

water

dark paper all round the sides of the tank to prevent algal growth

organic debris, such as compost

happens, some should be removed at regular intervals to prevent overcrowding. Single duckweed fronds should be handled with a small paintbrush.

Many manufactured substances can be investigated to see if they will kill the duckweed.

In very rural areas, some old houses may still have drains which empty straight into streams or rivers. This means that household waste water will flow straight into the streams.

1 Make a list of things in kitchen waste which might cause pollution.

Activity

a ▶ The effect of a washing powder on duckweed can be examined. Figures 15.5 and 15.6 show how a range of solutions of the washing powder could be set up. There must be the same final volume of water in each beaker. Label the beakers carefully. The duckweed fronds are carefully removed from the stock tank with a paintbrush. They are washed gently in distilled water and then placed in the beakers. About ten fronds per beaker is a suitable number for 100 cm³ beakers.

153

Fig. 15.5 Flow chart to show how to make up different concentrations of washing powder solution

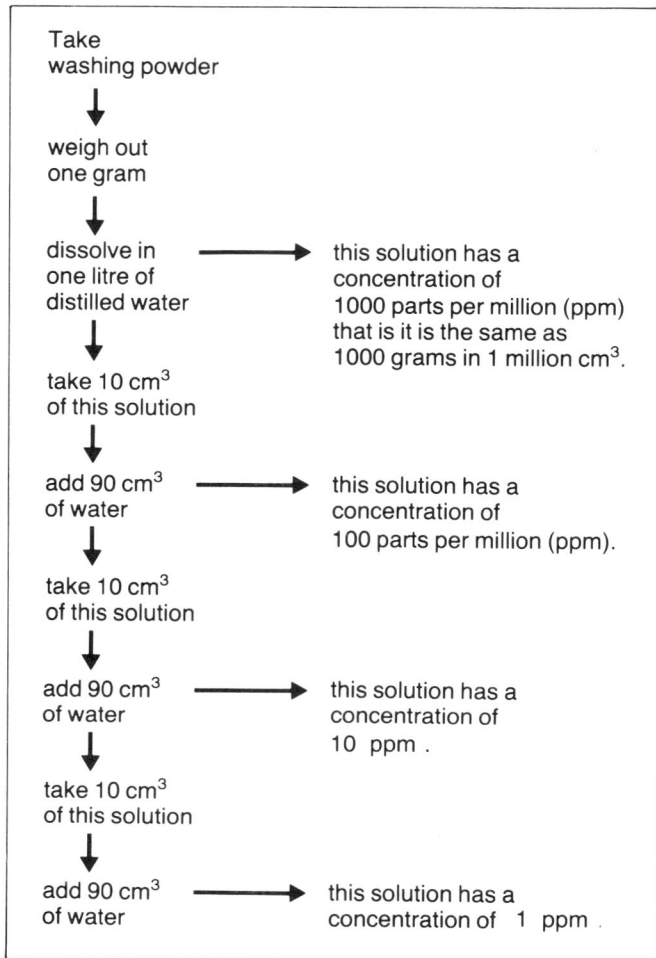

Take
washing powder

↓

weigh out
one gram

↓

dissolve in
one litre of ⟶ this solution has a
distilled water concentration of
1000 parts per million (ppm)
that is it is the same as
1000 grams in 1 million cm^3.

↓

take 10 cm^3
of this solution

↓

add 90 cm^3 ⟶ this solution has a
of water concentration of
100 parts per million (ppm).

↓

take 10 cm^3
of this solution

↓

add 90 cm^3 ⟶ this solution has a
of water concentration of
10 ppm .

↓

take 10 cm^3
of this solution

↓

add 90 cm^3 ⟶ this solution has a
of water concentration of 1 ppm .

even illumination

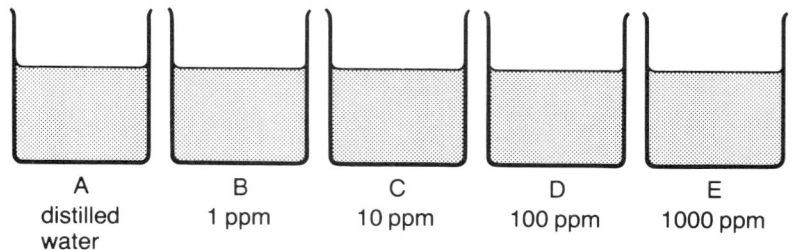

A	B	C	D	E
distilled water	1 ppm	10 ppm	100 ppm	1000 ppm

Fig. 15.6

b ▶ All the beakers must be evenly illuminated. They should be topped up with distilled water as necessary.
c ▶ Each day, count the total number and note the colour of the duckweed fronds in each beaker. You can go on for as long as there is no change in beaker A.

DAY	Concentration of washing powder (parts per million)				
	400 p.p.m	300 p.p.m	200 p.p.m	100 p.p.m	control
0	30	30	30	30	30
2	30 (all turning white)	38 (a few turning white)	31 (a few turning white)	37 (all fronds green)	40 (all green)
4 (week end)	30	38	31	51	52
7	30	38	40	74	60
9	30	38	40	80	70
11	30 (all white)	40 (half green half white)	40 (most green)	80 (all green except 1)	76 (all green)

Table 15.1 *A set of class results on the duckweed experiment. The table shows the number of duckweed fronds which grow in each solution.*

2 What is the name given to beaker A (distilled water only)?
3 Why is it necessary to include this beaker in the experiment?
4 Why is it necessary to wash the duckweed fronds before putting them into the beakers?
5 Some class results are given in Table 15.1. Which concentrations of washing powder killed the duckweed in Table 15.1?

The experiment can be repeated using other 'pollutants'. The most difficult thing is to try and find out if these concentrations of the washing powder are ever likely to be found in a stream.

3 The River Thames

In the past, rivers were regarded as useful places in which to get rid of rubbish and waste, especially sewage. If a small number of people are involved, the river can manage. The waste is diluted and decays harmlessly. However, when the waste from large towns and from factories enters a river it cannot be diluted. It overwhelms the river, which becomes an open sewer.

For hundreds of years the River Thames managed to cope with all the sewage that went into it. Indeed, in the early 1800s, the Thames was still a good fishing river with plenty of salmon. However, the rapidly increasing population along its banks proved too much for the river. The factories of the Industrial Revolution added to the problem. Their untreated waste went straight into the river. The Thames became an open sewer.

As early as the year 1191 King Richard I granted a Charter to the Corporation of the City of London to control the state of the River Thames up as far as Staines (Figure 15.7). However, very little was done to try and clean up the river until 1857. At about this time the smell from the river at Westminster was so dreadful that sheets soaked in disinfectant were hung up in the Houses of Parliament to try and hide the smell.

In 1857 the Thames Conservancy came into being. In 1866 the owners of 77 factories were prosecuted for polluting the Thames. In the same year many of the towns along the Thames above London (Figure 15.7) were ordered to stop passing sewage into the Thames. Sewage treatment plants had been built at all of these places by 1880.

London itself presented a huge problem. Up until the middle of the 19th century one third of London's water supply came from the river. The same river carried the city's sewage. By 1864 a system of sewers had been built. These merely carried the sewage down to points on the river below London. The sewers emptied into the river at Barking on the north bank and at Crossness on the south bank.

Fig. 15.7 Towns along the River Thames

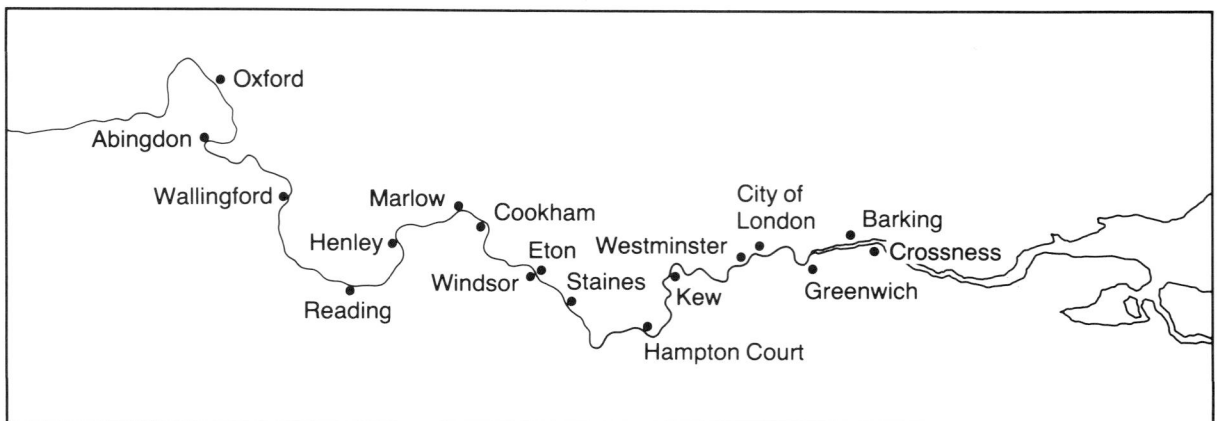

London produced so much sewage that this Victorian system never did solve the pollution problem in the river. It merely moved the problem downstream. In the 1950s and 1960s the river downstream from Greenwich had a foul smell over several miles, especially in the dry summer months. Recent efforts by the Greater London Council to clean up the river have been more successful. In 1957 there were no fish at all in the Thames in the London area. However, by 1975 the Thames Authority reported that 87 different types of fish had been found in the river. Salmon were reported in the Thames in 1974 after an absence of nearly 150 years.

4 Oil pollution of the sea

The worst oil pollution incident at sea so far occurred on 3rd June 1979 in the Gulf of Mexico. An exploration oil well called Ixtoc 1, 80 km off the Mexican coast, blew out and caught fire. The well belonged to the Mexican company Pemex. On 24th June the fire was put out, but oil continued to flow from the well into the surrounding sea. It was not until 24th March 1980 that the well was finally plugged.

1 For how many months did oil leak from Ixtoc 1 into the sea?

Within a week of the blow out, an oil slick 180 km long by 80 km wide had formed. This later split up into several slicks which spread 600 km up the Yucatan Peninsula. Oil came ashore on beaches along the Mexican and Texas coasts. The US Coast Guard is reported to have spent $8.5 million cleaning up the oil. The natural breakdown of oil is rapid in warm tropical waters. Luckily little oil got past the barrier islands off the coast of Texas. Precise information about damage to the Mexican coast is not available. However, this section of coast has the largest shrimp port in the world. The annual shrimp catch there was said to be worth £110 million in 1980. The effect on this industry is not known.

It is estimated that a total of 3.1 million barrels of oil escaped from the Ixtoc 1 oil well into the sea. There are between 7 and 7.5 barrels of oil to the ton (depending on the density of the oil). 3.1 million barrels is equal to about 430 000 tons of oil. This would have been enough to provide the whole of the United Kingdom with all of its energy needs for 18 hours in 1980, or total UK oil needs for nearly two days (44 hours).

Fig. 15.8 The oil tanker **Betelgeuse** *on fire at Bantry Bay oil terminal on 8th June 1979*

The Mexican oil company, Pemex, is said to have spent $133 million plugging the well and on trying to reduce damage to the environment. Pemex claims to have lost $87 million in oil revenues as a result of the disaster. The United States Senate investigated the blow out in November 1979. During the hearings, it was alleged that the drilling crew on the Ixtoc 1 oil rig lacked experience and qualifications.

There is no doubt that many oil pollution incidents at sea and at tanker terminals are caused by faulty machinery or carelessness or both. The behaviour of some oil tanker crews is very alarming.

On Thursday 10th January 1980, the Greek tanker *Scenic* was loading crude oil at Sullom Voe oil terminal in Shetland. Members of her crew were reported to be smoking on deck. Loading of oil was immediately stopped. On the next day loading continued but the crew allowed about 200 gallons of oil to be spilled into the sea. The captain of the *Scenic* was fined £3830. The cost of cleaning up the oil spill was £2830. The oil terminal's marine adviser then inspected the tanker. He found that the fire extinguishers were not available. The anchors were not available for use in an emergency (they were secured as at sea). There was smoking by the crew in unauthorised places. Loading of the tanker was stopped again. Matches and lighters were confiscated from the crew. Later the tanker was inspected by the Department of Trade. The port lifeboat engine caught fire when they tried to start it. Gas-tight covers of emergency lights were open. This exposed naked electric light bulbs. Crude oil was leaking from a deck hatch.

The *Scenic* was eventually allowed to sail on 14th January. However, she was banned from ever coming back to Sullom Voe in her present condition. On the next day there was an explosion in her engine room which injured five members of the crew. The tanker drifted helpless in the North Sea for three days while repairs were carried out. Records at the time showed that this tanker had been involved in fourteen other incidents around the world. These included another fire and explosion in her engine room, boiler trouble and repeated running aground. It is also alleged that five other tankers belonging to the company which owns the *Scenic* have also caused problems at Sullom Voe. The annual report of the Advisory Committee on Oil Pollution of the Sea (ACOPS) for 1980 says:

'ACOPS is deeply concerned at what appears to be an increasing number of vessels that are inefficient and

Fig. 15.9 Oil spills affect many seabirds, such as this guillemot

hell-bent on destruction . . .' despite this, the vessels . . . 'continue to be classed by their Classification Societies, insured by their Insurance Companies and registered by their flag states.'

2 How much oil is thought to have escaped into the sea when the Ixtoc 1 oil well blew out?
3 How much money was spent cleaning up the beaches of Texas by the US Coast Guard?
4 Make a list of all the things that were wrong with the tanker *Scenic*.
5 Why should there be strict regulations at oil terminals?
6 List as many animals and plants as you can think of which might have been affected by an oil spill such as the one at Ixtoc 1.

It ought to be pointed out that many owners of oil tankers insist on very high standards of safety on their ships.

5 Pollution of the sea by toxic chemicals

Fig. 15.10 Humans can get mercury poisoning via a marine food chain

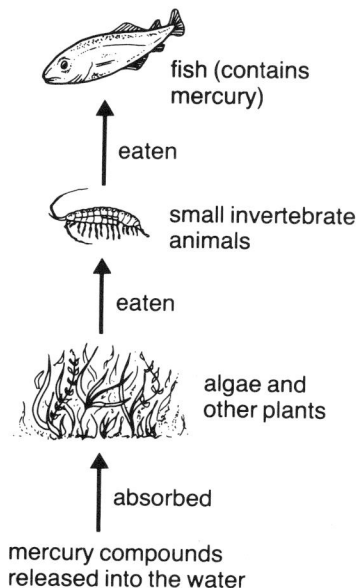

One of the most famous examples of pollution occurred in Japan at a place called Minimata Bay. A factory on the shore of the bay was making PVC and acetaldehyde. A mercury catalyst was used in the factory. In the early 1950s production was increased. An estimated 40 tons of mercury were emptied into Minimata Bay with the factory waste each year. The people living nearby caught and ate the fish which lived in the waters of the bay. They were poor people and relied heavily on these fish for basic food.

In 1953 the first signs of mercury poisoning appeared in these people. By 1956 the disease of Minimata had been identified as mercury poisoning from local fish. The symptoms of mercury poisoning include numbness of finger tips, slurred speech, unsteady walk, deafness and poor vision. By 1961 there had been 121 severe cases of mercury poisoning among the people of Minimata and 46 deaths.

The mercury finds its way into the fish via the food chains (see Figure 15.10).

1 Should the dumping of toxic waste like mercury be controlled? If so, how can this be done worldwide?

159

6 Pollution of the land

During the late 19th century a man named William T. Love decided to build a canal as part of a plan to bring industry to the town of Niagara Falls in New York State, USA. However, the work was abandoned when the canal consisted of a large trench fifteen yards wide and about a mile long. Later the canal came into the hands of a chemicals and plastics company. In the late 1940s and early 1950s this company used the canal as a dump for toxic waste products. There was no law preventing dumping of this sort then. About 20 000 tons of waste chemicals were dumped in the canal. Most of this waste was in 55 gallon steel drums. Later the drums were covered with earth. Houses and a school were built on the site.

From the beginning, the health of the people who lived on the site of the Love canal was affected. Children who swam in a pond on the site got painful skin rashes. Many children were born with defects. For example, so many of them were deaf that special street signs were put up to warn motorists.

Many pregnant women living in the Love canal area had miscarriages.

Heavy rain in 1978 washed away some of the earth which covered the canal. Many of the steel drums were exposed. A large number of the drums had corroded so that their toxic

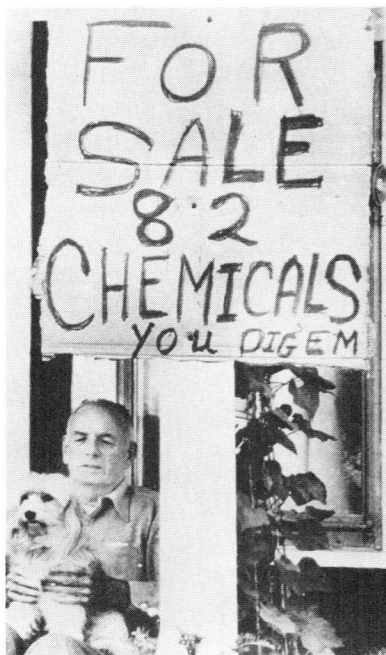

Fig. 15.11 This man lived near the Love Canal and will have to leave his home because of chemicals seeping into his basement from the dump

contents were leaking out. Following this, New York State found new homes for 239 families who lived closest to the site. The cost of this was $37 million. In 1980, President Carter declared a state of emergency in the area of the Love canal. Plans were made to find temporary homes, away from the site, for 710 families while the site was tested to see if it will ever be safe for them to return.

1 Why do motorists need to be warned if many children in an area are deaf?
2 Whose fault was the disaster at Love canal?

7 Accidents happen

In 1973 a firm in Michigan, USA was manufacturing two products. One was sold as a fire retardant, a substance for helping to fight fires. It was called Firemaster. It contained a highly poisonous compound called polybrominated biphenyl (PBB). The second product made by the firm was a substance which was added to animal food. This was called Nutromaster. The company usually packed Firemaster and Nutromaster in bags which were clearly labelled and coloured, one colour for Firemaster and another colour for Nutromaster. When the firm ran out of coloured bags, the products were packed in plain bags which were clearly labelled.

One day a lorry driver arrived for a load of Nutromaster. He could not read. However, he was normally able to tell which bags were which by their colour. On this day there were no coloured bags. For some reason he picked up 2000 bags of Firemaster (instead of Nutromaster) and delivered these to various farms in Michigan State. At the farms the people had never heard of Firemaster. They thought that it must be a new and better form of Nutromaster. It was mixed with the animal feed and fed to thousands of dairy cattle, beef cattle and poultry over a long period of time. The animals survived without showing signs of ill health.

It is estimated that the whole population of the State of Michigan (about 9 million people) ate the highly poisonous PBB in meat, eggs, butter, cheese etc. By 1977 there were about 1000 people showing symptoms of PBB poisoning.

1 Make a list of all the points in this story at which something might have been done to stop this disaster.
2 How might disasters like this be prevented in future?

16 Conservation

1 Introduction

Between the 1st century AD and 1800, at least thirty animals became extinct worldwide. These include the European lion.

Between 1800 and 1900, at least another thirty animals became extinct worldwide. These include the South African Quagga (a zebra-like animal), the Dodo, the Great Auk, and the north American passenger pigeon.

From 1900 to the present day, at least 100 animals have become extinct worldwide. These include the Caucasian bison, the Pyrenean ibex, the crested shelduck, the Texas grizzly bear, and the Arabian ostrich.

No one knows exactly how many animals and plants are still becoming extinct at the present time. One recent estimate stated that about one type of animal or plant becomes extinct every day. This may be an over-estimate. It may be an under-estimate. However, most people agree that plants and animals are becoming extinct faster than ever before.

2 Why do plants and animals become extinct?

There are two main reasons why plants and animals become extinct. Firstly, their **habitat**, the place where they live, is destroyed. Secondly, they are hunted for pets, for food, for skins, or, in the case of plants, because they are attractive.

1 Make a list of wild animals which are collected and sold as pets.
2 Which wild animals are killed for their skins?

The destruction of habitats is taking place all over the world. For example, 300 years ago most of England was covered by woodland. In those days a squirrel could probably have travelled from Cambridge to Bristol without touching the ground.

Since 1945, over 100 000 miles of hedgerows have been dug out in Britain to make bigger fields which are more efficient to farm.

Woodland and hedgerows both provide habitats for many wild plants and animals. Today, open land is disappearing under roads and industrial and urban development.

Fig. 16.1a The Great Auk

Fig. 16.1b The Dodo

Fig. 16.1c The Quagga

3 Why are bigger fields more efficient to farm?
4 Look at Figure 16.2. How much countryside was destroyed when this section of road was built?

Many tropical areas are less developed than Britain. There are still large areas of undisturbed land. However, development is spreading rapidly. For example, in Brazil the vast Amazon rain forest is being cleared rapidly for agriculture. This forest, once even larger than the whole of Europe, is disappearing fast.

Scientists are particularly worried about the three main surviving areas of tropical rain forest. (See Table 16.1.) It has been estimated that, every year, about 15 million hectares of rain forest are lost (more than the combined areas of England and Wales). In the Amazon forest alone, the loss may be as much as 11 million hectares each year. Clearing for timber, mining and agriculture are the main reasons for the loss of rain forest.

As the forests disappear, so do the plants and animals which live in them. Tropical habitats contain many more

Rain forest area	Estimated area in 1980, in million hectares
Amazon and Orinoco river basins (S America)	472
South East Asia	187
West and Central Africa	175

Fig. 16.2 The portion of motorway you can see in this photograph is 2 kilometres long. Including its embankment it is 40 metres wide

Table 16.1 The three main surviving areas of tropical rain forest

Fig. 16.3 The Amazon rain forest is being destroyed at an alarming rate

163

different plants and animals than the temperate habitats of Europe. For example, there are about 300 different known land mammals in Tanzania. In addition, there must be many smaller mammals there which have still not been described and named, such as bats and rodents. In Britain, there are only 47 living native land mammals. Make sure that you know what a mammal is (see Chapter 17).

5 Make a list of as many different wild British land mammals as you can.

Over 800 different land birds breed in Kenya. About 200 different land birds breed in Britain. In Uganda, in one forest alone, about 78 different types of butterfly have been recorded. In the whole of Britain, there are only about 68 different types of butterfly. In a small area of tropical rain forest, there may be over 300 different types of trees and shrubs. In a similar area of British woodland, you will probably find about 20 different trees and shrubs at the most. The message is clear. If large areas of tropical forest are destroyed, thousands of plants and animals are threatened with extinction.

3 Does it matter if plants and animals become extinct?

If forests are cleared to make way for agriculture, this is surely a good thing. After all, we need more food for the world's poor and hungry. This is true. However, there are several reasons why scientists and other people are becoming more and more worried, especially by the disappearance of rain forests.

No one really knows what effect the loss of such huge forest areas will have on the climate. For example, forests release large amounts of moisture into the air. Sooner or later, this returns to the ground as rain. Forests also act like gigantic sponges. They soak up large amounts of water when it rains and probably prevent flooding in nearby areas.

Another reason why people are worried about the extinction of increasing numbers of plants and animals is the thought that these might become useful to us if they survive. This is particularly true of plants. Man makes use of an enormous number of different plants from all over the world. Many of these plants are now cultivated. All of them were once wild and many of them still have wild relatives. Sometimes the wild relative can be useful. For example, some British tomatoes may look good, but they have little flavour and contain very little vitamin C. The tomato came originally from South America. Our cultivated tomatoes are descended from the tiny, yellow, wild tomatoes which still grow in parts of South America. These tiny, wild tomatoes contain much more vitamin C than our cultivated ones. It may be possible to breed the cultivated tomato with the wild tomato. Some of the offspring may combine the best features of both. These offspring may have a better vitamin C content together with large size and red colour. This is an example of the way in which a wild plant might be useful.

There are other ways. For example, we get many useful substances from plants. Look at Tables 16.2 and 16.3.

Bilharzia is a common disease in Africa. It is caused by a parasitic flatworm which spends part of its life in man (causing the disease), and part in a certain type of water snail. People get infected with bilharzia by washing or

Table 16.2 Some of the many useful drugs which we obtain from plants

Name of useful substance	What it is used for	Name of plant from which we obtain the substance
Atropine	Medical uses. It dries up saliva and dilates the pupils.	Deadly nightshade
Caffeine	Stimulant	Tea and coffee plants
Cocaine	Used medically as a local anaesthetic.	Leaves of the Coca tree
Curare	Used medically as a muscle relaxant; also South American Indian arrow poison.	Barks of various South American forest trees
Digitalis	Used medically as a heart stimulant	Foxgloves
Morphine	Used medically as a pain killer	Opium poppy
Penicillin	Used medically as an antibiotic	Penicillium fungus
Quinine	Used medically as an antimalarial drug	Bark of the Cinchona tree
Theophylline	Various medical uses	Leaves of *Camellia sinensis*
l-Dopa	Treatment of Parkinson's disease	*Mucuna pruriens*

Name of product	What the product is	What the product is used for	Name of the plants from which we obtain the product
Copra	Dried kernel of the coconut. It contains oil	The oil is used for making soap. Fibres used for matting etc.	Coconut palm
Cotton	Long hairs covering the ripe seeds	Making cloth for clothing.	Cotton shrub
Flax	Fibres from the stem	Making linen.	Flax plant
Hemp	Fibres from the stem	Making rope, string and coarse cloth.	Hemp plant
Jute	Fibres from the stem	Making string, rope and, in the past, sails.	Jute plant
Linseed oil	Oil from the seeds	Treating timber.	Flax plant
Nicotine	Substance obtained from the dried leaves	Used as a powerful insecticide in greenhouses	Tobacco plant
Palm oil	Oil from the outer layers of the fruit	Making soap, margarine, cooking fats and candles.	Oil palm
Pyrethrum	Substance obtained from the flowers	Useful insecticide.	Pyrethrum chrysanthemum
Rubber	Latex (sap) from the tree's trunk	Making tyres, gloves, footwear, flooring and adhesives.	Various shrubs and trees called Rubber trees (especially *Hevea braziliensis*)
Sisal	Fibres from the leaves	Making rope, cord, matting and sacking.	Sisal plant
Tobacco	Dried leaves	Making cigarettes, cigars pipe tobacco and snuff.	Tobacco plant
Timber	The trunks of mature trees are felled and the wood cut into timber	Building, furniture, telegraph poles, fuel.	Oak, Pine, Mahogany, Teak, Cedar, Walnut etc.

Table 16.3 Some other useful products which we obtain from plants. This does not include food (see facing page)

swimming in infected water or drinking it. One way to control the disease is to kill the snail. It was discovered that the snails were completely absent from some parts of certain streams in Ethiopia. These snail-free places were always downstream from the places where people washed clothes. The people used the dried berries of the soap berry plant as soap for washing their clothes. These berries contain a substance which kills the bilharzia snails. It is possible that this substance could be extracted from the plants and used to help control bilharzia.

Only a very small number of the hundreds of thousands of known plants have been thoroughly examined to see if they could be useful to us.

Wild animals could also be useful. For example, at one time the island of Rhum, off the west coast of Scotland, was used for sheep farming. Later, the island passed into the hands of the Nature Conservancy. They removed all the sheep and let the wild red deer graze there instead. The deer were completely protected and their numbers increased very rapidly. Finally, it became necessary to start killing the deer to prevent them from completely destroying the grazing land. The deer were killed humanely and the meat sold on the mainland as venison. Then it was discovered that the island was producing more meat as a by-product of con-servation management, than it did when a good sheep farmer farmed it for sheep! Deer need no shepherds and make much better use of the grass and other plants than sheep do. In some parts of Africa, a large antelope called the eland is being 'farmed' in the same way.

4   Buffalo Bill: was he really a hero?

In the early 1800s, herds of the North American buffalo or bison contained an estimated 60 million animals. The prairies of North America appeared black at certain times of year because there were so many buffalo. The Indians hunted the buffalo, but it was the white settlers, trappers, travellers and meat hunters who brought this animal so close to extinction.

Buffalo Bill Cody is said to have killed over 4000 buffalo in one year. By 1879 the great southern buffalo herd had been completely wiped out. In 1883 the last animals in the northern herd were rounded up and shot. Only about 300–600 buffalo survived this dreadful slaughter. They found refuge in wildlife reserves and national parks in the USA and Canada. They started to breed and their numbers slowly

Fig. 16.4 Joe's Pride, a beefalo bull

increased. But nearly 100 years after the end of the great slaughter, there are still not many buffalo. In 1980, it was estimated that there were between 50 000 and 60 000 buffalo in the USA and less than 20 000 in Canada.

Today there is great interest in the buffalo. Farmers are willing to pay as much as $700 each for surplus buffalo from the parks and reserves. The reason for this is that the buffalo is better than cattle for meat production. Buffalo need less care than cattle. They put up with the hard prairie winter better than cattle do and can find their own food by foraging. Cattle must be fed in winter. Buffalo live happily on land that is too poor to support cattle. 65% of a buffalo carcass can be used commercially against only 55% for cattle. Buffalo meat is said to taste like beef and it contains 25% more protein than beef. It also contains 20% less cholesterol. Some people think that heart disease in man may be caused by too much cholesterol in the diet.

For more than a hundred years American biologists have been trying to cross the buffalo with domestic beef cattle. Success came recently, and the new animal is called a 'beefalo'. A beefalo bull called Joe's Pride was recently sold for a record £1.3 million. (See Figure 16.4.)

Beefalo breeders claim that the new animal is, like the buffalo itself, better than cattle in many ways. They say it gives more meat, but does this on much poorer food than cattle need. The meat has less fat, is quicker to cook and is a quarter of the cost of beef. They also say that the skin can be used to make fur coats. One of the problems is that people are used to eating beef and lamb. They may not be willing to eat venison, eland, beefalo or buffalo instead, even if they are cheaper.

The story about the buffalo slaughter shows how close this animal came to extinction. It also shows how important it could be for us to prevent more wild animals from becoming extinct.

There are many other ways in which wild animals and plants could be of use to man. People also enjoy just looking at them. However, if they become extinct, we may never have a chance to find out if they are useful, or to share the pleasure of looking at them with our own children.

At a recent wildlife exhibition there was a large mirror hanging on the wall. A notice under the mirror said: 'The most dangerous animal in the world.'

6 What did the visitors see when they looked in the mirror?
7 Why was that notice put under the mirror?

Classification

1   The need for classification

There are nearly 1 million different kinds of animal living in the world today. We also know that many other animals once lived on Earth but are now extinct, for example, the dinosaurs and the Dodo.

People are still discovering and naming 'new' animals, that is, animals which have not previously been named. Many of these new animals are tiny insects. At the same time, some animals become extinct each year.

We know of just over 340 000 different kinds of plant living in the world today. Some plants, like animals, have become extinct. Occasionally new plants are discovered and named.

We find it convenient to arrange plants and animals into groups. Similar animals are put into the same group, while similar groups of animals are also put together. The need for grouping is obvious if you think of a large collection of books in a library, or a large collection of stamps. It is easier to use the books and study the stamps if they are arranged in groups. The same is true of animals. Stamps can differ in price, colour, shape, name of country, picture on the stamp, etc. They could be arranged in groups according to any of these differences. For example, all stamps showing birds could be put into one group, stamps showing people in another group, stamps showing buildings in a third, and so on.

   1 In what other ways could stamps be arranged?

Animals and plants differ from each other. They show variation. For example, animals may have wings and legs, legs only, fins only, flippers only or no limbs at all. (See Figure 17.1.) They vary in size, in shape, in colour, in the places where they live, and above all in structure.

   2 Do you think there is only one way of grouping plants and animals? Give reasons for your answer.

The fact that living things can be grouped and named in many different ways causes problems. Scientists often meet to talk about plants and animals. It would be difficult or impossible for them to actually bring the plants or animals to

Fig. 17.1 Different animals
have different sorts of limbs.
These animals are not drawn
to the same scale.

their meetings. In order to be sure that they are all talking about the same plant or animal, they need to use the same system of grouping and naming. For example, scientists from Britain, France, Germany and Tanzania may be meeting to discuss an important crop plant. In Kiswahili, the language of Tanzania, it is called *kiazi cha kizungu*. In German, it is called *kartoffel*. In French it is called *pomme de terre*. You know it as the potato. Fortunately, the potato also has a scientific name: *Solanum tuberosum*. All scientists throughout the world know it by this name.

Sometimes problems arise when different things have been given the same common name. For example, in England there are several small plants with blue flowers. One is called a bluebell. In Scotland a completely different plant is called a bluebell. These two plants have different scientific names. The English bluebell is *Endymion non-scriptus*. The Scottish bluebell is *Campanula rotundifolia*.

Scientists sometimes disagree about what groups some plants and animals should be put into. Their arguments are often complicated and need not worry us. One commonly used system of grouping living things is shown in Figure 17.2.

Fig. 17.2 Living things can be
divided into four groups

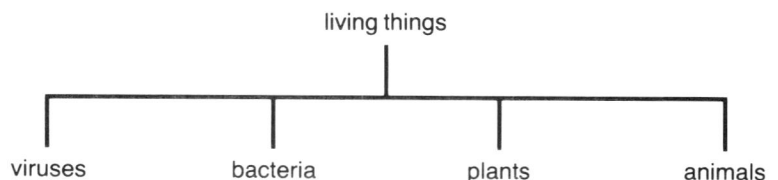

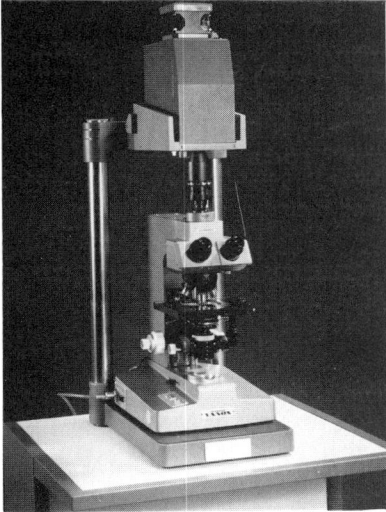

Fig. 17.3 A high quality light microscope

Fig. 17.4 A modern electron microscope

Fig. 17.5 An electron-micrograph of a human warts virus. The magnification is × 250 000

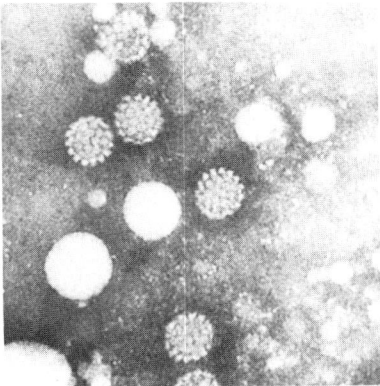

Viruses

Viruses are so small that they are invisible even using the best light microscope (Figure 17.3). However, they can be seen with an **electron microscope** (Figures 17.4 and 17.5). Viruses can only multiply inside the living cells of a bacterium, a plant or an animal. The host cells are killed when viruses multiply inside them. This is why viruses cause diseases. For example, smallpox, yellow fever, polio, common cold, chicken pox, mumps, influenza and measles are all examples of human virus diseases. Viruses also cause serious diseases in plants, for example barley yellow dwarf virus, which attacks oats, wheat, barley and maize. This virus makes the plants shorter than they should be and reduces the yield of the crop.

Bacteria

Bacteria are not as small as viruses, but a good light microscope is needed to see them. Bacteria are made of a single cell, but they have no enclosed nucleus like plant and animal cells. They have a cell wall made of protein and carbohydrate. Some bacteria cause diseases and are therefore harmful. For example, the following human diseases are caused by bacteria: typhoid, cholera, anthrax, pneumonia and tuberculosis (TB). Many bacteria are harmless. Some are very useful to us. For example, one type of bacteria converts milk into yoghurt. Another type changes milk into cheese.

171

plants

plants without seeds   plants with seeds

plants without seeds

Algae	Fungi	Mosses and Liverworts	Ferns and Horsetails
Features: Very simple plants, no roots, stems or leaves and no seeds	Features: Do not contain the usual green colouring of plants and have no seeds	Features: These are simple plants. Many have leaves and stems, but no proper roots or seeds	Features: These have roots, stems and leaves and they have tiny spores instead of seeds
For example seaweeds *Pleurococcus*	For example mushrooms toadstools moulds	For example cushion moss peat moss	For example bracken fern parsley fern

plants with seeds

plants with flowers, and seeds in a fruit

Plants with cones and naked seeds	Flowering plants	Flowering plants
Features: Trees with needle-shaped leaves	Features: With long thin leaves and non-branching veins, (monocotyledons)	Features: Having broad leaves with branching veins, (dicotyledons)
For example scots pine yew fir spruce juniper	For example all grasses and cereals daffodil, orchids, onion, leek, iris	For example oak, ash, beech, rose, potato, daisy

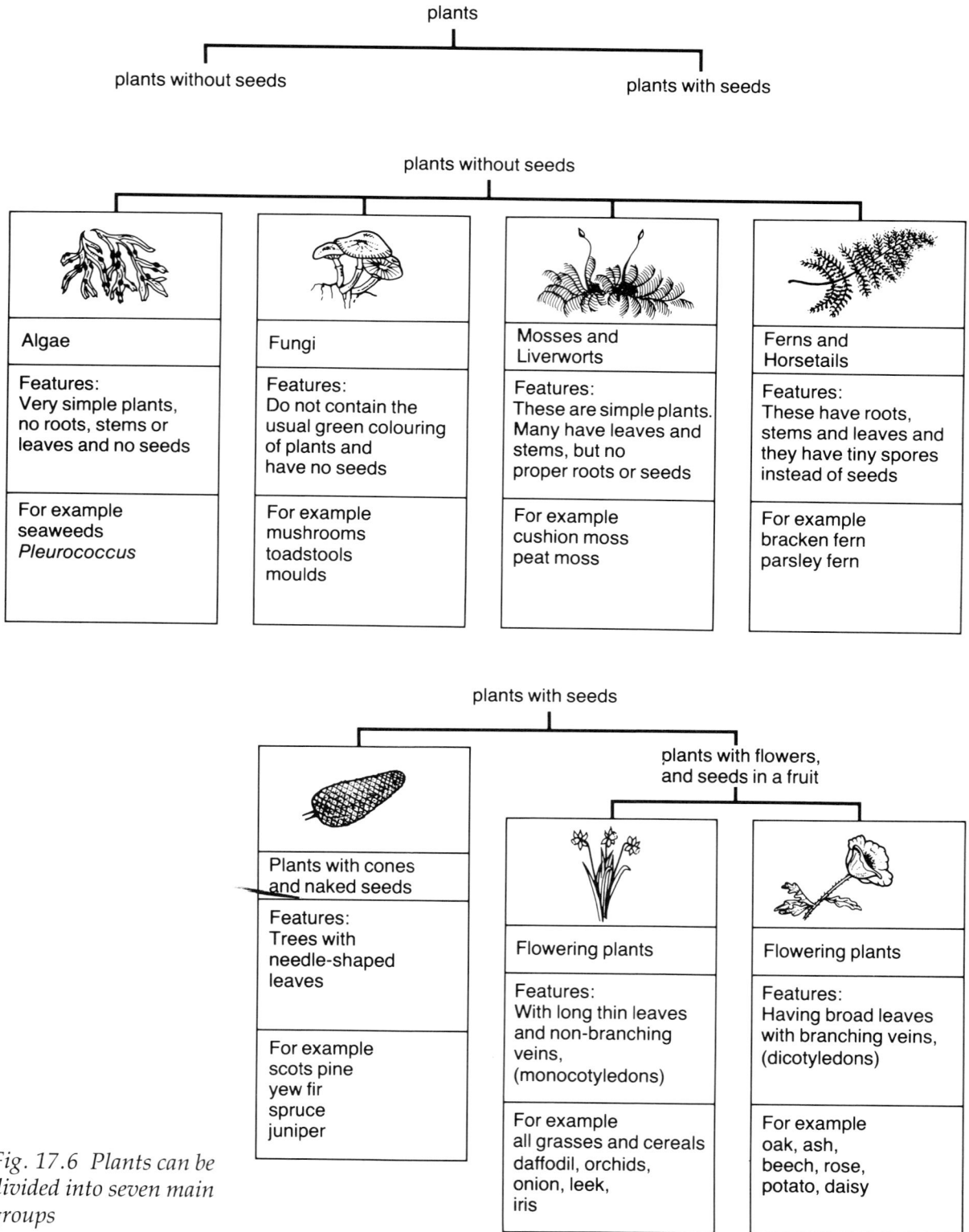

Fig. 17.6 Plants can be divided into seven main groups

172

Fig. 17.7 Animals can be divided into two main groups, vertebrates and invertebrates

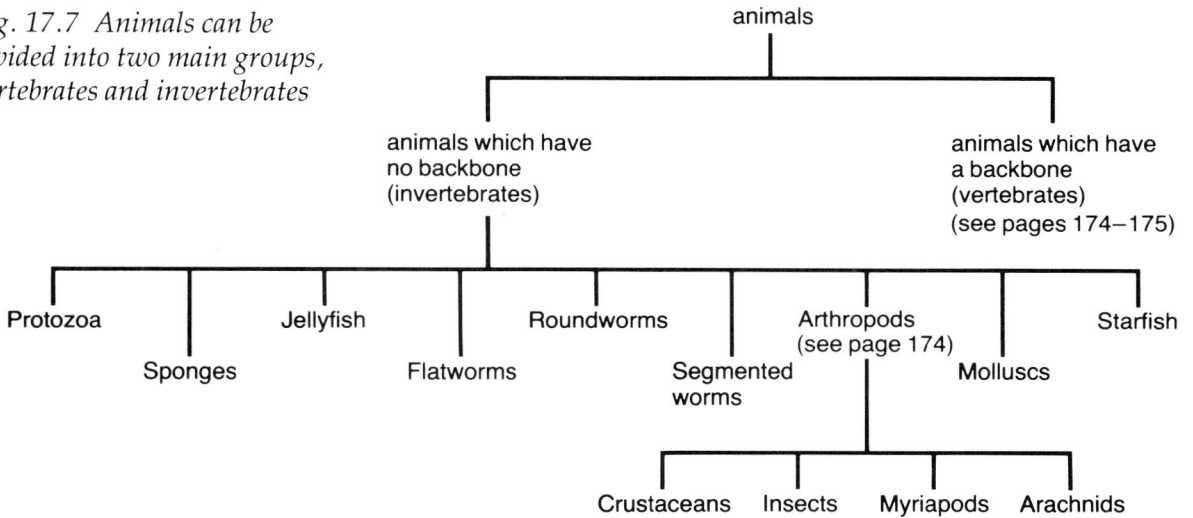

Fig. 17.8a There are nine main types of invertebrates. The arthropods are shown on the next page.

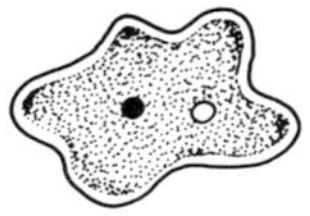

Protozoa	Jellyfish	Roundworms	Molluscs
Features: Single celled microscopic animals	Features: Body has one opening surrounded by tentacles	Features: Round body with no segments	Features: Soft body with a muscular foot and a shell
For example amoeba malaria parasite	For example sea anemone jellyfish hydra	For example hookworm filaria parasite	For example snail limpet otcopus

Sponges	Flatworms	Segmented worms	Starfish
Features: Bag-like body with many holes	Features: Flat body with no segments	Features: Round body with segments	Features: Five or ten radial arms or segments
For example sponges	For example tapeworm liver fluke bilharzia parasite	For example earthworm leech lugworm	For example sea urchin brittle star

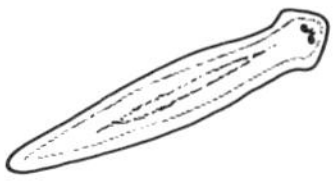

Fig. 17.8b The arthropods

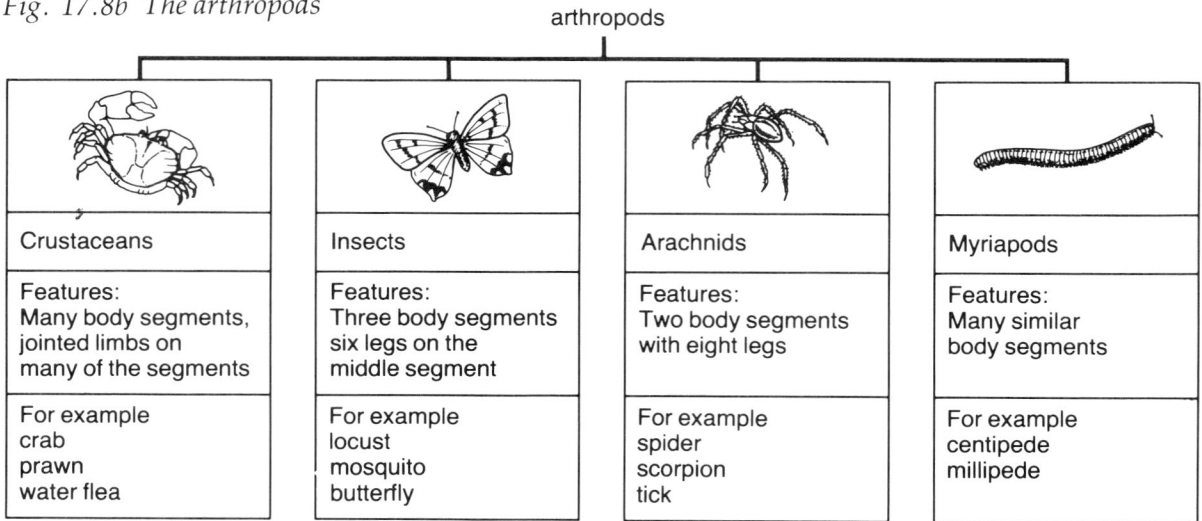

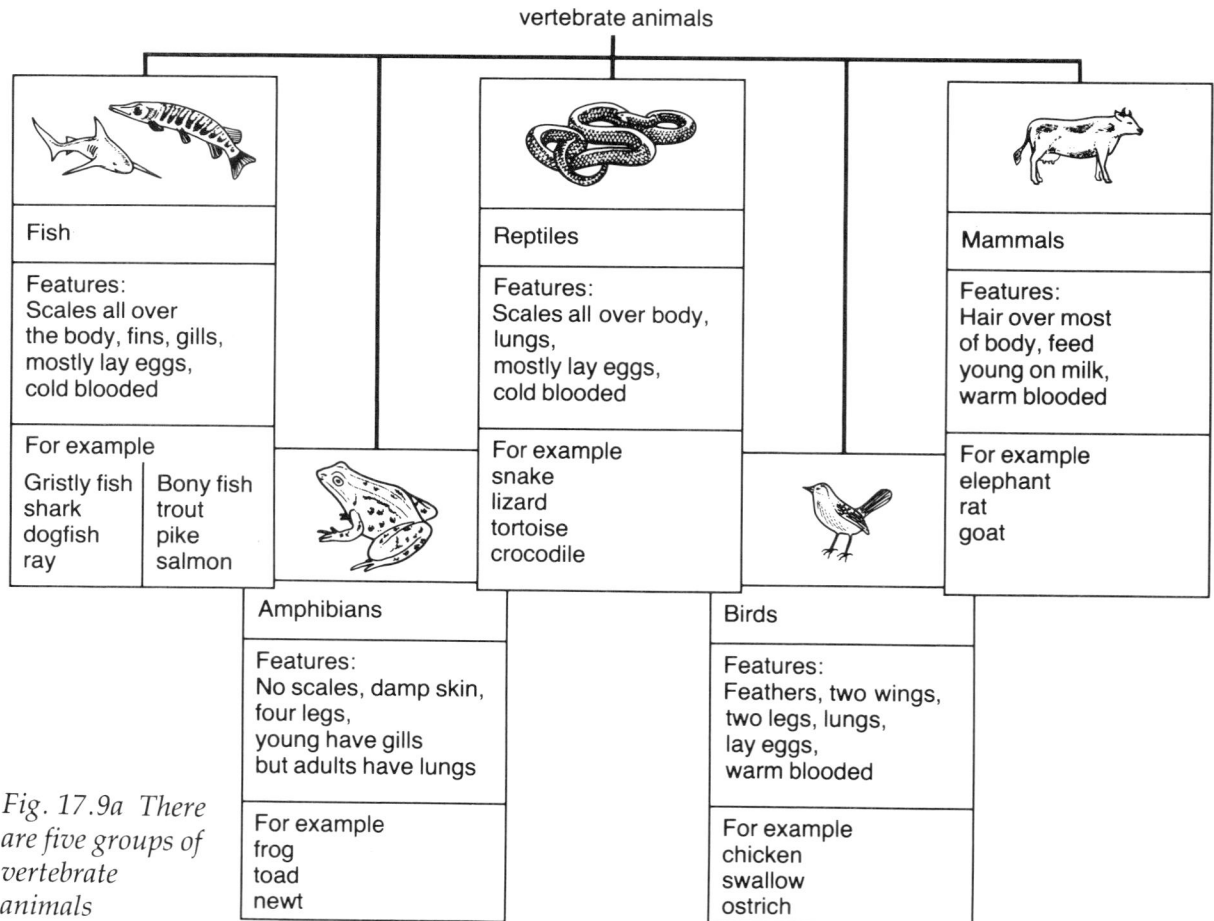

arthropods

Crustaceans	Insects	Arachnids	Myriapods
Features: Many body segments, jointed limbs on many of the segments	Features: Three body segments six legs on the middle segment	Features: Two body segments with eight legs	Features: Many similar body segments
For example crab prawn water flea	For example locust mosquito butterfly	For example spider scorpion tick	For example centipede millipede

vertebrate animals

Fish		Reptiles	Mammals
Features: Scales all over the body, fins, gills, mostly lay eggs, cold blooded		Features: Scales all over body, lungs, mostly lay eggs, cold blooded	Features: Hair over most of body, feed young on milk, warm blooded
For example		For example snake lizard tortoise crocodile	For example elephant rat goat
Gristly fish shark dogfish ray	Bony fish trout pike salmon		

Amphibians	Birds
Features: No scales, damp skin, four legs, young have gills but adults have lungs	Features: Feathers, two wings, two legs, lungs, lay eggs, warm blooded
For example frog toad newt	For example chicken swallow ostrich

Fig. 17.9a There are five groups of vertebrate animals

Fig. 17.9b The mammals may be divided in three groups

mammals

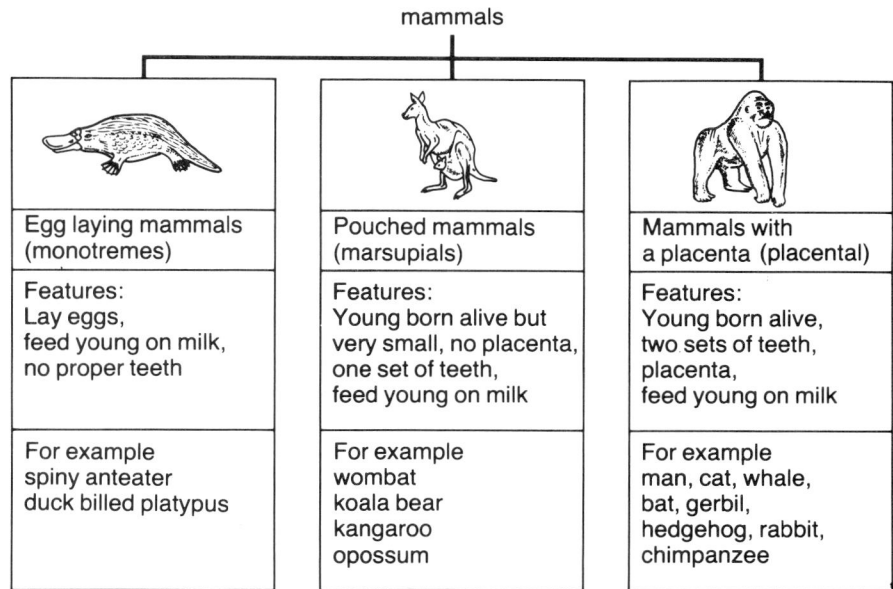

Egg laying mammals (monotremes)	Pouched mammals (marsupials)	Mammals with a placenta (placental)
Features: Lay eggs, feed young on milk, no proper teeth	Features: Young born alive but very small, no placenta, one set of teeth, feed young on milk	Features: Young born alive, two sets of teeth, placenta, feed young on milk
For example spiny anteater duck billed platypus	For example wombat koala bear kangaroo opossum	For example man, cat, whale, bat, gerbil, hedgehog, rabbit, chimpanzee

2 Practising classification

1 Describe the surface covering of the animal shown in Figure 17.10.
2 How many limbs does this animal have?
3 Look at Figure 17.9. What group does the animal in Figure 17.10 belong to?
4 The animal in Figure 17.10 has a placenta. What other features would you expect it to have?

Fig. 17.10 This type of animal is in danger of extinction

175

Your teacher may be able to show you living or preserved animals and plants, or pictures of them. Look for features which will help you to place them into their groups. For each one you could write down:

Animal ____ (give its number, letter or name) belongs to

the ____ group because ____ (give a list of reasons).

5 Here are some other examples for you to try.

Animal A has backbone, breathes with gills, has scales all over body, lays eggs, and is cold blooded.

Animal B has fur, breathes with lungs, is warm blooded, has two wings and two legs.

Animal C has warm blood, lives in water, has no hair, has lungs, and its young are born alive.

Animal D has a backbone, breathes with lungs, has scales all over its body, lays eggs, is cold blooded, and lives mostly in water, but comes onto land.

Animal E has six legs, no backbone, and a hard skin.

Animal F has a mouth surrounded by tentacles, and no backbone.

Animal G has a long, round body with no segments and no backbone.

Animal H has two body segments, eight legs and no backbone.

Plant A has seeds enclosed in a fruit, and parallel veins in leaves.

Plant B has naked seeds attached to cones.

Plant C has tiny leaves, but no proper roots.

Plant D has enclosed seeds, and branching veins in leaves.

Fig. 17.11 A mystery animal

6 Describe the surface covering of the animal in Figure 17.11.

7 How many limbs does it have?

8 If you had no more information about it, which group would you put this animal into? (See Figure 17.9.)

9 Here is some more information about the animal in Figure 17.11. It has a constant body temperature of about 37 °C. It does not lay eggs, nor does it have a pouch. Now which group of animals do you think it belongs to? You can find out the name of this animal in the Reference Section.

This example shows that you need more than just one or two pieces of information before you can put an animal into the correct group.

Ant-eaters, armadilloes, sloths

Whales, porpoises, dolphins

Moles, hedgehogs, shrews

Bats

Monkeys, apes, man

Pangolins

Hares, rabbits

Rodents such as squirrels, rats, gerbils, porcupines

Carnivores such as dogs, jackals, weasels, otters, cats, badgers, mongooses

Elephants

Hoofed animals (odd number of toes) such as zebras, horses, rhinoceroses

Hoofed animals (even number of toes) such as pigs, hippos, cows, sheep, giraffes, antelopes

Table 17.1 The twelve major orders of placental mammals

3 Classifying the tiger

Biologists divide all groups of animals (mammals, amphibians, insects, etc.) into smaller and smaller groups. For example, the mammals are divided into several orders. Each order is divided into several families. Each family is divided into several genera, and finally each genus has several species in it.

Twelve of the mammal orders are shown in Table 17.1. One of these orders is then broken down into families in Table 17.2. In Table 17.3 one of these families is broken down into genera. Finally, one of these genera is broken down into species in Table 17.4.

Dogs, wolves, jackals, foxes
Bears
Racoons, giant pandas
Weasels, ferrets, stoats, badgers, otters
Cats, pumas, leopards, lions, tigers, jaguars
Civets, mongooses
Hyenas
Sea lions
Walruses
Seals

Table 17.2 There are ten main families of carnivores

Felis (small cats)
Lynx (lynxes)
Panthera (large cats)
Acinonyx (cheetahs)

Table 17.3 There are four genera in the cat family

Panthera pardus (leopard)
Panthera leo (lion)
Panthera tigris (tiger)
Panthera concolor (cougar or puma)
Panthera onca (jaguar)
Panthera uncia (snow leopard)

Table 17.4 There are at least six different species of large cat

Table 17.4 shows that each animal has a double name. For example, the proper scientific name for the tiger is *Panthera tigris*. The first is the name of the genus. It shares this name with other members of the same genus. The second name, *tigris,* is the name of the species. The full classification of the tiger is this:

Phylum: Chordates (includes all animals with a backbone)
Class: Mammals
Order: Carnivores (meat eaters)
Family: Felidae (cats)
Genus: *Panthera* (large cats)
Species: *Panthera tigris* (tiger)

Looking ahead

What subjects are needed for biological careers?

At some time during your school career, perhaps while you are using this book, you may have to decide to give up some subjects, while continuing to study others.

These decisions are among the most important that you make in your life. This is because if you give up some subjects now, certain jobs, courses and careers may be closed to you later.

The most important question to ask about each subject that you are thinking of giving up is this: 'If I give up this subject (whatever it is), what jobs or courses may be closed to me later?' The answers to this question will sometimes surprise you.

English language and mathematics are important subjects for all of us, whatever we do. They are essential for most careers and you should certainly try to avoid dropping them.

If you give up subjects like physics or chemistry, some biological careers may be closed to you. (See Table 18.1.)

There are several people and publications which will help you to make up your mind about which subjects to continue with and which to drop. Many schools have an excellent careers department. You may also find it helpful to talk to your subject teachers and, of course, to your parents. It is also a good idea to talk to people who do the sort of jobs that you think you might be interested in. You should try to talk to employers as well. All local authorities have a careers service. Your school careers department may be in touch with this service.

This subject is dealt with very thoroughly in Chapter 7 of the book *Your Choice at 13+*. This gives full lists of careers that may be closed to you if you give up certain subjects. It contains good advice and is strongly recommended. (See Reference Section for full details of this book and other useful publications.)

As far as biology is concerned, you may find it quite easy to decide whether or not to go on with it. The important decisions involve what *other* subjects to do if you think you want to make a career in a biological sort of job. If you do want a biological sort of job later, then chemistry will be a very important subject (or physical science) and perhaps physics as well. Most careers or courses in biological subjects demand chemistry and many need physics as well. Oddly

Table 18.1 *These biological careers may be closed to you if you give up science, biology, chemistry or physics. Table reproduced from 'Your Choice at 13+' (CRAC)*

Science subjects	Biology	Chemistry	Physics
Animal nursing auxillary	Animal technician	Biology	Audiology
Animal technician	Audiology Technician	Brewing	Dentistry
Baking technology	Biology	Dental hygiene	Medicine
Beauty therapy	Dental hygiene	Dentistry	Ophthalmic optics
Beekeeping	Dental therapy	Dietetics	Pharmacy
Brewing	Dentistry	Dispensing	Physiotherapy
Chiropody	Medicine	Pharmacy technician	Radiography
Dairy technology	Nature conservancy	Leather technology	Radiotherapy
Dental hygiene	Nursing	Medicine	Veterinary work
Dental therapy	Orthoptics	Museum work	
Dentistry	Osteopathy	Nursing	
Dietetics	Pharmacy	Osteopathy	
Environmental health	Physiotherapy	Pharmacy	
Farming	Veterinary work	Physiotherapy	
Fashion design		Veterinary work	
Fashion production			
Food technology			
Forestry			
Hairdressing			
Home economics			
Horticulture			
Laboratory technician work			
Leather technology			
Medical laboratory science			
Medical physics technician			
Medicine			
Midwifery			
Nature conservancy			
Neurophysiology technician			
Nursing			
Occupational therapy			
Ophthalmic optics			
Pharmacy			
Photography			
Physiotherapy			
Psychology			
Surgery			
Radiography			
Radiology			
Remedial gymnastics			
Veterinary work			

Fig. 18.1 *Biologists discuss their results*

enough, if you give up biology and continue with chemistry and physics, most of these biological careers or courses will still be open to you. For example, you could probably do biology 'A' level, even if you do not do it at 'O' level, provided that you get good passes in chemistry and perhaps physics.

Whatever subjects you choose, it is obviously essential to get good advice before you make the decision about which subjects to give up. Your teachers will help you to make the right decisions. The most important thing is not to close the door on too many careers at this early stage. Therefore, you should try to choose a balanced combination of subjects. This might include english, mathematics, one or more humanities subjects (history, geography), one or more modern languages, one or more sciences, and a creative subject.

1 Give the names of twelve biological careers which may be closed to you if you give up chemistry.
2 Name six biological careers which may be closed to you if you give up physics.
3 Choose three careers from the lists given in this chapter which look interesting to you. Find out more about them.
4 Is the study of biology useful for someone who does not go on to a biological career? Give reasons for your answer.

Fig. 18.2 A biologist working with plants

Students' Reference Section

Chapter 1 Photosynthesis

Section 7

Air is a mixture of gases, mostly nitrogen (about 79%) and oxygen (about 21%). It also contains small amounts of carbon dioxide and of various inert gases such as argon. In addition air contains variable amounts of water vapour.

Chapter 2 Food chains

Section 4

A cow weighs 590 kilograms (kg) and eats 1020 kg of hay in 120 days. During this time the cow will put on 109 kg in weight.

300 rabbits weigh 590 kg. They eat 1020 kg of hay in 30 days. During this time all the rabbits together will put on a total of 109 kg in weight.

Which of these animals produce meat faster?

Section 5

The address of the Royal Society for the Protection of Birds (RSPB) is: The Lodge, Sandy, Bedfordshire, SG19 2DL. Always enclose a stamped and addressed envelope when sending for information leaflets. The RSPB runs a special organisation for young people called The Young Ornithologists' Club (YOC).

Chapter 3 Diet

Section 2

Normal human body temperatures is 37 °C. Athletes sometimes have higher temperatures than this. For example, during hot weather a marathon runner may have a temperature as high as 41 °C.

For Sections 3, 4 and 5 see Table 1 on pages 183–185.

Table 2 Approx. composition of the body (% by weight)

Water	60	Phosphorus	1
Fat	18 (variable)	Other minerals	0.5
Protein	18	Carbohydrate	0.5
Calcium	2		

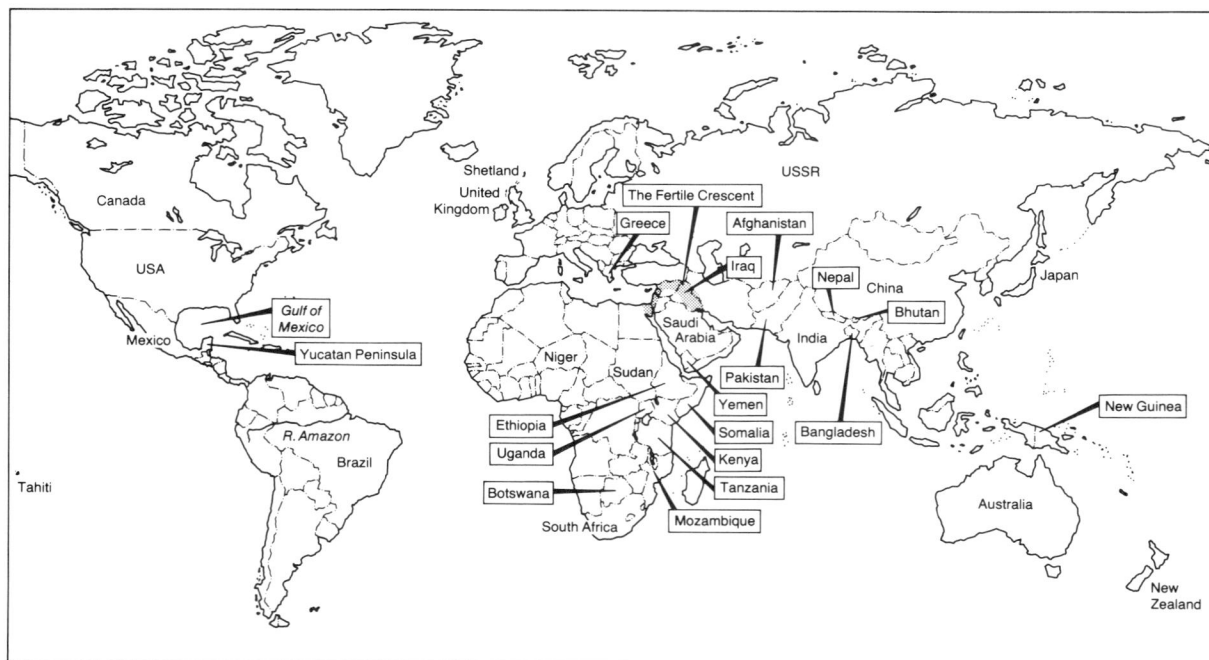

Fig 1   A map of the world showing the countries mentioned in this book

Table 1 Composition per 100 g (raw edible weight except where stated)

Food	Energy kJ	Protein g	Fat g	Carbohydrate g	Water g	Calcium mg	Iron mg	Vitamin A (retinol equivalent) µg	Thiamin (B₁) mg	Riboflavin (B₂) mg	Nicotinic acid equivalent mg	Vitamin C mg	Vitamin D µg
Milk, Cheese, Eggs													
Cream, double	1841	1.5	48.2	2.0	49	50	0.2	500	0.02	0.08	0.4	1	0.28
Milk, liquid, whole	272	3.3	3.8	4.7	87	120	0.1	46	0.04	0.19	0.9	2	0.03
Yogurt, low fat, natural	216	5.0	1.0	6.2	86	180	0.1	10	0.05	0.26	1.2	2	0.01
Yogurt, low fat, fruit	405	4.8	1.0	17.9	75	160	0.2	22	0.05	0.23	1.1	2	0.01
Cheese, Cheddar	1682	26.0	33.5	0	37	800	0.4	412	0.04	0.50	6.2	0	0.26
Cheese, cottage	402	13.6	4.0	1.4	79	60	0.1	41	0.02	0.19	3.3	0	0.02
Eggs, fresh	612	12.3	10.9	0	75	52	2.0	140	0.09	0.47	3.7	0	1.75
Meat													
Bacon, rashers, cooked	1851	24.5	38.8	0	32	12	1.4	0	0.40	0.18	9.2	0	0
Beef, average, raw	1107	17.1	22.0	0	64	8	1.8	0	0.05	0.17	7.3	0	0
Beef, stewing steak, raw	736	20.2	10.6	0	69	8	2.1	0	0.06	0.23	8.5	0	0
Beef, stewing steak, cooked	932	30.9	11.0	0.	57	15	3.0	0	0.03	0.33	10.2	0	0.
Chicken, raw	954	17.6	17.7	0	65	10	0.7	0	0.08	0.14	9.3	0	0
Chicken, roast, light meat	599	26.5	4.0	0	69	9	0.5	0	0.08	0.14	15.3	0	0
Ham, cooked	1119	24.7	18.9	0	54	9	1.3	0	0.44	0.15	8.0	0	0
Lamb, roast	1209	23.0	22.1	0	54	9	2.1	0	0.10	0.25	9.2	0	0
Liver, fried	1016	24.9	13.6	5.6	56	14	8.8	19 010	0.26	4.30	20.4	12	0.38
Pork chop, grilled	1380	28.5	24.2	0	46	11	1.2	0	0.66	0.20	11.0	0	0
Sausage, pork	1520	10.6	32.1	9.5	45	41	1.1	0	0.04	0.12	5.7	0	0
Steak and kidney pie, cooked	1195	15.2	18.3	14.6	49	37	2.8	126	0.14	0.52	6.8	2	0.55
Fish													
White fish, filleted	322	17.4	0.7	0	82	16	0.3	0	0.08	0.07	4.9	0	0
Cod, fried in batter	834	19.6	10.3	7.5	61	80	0.5	0	0.04	0.10	6.7	0	0
Fish fingers	749	12.6	7.5	16.1	64	43	0.7	0	0.09	0.06	3.1	0	0
Salmon, canned	649	20.3	8.2	0	70	93	1.4	90	0.04	0.18	10.8	0	12.50
Sardines, canned in oil, fish only	906	23.7	13.6	0	58	550	2.9	0	0.04	0.36	12.6	0	7.50
Fats													
Butter	3041	0.4	82.0	0	15	15	0.2	985	0	0	0.1	0	0.76
Lard; cooking fat; dripping	3667	0	99.1	0	1	1	0.1	0	0	0	0	0	0
Margarine, average	3000	0.1	81.0	0	16	4	0.3	900[1]	0.	0	0.1	0	7.94[1]
Preserves, etc.													
Chocolate, milk	2214	8.4	30.3	59.4	2	220	1.6	6.6	0.10	0.23	1.6	0	0
Honey	1229	0.4	0	76.4	23	5	0.4	0	0	0.05	0.2	0	0
Jam	1116	0.5	0	69.2	30	18	1.2	2	0	0	0	10	0
Marmalade	1114	0.1	0	69.5	28	35	0.6	8	0	0	0	10	0
Sugar, white	1680	0	0	105.0	0	2	0	0	0	0	0	0	0

Table 1 continued

Food	Energy kJ	Protein g	Fat g	Carbo-hydrate g	Water g	Calcium mg	Iron mg	Vitamin A (retinol equivalent) µg	Thiamin (B₁) mg	Riboflavin (B₂) mg	Nicotinic acid equivalent mg	Vitamin C mg	Vitamin D µg
Vegetables													
Beans, canned in tomato sauce	270	5.1	0.5	10.3	74	45	1.4	50	0.07	0.05	1.3	0	0
Beans, broad	293	7.2	0.5	9.5	77	30	1.1	22	0.28	0.05	5.0	30	0
Beans, runner	102	2.3	0	3.9	89	27	0.8	50	0.05	0.10	1.3	20	0
Cabbage, green, raw	92	2.8	0	2.8	88	57	0.6	50	0.06	0.05	0.8	53	0
Cabbage, green, boiled	66	1.7	0	2.3	93	38	0.4	50	0.03	0.03	0.5	23	0
Carrots, old	98	0.7	0	5.4	90	48	0.6	2 000	0.06	0.05	0.7	6	0
Cauliflower	56	1.9	0	1.5	93	21	0.5	5	0.10	0.10	1.1	64	0
Crisps, potato	2224	6.3	35.9	49.3	3	37	2.1	0	0.19	0.07	6.1	17	0
Lettuce	36	1.0	0	1.2	96	23	0.9	167	0.07	0.08	0.4	15	0
Mushrooms	31	1.8	0	0	92	3	1.0	0	0.10	0.40	4.6	3	0
Onions	99	0.9	0	5.2	93	31	0.3	0	0.03	0.05	0.4	10	0
Peas, frozen, raw	212	5.7	0	7.2	79	33	1.5	50	0.32	0.10	3.0	17	0
Peas, frozen, boiled	161	5.4	7.7	4.3	81	31	1.4	50	0.24	0.07	2.4	13	0
Peas, canned, processed	325	6.2	0	13.7	72	27	1.5	67	0.10	0.04	1.5	0	0
Potatoes, boiled	339	1.4	0	19.7	81	4	0.3	0	0.08	0.03	1.1	5–18[2]	0
Potato chips, fried	1065	3.8	10.9	37.3	47	14	0.9	0	0.10	0.04	2.1	6–21[2]	0
Potatoes, roast	662	2.8	4.8	27.3	64	10	0.7	0	0.10	0.04	1.9	6–21[2]	0
Spinach	91	2.7	0	2.8	91	70	3.2	1 000	0.12	0.20	1.3	60	0
Sweet corn, canned	325	2.9	0.5	16.1	73	3	0.6	35	0.05	0.08	0.3	4	0
Tomatoes, fresh	60	0.9	0	2.8	93	13	0.4	100	0.06	0.04	0.8	20	0
Fruit													
Apples	196	0.3	0	11.9	84	4	0.3	5	0.04	0.02	0.1	5	0
Bananas	326	1.1	0	19.2	71	7	0.4	33	0.04	0.07	0.8	10	0
Blackcurrants	121	0.9	0	6.6	77	60	1.3	33	0.03	0.06	0.4	200	0
Grapefruit	95	0.6	0	5.3	91	17	0.3	0	0.05	0.02	0.3	40	0
Oranges	150	0.8	0	8.5	86	41	0.3	8	0.10	0.03	0.3	50	0
Orange juice, canned, unsweetened	143	0.4	0	8.5	89	9	0.5	8	0.07	0.02	0.3	35	0
Pineapple, canned (including syrup)	328	0.3	0	20.2	77	13	0.4	7	0.05	0.02	0.2	12	0
Prunes, dried	686	2.4	0	40.3	23	38	2.9	160	0.10	0.20	1.9	0	0
Raspberries	105	0.9	0	5.6	83	41	1.2	13	0.02	0.03	0.5	25	0
Rhubarb	26	0.6	0	1.0	94	100	0.4	10	0.01	0.03	0.4	0	0
Strawberries	109	0.6	0	6.2	89	22	0.7	5	0.02	0.03	0.5	60	0
Sultanas	1066	1.8	0	64.7	18	52	1.8	5	0.10	0.08	0.6	0	0

Table 1 continued

Food	Energy kJ	Protein g	Fat g	Carbo-hydrate g	Water g	Calcium mg	Iron mg	Vitamin A (retinol equivalent) μg	Thiamin (B₁) mg	Riboflavin (B₂) mg	Nicotinic acid equivalent mg	Vitamin C mg	Vitamin D μg
Nuts													
Peanuts, roasted	2364	24.3	49.0	8.6	5	61	2.0	0	0.23	0.10	21.3	0	0
Cereals													
Biscuits, chocolate	2197	5.7	27.6	67.4	2	110	1.7	0	0.03	0.13	1.4	0	0
Biscuits, cream crackers	1857	9.5	16.3	68.3	4	110	1.7	0	0.13	0.08	2.5	0	0
Biscuits, rich, sweet	1966	6.2	23.4	62.2	3	87	1.8	0	0.16	0.04	1.7	0	0
Bread, brown	948	8.9	2.2	44.7	40	100	2.5	0	0.24	0.06	2.4	0	0
Bread, white	991	7.8	1.7	49.7	39	100	1.7	0	0.18	0.03	2.2	0	0
Bread, wholemeal	918	8.8	2.7	41.8	40	23	2.5	0	0.26	0.06	1.7	0	0
Cornflakes	1567	8.6	1.6	85.1	3	3	6.7[1] / 0.6[3]	0	1.80[1] / 0[3]	1.60[1] / 0.03[3]	21.3[1] / 0.9[3]	0	2.8[1] / 0[3]
Rice	1536	6.5	1.0	86.8	12	4	0.5	0	0.08	0.03	1.5	0	0
Spaghetti	1612	13.6	1.0	84.0	11	23	1.2	0	0.14	0.06	2.8	0	0
Beverages													
Coffee, instant powder	424	14.6	0	11.0	3	160	4.4	0	0	0.11	25.1	0	0
Coca cola	168	0	0	10.5	90	4	0	0	0	0	0	0	0
Tea, dry	0	0	0	0	—	0	0	0	0	0.90[4]	6.0[4]	0	0
Squash, fruit, undiluted	521	0.1	0.1	32.2	63	16	0.2	0	0	0.01	0	1	0
Alcoholic beverages per 100 ml													
Beer, keg, bitter	129	0.3	0	2.3	—	8	0	0	0	0.03	0.5	0	0
Spirits, 70° proof	919	0	0	0	—	0	0	0	0	0	0	0	0
Wine, red	284	0.2	0	0.3	—	7	0.9	0	0.01	0.02	0.01	0	0
Puddings and cakes etc.													
Apple pie	1179	3.2	14.4	40.4	42	42	0.8	2	0.08	0.02	0.9	2	0
Custard	496	3.8	4.4	16.8	75	140	0.1	43	0.05	0.21	1.0	0	0.03
Fruit cake, rich	1403	3.7	11.0	58.3	21	75	1.8	121	0.08	0.08	1.2	0	1.14
Jam tarts	1616	3.5	14.9	62.8	19	62	1.6	0	0.08	0.01	1.1	4	0
Rice pudding	552	4.1	4.2	20.2	72	130	0.1	33	0.04	0.14	1.1	1	0.02
Marmite	730	39.7	0.7	1.8	25	95	3.7	0	3.10	11.00	67.0	0	0
Ice-cream, vanilla	698	3.5	7.4	22.8	65	130	0.3	7	0.04	0.17	1.0	1	0

[1] fortified.
[2] vitamin C falls during storage.
[3] unfortified.
[4] 90 to 100 per cent goes into the tea you drink.

Chapter 4   Teeth

Section 4

Some animals have teeth which are worn down continuously by the hard food which they eat. These include rats, mice and rabbits. The teeth of these

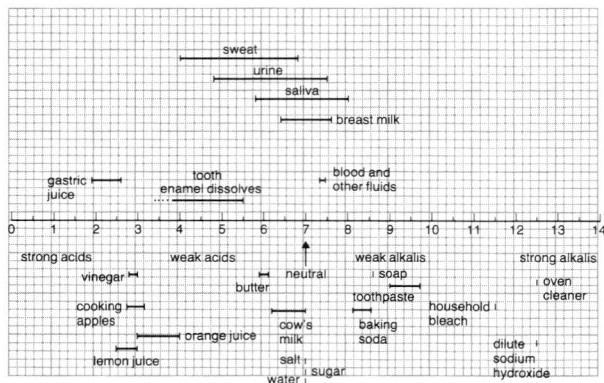

Fig 2   Chart to show the pH values of various household substances and some body fluids

animal grow all the time, from their roots, to replace the chewing suface as it is worn away (rather like the growth of human finger nails). Human teeth do not grow in this way.

Chapter 5   Digestion

Section 5

How rabbits digest cellulose. Rabbits have a gut which is similar to the gut of a rat (see Figure 5.3). However, rabbits have a very large caecum. This caecum contains millions of cellulose-digesting microbes. When rabbits eat food it passes through the gut in the normal way. When the food reaches the caecum it mixes with the microbes, and cellulose digestion begins. However, by this time, the food has already passed through the ileum which is where the digested food is absorbed into the blood. The food cannot go backwards. Therefore the rabbit eats the first droppings so that when the food passes through the ileum for the second time, the products of digestion can be absorbed. The second droppings are hard and black. The rabbit does not eat these.

In animals such as the elephant and the horse there is a third method of cellulose digestion. They do not have a four-chambered stomach as in cattle, nor do they eat their droppings as in rabbits. The elephant has a huge gut which contains the cellulose-digesting microbes. The food takes as long as three days to pass through the gut which gives time for the microbes to break down the cellulose before it passes beyond the ileum.

Chapter 6   Crops

Table 3   Some important wheat-producing countries

Country	Wheat production (million tonnes) 1979	1980
USSR	90.2	98.1
USA	58.0	64.5
China estimate	62.8	54.2
India	35.5	31.6
France	19.4	23.7
Canada	17.2	19.1
Australia	15.7	10.8
Pakistan	10.0	10.8
West Germany	8.1	8.2
Argentina	8.1	7.8
United Kingdom	7.2	8.1

Table 4   Wheat-growing countries with the best yields

Country	Wheat yield (tonnes per hectare) 1979	1980
Netherlands	5.9	6.2
United Kingdom	5.2	5.7
Eire	5.3	5.0
France	4.8	5.2
West Germany	5.0	4.9
USA	2.3	2.3
USSR	1.6	1.6

Chapter 8   Animals

There are many religious and other beliefs connected with animals. For example, cattle are sacred to the Hindu people. In some places chickens are linked with human fertility, perhaps because they lay a lot of eggs. You may be able to find other examples of special beliefs about animals.

Chapter 9   Breathing

Section 2

Table 5   Normal human breathing rates

	average breaths per minute	Extreme range
Infants, 11 weeks	63	40–87
Children, 4–5 years	23	11–30
Boys, 14 years	17	13–21
Girls, 14 years	16	11–20
Men, resting	12	10–13
Men, light work	17	16–18
Men, heavy work	21	19–23

Chapter 10 Smoking *or* health

Some studies suggest that smoking may reduce male fertility by making the sperms less active. Women who smoke may have a shorter reproductive life than non-smoking women.

Chapter 11 The heart

Table 6 Normal human adult pulse rates (resting)

women 78–82 per minute
men 70–72 per minute.

Table 7 Reported heartbeat rates in other animals (beats per minute)

Swallow	600	Frog	30
Mouse	500	Bull	25
Rabbit	200	Elephant	20

There are about 70 cm³ of blood for each kilogram of body weight in human beings. Thus a man who weighs 70 kg has about 4.9 litres of blood in his body.

Chapter 12 Human population

Information about the human population changes rapidly. For example, a few months after Chapter 12 in this book was written the United Nations Fund for Population Activities published some new world population predictions. The Fund says that the human population now seems likely to level off at about 10.5 billion people by the year 2110.

Chapter 13 Human reproduction

Venereal diseases (VD) are disease which may be passed from an infected person to another person during sexual intercourse. People who get venereal diseases are always advised to seek medical treatment as soon as possible. If they do not get treated they may become sterile or suffer in other ways. There are special VD Clinics in most towns.

Chapter 14 Diseases

The diseases which people get fall into five main groups:
   (i) Inherited diseases. These diseases are present at birth. An example is the bleeding disease haemophilia.
  (ii) Deficiency diseases. Some examples are given in Chapter 3.
 (iii) Diseases caused by poisoning, for example lead poisoning or mercury poisoning (see Chapter 15).
 (iv) Diseases caused by non-living external factors, e.g. radiation sickness and hypothermia.
  (v) Diseases caused by living things. Smallpox and malaria are both examples.

In Britain a great deal of money is spent on treating people who have diseases. Some people say that we should spend more money on trying to prevent people from getting diseases.

Chapter 15 Pollution

The chapter gives several examples of water pollution but air pollution is also important. Here are some examples:

   (i) Wood and coal fires produce smoke. Smoke contains gases such as carbon dioxide together with small particles of carbon. When these particles settle they form a black layer which we call soot.
  (ii) The exhaust from petrol engines contains carbon monoxide and lead compounds. Both are poisonous.
 (iii) The smoke from brickworks contains fluorine, a very poisonous substance.
 (iv) One of the most widespread pollutants in air is sulphur dioxide, a poisonous gas. It is produced when fuels such as coal and oil are burnt.

Chapter 16 Conservation

Recently, one expert said this:
   'Food is essential; conservation is a luxury'.
   You might agree with this. On the other hand you could use some of the information in Chapter 16 to point out that conservation may help food production.

Chapter 17 Classification

Section 2

Q 6 to Q 9   The animal in Figure 17.11 is a pangolin, sometimes called the scaly ant-eater. It lives in Asia and Africa. Pangolins have very long sticky tongues. They feed on insects especially ants and termites. The African pangolins have no external ears and no teeth. It is a placental mammal.

Teachers' Guidelines

Chapter 1   Photosynthesis

Section 2

Iodine is slow to dissolve so make up the solution at least 24 hours before it is needed. Dissolve 6 g of potassium iodide in 200 cm³ of distilled water. Then add 3 g of iodine crystals. This should be labelled 'Iodine solution'.

Section 3

The roots of many plants contain starch, but the amount may vary with time of year and condition of the plant. It is wise to try out this experiment beforehand. In procedure **e**, it is essential to cool before adding the iodine solution. The blue-black colour may not be seen if the contents of the test tube are still hot. The difference between treatments A and B should illustrate the benefit of crushing up any substance to be tested.

Section 4

A healthy, well-illuminated variegated geranium is required. Ethanol is highly inflammable. It is important therefore to use a water bath for heating the ethanol.

Section 5

Removing the petiole from one leaf (but not from the other) provides a means of identifying the leaves after the removal of the chlorophyll. One of the aims here is to introduce control experiments (see question 6).

Section 7

Make up a stock solution of biocarbonate indicator which can be diluted for use when it is needed. The colour of the indicator may be affected by traces of dust so very clean glassware must be used, and dust must be excluded from the distilled or deionised water which is used.

To make 1 litre of stock solution dissolve 0.84 grams of Analar sodium hydrogen carbonate in about 900 cm³ distilled (or deionised) water. Do this in a 1 litre volumetric flask. Then dissolve 0.2 g of thymol blue and 0.1 g of cresol red in 20 cm³ ethanol. Add this alcoholic solution of the dyes to the sodium hydrogen carbonate solution. Top up the mixture to the 1 litre mark with distilled (or deionised) water.

To dilute the stock solution for use, use a pipette to transfer 25 cm³ of stock solution to a 250 cm³ volumetric flask. Add distilled (or deionised) water to give a total volume of 250 cm³. Before use this solution must be equilibrated with the carbon dioxide in the air. Do this by bubbling air (preferably from outside the laboratory and well away from chimneys, roads and cars) through the solution until no further colour change takes place. When it is ready for use the indicator should look deep red in the bottle or orange-red in a test tube.

The addition of bicarbonate ions to the water often increases bubble production in *Elodea*, (sodium bicarbonate is suitable). Bubbles will often appear readily from a freshly broken piece of *Elodea* stem.

Revised Nuffield Biology, Text 2: Living Things in Action (and Teachers Guide 2) Longman (1975).

Chapter 2   Food chains

Section 2

Answer to question 8: grass $\longrightarrow$ zebra $\longrightarrow$ lion.

Section 5

The RSPB (address in Pupils' Reference Section) is an excellent source of information about birds. They welcome enquiries from teachers. They publish a Teachers' Newsletter, Teachers' Guides on a variety of topics, posters, booklets and leaflets. If you write to the RSPB for information, please enclose stamps to cover return postage.

Another source of information about birds is the British Trust for Ornithology (BTO), Beech Grove, Tring, Herts, HP23 5NR. The BTO runs the national bird ringing scheme, the common bird census, the nest record scheme etc. They issue various publications including some very useful Guides, (such as No. 16 Bird Ringing), and a regular Newsletter for members.

Nature at Work: Introducing Ecology, British Museum (Natural History) and Cambridge University Press, (1978).
Ecological Energetics, Phillipson, J., Edward Arnold, (1966).

Chapter 3   Diet

Section 1

Malnutrition and its effects are not confined to the people of the developing countries. Many people in the rich nations have diets which lack sufficient fresh fruit, fresh vegetables or fibre.

Section 3

A convenient way in which to run this experiment is to provide ready weighed half peanuts each on a small piece of paper. The mass of each one is written clearly beside the peanut. It does not matter if they have different masses. Question 2 assumes that the peanuts will have different masses. Values for the energy released per gram of peanuts are likely to be well below the value given in Table 1 in the Reference Section for obvious reasons.

Section 4

Question 8: as far as possible, all places mentioned in the text are labelled on the map on page 182.

Manual of Nutrition, (Ministry of Agriculture, Fisheries and Food), HMSO. It is updated from time to time.
World Health is published ten times a year by the World Health Organisation (WHO). It is sent to many schools and is a good source of information and photographs. The address is: WHO, Av. Appia, 1211 Geneva 27, Switzerland.

Chapter 4   Teeth

Section 4
Many pupils believe that sugar alone or the bacteria in plaque damage the enamel. This exercise aims to show that neither of these alone will damage the enamel.

Section 5

Question 3: the molars and premolars will almost certainly have more fillings than the other teeth. The reasons for this might form the basis for discussion.

Section 7
The addition of fluoride to drinking water is a controversial issue. The National Pure Water Association opposes it and publishes a variety of booklets and leaflets. Its address is: 213 Withington Road, Manchester M16 8NB. The Royal College of Physicians recommends fluoridation of water supplies in areas where the natural fluoride level is below a certain level.

Fluoride, Teeth and Health, A report of The Royal College of Physicians, Pitman, (1976).
Various publications from The National Pure Water Association, (for their address see above).
The Health Education Council, 78 New Oxford Street, London WC1A 1AH, publishes posters and leaflets.
The General Dental Council, 37 Wimpole Street, London W1M 8DQ, publishes a *Catalogue of Dental Health Education Material*.
Your local Health Education Officer will have material on dental health education.

Chapter 5   Digestion
Section 3
Make up fresh starch/glucose mixture when needed. Heat 250 cm³ distilled (or deionised) water to boiling. While it is heating, mix 2.5 g of starch thoroughly with a little cold water. Add this to the boiling water and stir well. Stop heating and add 15 g of glucose. Allow this mixture to cool before using it. It can be stored in a fridge for up to 24 hours.

Section 4

To make starch suspension for hydrolysis by salivary amylase, take 0.25 g of sodium chloride and 2.5 g of Analar soluble starch (free of reducing sugars). Mix the two thoroughly in a little cold water and add to 250 cm³ of boiling distilled (or deionised) water. Stir well while continuing to heat. This should stop any lumps from forming. Cool before use.
   Question 8: it might be argued that the glucose detected in the syringe at the end of the experiment has been there all the time, perhaps a constituent of saliva. This question is designed to get pupils to think about how to find out whether or not this is true.

Revised Nuffield Biology, Text 2, Living Things in Action (and Teachers' Guide 2). Longman (1975).
Guts, (2nd Edition 1979), Morton, J., Edward Arnold (Cellulose digestion in ruminants and rabbits).

Chapter 6   Crops
Section 3
The leaflet *Recommended varieties of cereals* is published by The National Institute of Agricultural Botany (NIAB), Huntingdon Road, Cambridge, CB3 0LE.
   Seeds should be sown at the density recommended in the text. If the seeds are spaced more widely than this or in much smaller plots, the tillers are produced over a longer period so that by July or August there are lots of tillers, of varying ages, some ripe and others much younger. Such plants are unsuitable for harvesting.

Wheat: a guide to varieties from the Plant Breeding Institute, published by The National Seed Development Organisation (NSDO), Newton Hall, Newton, Cambridge. This is useful booklet which covers trends in UK wheat production and utilisation, grain quality, husbandry, and information about current recommended varieties of wheat.
Food, Energy and Society, Pimental, M. Edward Arnold, (1979).
Food and Agriculture, Scientific American, Freeman and Co. (September 1976). Contains articles about the origins of agriculture, the 'Green Revolution' etc.

FAO Production Yearbook, published annually by the FAO, Rome, provides a vast amount of data on world agricultural production.

Cereal Development Guide, Kirby E. M. J. and Appleyard, M, (1981). Published by Cereal Unit, National Agricultural Centre, Stoneleigh, Kenilworth, Warwickshire CV8 2LZ. This is a superbly illustrated, loose leaf folder, showing internal development and growth of cereals from germination to harvest.

(RDP 53), and many others. These are obtainable from the Ministry of Agriculture, Fisheries and Food (Publications), Tolcarne Drive, Pinner, Middlesex HA5 2DT.

The Overseas Centre for Pest Research, College House, Wrights Lane, London W8 5SJ, publishes some useful booklets and leaflets, especially on locusts.

Chapter 7 Pests

Section 2

The African Migratory Locust is easier to breed in a school laboratory than the Desert Locust. Very full information about the care of locusts is given in *Revised Nuffield Biology, Text 1, Introducing Living Things* and in the accompanying Teachers' Guide.

Question 8: one ocellus is in the centre of the 'forehead'. The other two are near the base of the antennae.

Section 3

Starve the locusts for a day before trying this activity. Even after this, some will feed and others will not. They will often feed more readily when they have got used to being in the tubes. If several locusts are studied by a class you should get at least some data.

Section 6

Wild oats normally shed their seeds in August just before the crops in which they grow are harvested. Local farmers, if approached tactfully by teachers, with an explanation of why the seeds are needed, will often give permission for them to be collected. For teachers in urban schools, a nearby branch of the National Union of Farmers may be able to help with farm contacts. Alternatively, local offices of the Ministry of Agriculture may be able to help.

It is certainly worth getting hold of the seeds because the behaviour of the awn is quite dramatic. The awn rotates very rapidly, especially when dry seeds are exposed to moisture. Moist seeds take longer to dry out and thus rotation of the awn in the opposite direction is slower. This behaviour seems to be an adaptation which enables the seeds to bury themselves in crevices.

The Ministry of Agriculture, Fisheries and Food publishes a series of Advisory leaflets. There is one on *The Woodpigeon* (No. 165), and another on *Rabbits* (No. 534). There are also leaflets on *Wild Oats* (452), *Cereal Mildew* (579), *Cereal Aphids* (586), *Colorado Beetle*

Chapter 8 Animals

Section 3

One film loop on peck order in chickens is *Social Behaviour in Chickens*, Biological Sciences Curriculum Study (BSCS), Hubbard Scientific Co.

King Solomon's Ring, Lorenz, K. Methuen, (1952), provides an interesting and amusing account of the author's study of animal behaviour.

Food and Agriculture, Scientific American, Freeman and Co. (September 1976), contains several articles including one on the origins of domestic animals.

FAO Production Yearbook, see references for Chapter 3.

Chapter 10 Smoking *or* Health

Section 4

A variety of different health warnings now appear on cigarette packs and on advertisements. The sponsorship of sport by the tobacco companies is a controversial issue. It certainly provides these companies with hours of TV advertising through the televising of sporting events, and enables them to get round the ban on cigarette advertising on television.

Smoking or *Health*, The Third Report of the Royal College of Physicians, Pitman, (1977).

Tobacco and the Third World: Tomorrow's Epidemic, Muller, M. (1978), published by War on Want, 467 Caledonian Road, London N7 9BE.

ASH (Action on Smoking and Health), 27–35 Mortimor Street, London W1N 7RJ, was set up in 1971 by the Royal College of Physicians and is supported by the Department of Health and Social Security. ASH acts as a pressure group and as a source of information for the media, MPs, and the public.

The Health Education Council, 78 New Oxford Street, London WC1A 1AH, publishes posters, leaflets etc.

The Tobacco Advisory Council, Glen House, Stag Place, London SW1E 5AG, puts forward the tobacco industry's view on smoking.

Chapter 11   The heart

Section 1

When pupils locate the neck pulse they should be warned about the danger of reducing the blood supply to the brain if they press too hard.

The National Blood Transfusion Service distributes a number of colourful leaflets on blood. (You have to be between 18 and 65 to be a blood donor.)

The Health Education Council, (see above for the address), publishes information about keeping fit and about coronary heart disease.

Chapter 12   Human population

Oxfam Education Department, 274 Banbury Road, Oxford OX2 7DZ, publishes some useful educational materials about the problems which face the poor countries. These include several games and simulations. One of the best of these is called the Poverty Game which illustrates the vulnerability of African subsistence farmers to disease, adverse weather and so on. It can be played by between 8 and 30 players and costs £1.00.

Data about world population appears regularly in various UN population studies, such as *World Population Prospects* and *Population Bulletin*, both of which are published at regular intervals.

The *FAO Production Yearbook* contains data about populations by countries.

The Brandt Report provides interesting reading about relations between the rich and the poor nations. The full title is *North-South: A programme for survival*, (1980), Pan Books.

Chapter 13   Human reproduction

Sometimes pupils who want to ask questions about sexual reproduction and related topics are inhibited from doing so for fear that their questions will hold them up to ridicule among their peers. A way round this is to ask for anonymous written questions. The folded pieces of paper are put into a box, drawn out one at a time and dealt with as appropriate.

Chapter 15   Pollution

Section 2

Clones of duckweed (*Lemna minor*) are easy to grow in the way described in the text. However, the plant will not grow well in winter unless it is kept warm and well illuminated. A bench lamp shining down on the tank provides both. It should be left on day and night. Growth of algae in the water and on the sides of the tank can be reduced by sticking black paper around the sides of the tank.

Philip Harris Biological Ltd., Oldmixon, Weston-super-Mare, Avon, sells study packs on *Air Pollution* (using lichens), and on *Stream and River Pollution*.

The Biology of Pollution, 2nd Edition, Mellanby, K., Edward Arnold.

The Advisory Committee on Oil Pollution of the Sea (ACOPS) publishes a very readable annual report. The address is: 60 New Oxford Street, London WC1A 1ES.

The Pollution Handbook, Mabey, R. Penguin Education.

Chapter 16   Conservation

Section 3

There are many examples of wild animals and plants which are of use to man. A few are given in this section. However, the more glamorous species, especially animals, tend to attract the most attention. For this reason it is worth spending some time on plants.

Local Conservation or Naturalists' Trusts will be able to provide information about threatened habitats or species in your area. Many of them run Conservation Corps activities for young people.

Organisations connected with conservation include:

Fauna and Flora Preservation Society, London Zoo, Regent's Park, London NW1 4RY. (The Zoo itself has an Education Department.)

World Wildlife Fund (UK), Panda House, 11–13 Ockford Road, Godalming, Surrey GU7 1QU.

International Union for the Conservation of Nature and Natural Resources, 1196 Gland, Switzerland.

Friends of the Earth, 9 Poland Street, London W1V 3DG.

How to Save the World: Strategy for World Conservation, Allen, R., Kogan Page Ltd, (1980).

Chapter 18   Looking ahead

The inclusion of this chapter should not be seen as providing an opportunity to recruit biologists. The intention is merely to try and help pupils when they are trying to decide whether or not to continue to study the subject (if this option is open to them).

The Institute of Biology, 41 Queen's Gate, London SW7 5HU, publishes a useful booklet called Careers in Biology.

The Careers Research and Advisory Centre (CRAC), Bateman Street, Cambridge CB2 1LZ, publishes a number of useful books and booklets. These include *Your Choice at 13+*, which is highly recommended for all pupils at this stage in their education.

Revision questions

The section of each chapter in which the answers to these questions may be found, is shown in brackets after each question.

Chapter 1   Photosynthesis

1 Give the name of the chemical reagent which is used in the test for starch. (2)
2 What does the ending -ate mean (as in carbohy-drate)? (3)
3 Name the two main types of energy which reach the surface of the earth and which come from the sun. (6)
4 What sort of energy can be captured by most plants? (6)
5 What is the name of the substance in plants which enables them to capture energy from the sun? (6)
6 What does the word photosynthesis mean? (6)
7 What colour is chlorophyll? (6)
8 Why are plants called producers? (6)
9 What do all living things need energy for? (6)
10 Why are animals called consumers? (6)
11 Give two reasons why plants are so important to all of us. (6 and 7)
12 What is the name of the waste gas which is produced during photosynthesis? (7)

Chapter 2   Food chains

1 Plants are able to capture light energy. Why are animals unable to capture light energy? (1)
2 How do animals get their energy? (1)
3 Cats eat sparrows. Sparrows eat seeds. Draw a food chain to show this. Be careful to draw the arrows pointing in the correct direction. (2)
4 Give one important difference between plants and animals. (2)
5 Human beings do not eat grass, but grass is a very important plant for us. Explain why. (4)
6 A caterpillar eats 200 g of leaf. Roughly how much of this will go into making new caterpillar material? What will happen to the rest? (3)
7 What is a bird pellet? (5)
8 Whereabouts would you look for bird pellets? (5)
9 Look at the food web in Figure 2.6. Which other animal or animals would suffer most if a lot of the rabbits were killed by myxomatosis? Give reasons. (5)

Chapter 3   Diet

1 Give the names of two nutritional diseases and say what causes them. (1)
2 Give the name of a nutritional disease *common* in Britain today. What causes this disease? (1)
3 Nutritional diseases do not often kill those who suffer from them. Why, then, are these nutritional diseases so dangerous? (1)
4 Why should a healthy diet contain protein? (1)
5 Why do some people need more energy-containing food in their diet than other people? (2)
6 Look at Table 1 in the Reference Section. This table gives the amount of each nutrient in 100 g of every food listed. Which food in the table gives more energy (per 100 g) than any other food? What is this food used for?
7 When he sits in a chair, an average 25 year old man, weighing 65 kg, needs about 6 kJ of energy each minute to keep him alive. If he ate 100 g of tomatoes how long would the energy from these keep him going? (4)
8 Name the chemical reagents which are used in the test for proteins. (5)
9 Look at Figure 3.5. If, after treatment, a piece of food gives a red precipitate when it is boiled with Benedict's solution (or Fehling's A and B), what does this tell you?
10 If another piece of food does not give a blue-black colour with iodine solution what does this tell you? (5)
11 Why should milk not be left on the doorstep for too long? (Table 3.9)

Chapter 4   Teeth

1 How long should your teeth last if you look after them? (1)
2 How many teeth would you normally expect to find in the mouth of each of the following: a 4 year old child, a 13 year old boy, a 28 year old woman? (2)
3 At what age do the milk teeth start being replaced by the permanent teeth? (2)
4 What is the name of the very hard material which is found on the surface of teeth? (3)
5 Give the names of two minerals which are found in teeth. (3)
6 Why should decaying teeth be filled or removed? (4)
7 Dental caries (tooth decay) begins when acids dissolve the enamel layer on the surface of teeth. Where do these acids come from? (4)

8 Sweets *alone* will not damage teeth. Explain why. (4)
9 At what pH (acid level) does tooth enamel start to dissolve? (4)
10 In one class survey a group of students discovered that they had a total of 115 fillings between them. However, only three of these fillings were in front (incisor) teeth. The rest were in the molars and premolars. Give as many reasons as you can to explain why fillings are more often found in molars and premolars. (4 and 5)
11 Why do some people object to the addition of fluoride to water supplies? (7)
12 Roughly how many working days are lost each year because of dental disease? (7)
13 Why do people with dental disease miss work? (7)

Chapter 5   Digestion

1 What is peristalsis? (2)
2 Which part of the gut lies between the mouth and the stomach? (1)
3 Why should your diet contain fibrous food (roughage)? (2)
4 What might happen if your diet contains insufficient fibrous food? (2)
5 If you ate a mixture of starch and glucose, which of these would be able to pass through the wall of the gut and into the blood without being digested? Explain why. (3)
6 Copy down and complete this diagam:

salivary amylase   ?
starch ——————→ maltose ——————→ glucose

7 Why are human beings unable to digest cellulose? (5)
8 What is it that helps rabbits and cattle to digest cellulose? (5)
9 What is a ruminant? (5)
10 What is symbiosis? (5)

Chapter 6   Crops

1 In what part of the world do the Kung bushmen live? (1)
2 What is their main energy food? (1)
3 Do the Kung bushmen plant crops? (1)
4 In what part of the world do we think that the first crops were grown by man? How long ago did this happen? (2)
5 Why are the New Guinea farmers unable to grow crops on the same field for longer than two to three years? (2)

6 What sort of wheat, winter or spring, is grown mostly in Britain? (3)
7 When should spring wheat be sown? (3)
8 When could you expect to harvest spring wheat? (3)
9 Wheat is used for three main purposes in Britain. What are they? (4)
10 Britain is not yet self-sufficient in wheat. What does this mean? (4)

Chapter 7   Pests

1 When a farmer plants a crop he may harvest less than half the food value of the crop. What happens to the rest? (1)
2 When climatic conditions are suitable, some grasshoppers change their behaviour and become locusts. Describe two ways in which their behaviour changes when they become locusts. (2)
3 Make a list of all the sense organs which you have found on a locust. (2)
4 Think of a swarm of Desert Locusts containing one million locusts. How much food (in kilograms) would you expect this swarm to eat in 20 days? (3)
5 Which locust seems to be easier to control, the Desert Locust or the African Migratory Locust? Explain why. (4)
6 What crops, which are grown in Britain, are damaged by woodpigeons? (5)
7 Why are rabbits a pest? (5)
8 Why are wild oats such a serious pest? Give several reasons. (6)

Chapter 8   Animals

1 Why is the bird described in Section 1 called a Honey-guide? (1)
2 For how long have dogs probably been domesticated animals? (2)
3 What is the date of the earliest remains of domesticated cattle? (2)
4 How long ago were the first horses tamed? (2)
5 What is a hierarchy? (3)
6 Why is a stable peck order a good thing for social animals? (3)
7 Describe one way in which a dominant monkey may show his dominance over another monkey which is beneath him in the hierarchy. (4)
8 When two soldiers meet, how can you tell which one has the higher rank?
9 Is there a hierarchy among the students in your year group or house? If so, how could an outsider tell who the 'dominant' students are?

193

Chapter 9   Breathing

1 Make a list of the differences between inspired and expired air. (1)
2 Which blood will contain more oxygen: blood travelling into the lungs or blood travelling away from the lungs? (2)
3 Where are goblet cells found and what do they do? (3)
4 What important function do cilia have in your air passages. (3)
5 What sort of things are thought to be the most likely causes of chronic bronchitis? (4)
6 Describe what it must feel like to have chronic bronchitis and emphyséma. (4)
7 Name a lung disease which people may get if they already suffer from chronic bronchitis. (4)
8 The proportion of people who die from chronic bronchitis and emphysema has been going down in recent years. Make a list of the probable reasons for this. (4)
9 What sort of things may cause asthma? (4)
10 What is a carcinoma? (4)
11 Why is lung cancer a particularly dangerous disease? (4)

Chapter 10   Smoking *or* health

1 What are carcinogens? (1)
2 Give the name of a substance in tobacco smoke which makes people cough. (1)
3 What happens to the cilia (tiny hairs) in their air passages when people inhale cigarette smoke? Does the same thing happen when cigar or pipe smoke is inhaled? (1)
4 Why is carbon monoxide very dangerous? Is it found in cigarette smoke? (1)
5 If a pregnant woman smokes, what effect might this have on her baby? (1)
6 What is nicotine? (1)
7 If a person smokes 20 cigarettes a day for two years how many weeks of life are they likely to lose? (2)
8 If cigarettes cost £1 for a pack of 20 and a person smokes one pack each day for 40 years, how much money will they spend on smoking in that time?
9 Why do people smoke?
10 Cigarette sales in the poorer countries of the world have increased recently. What advantages and disadvantages could this bring to these countries? (4)

Chapter 11   The heart

1 What is the name given to the blood vessels on which a throbbing movement (the pulse) can be felt? (1)

2 When you count your pulse rate what does this tell you about your heartbeat rate? (2)
3 What is the function of the heart? (2)
4 Blood is made of various things. Give the names of four of them. (4)
5 Who was the famous English doctor who studied the heart and the blood? (5)
6 What discoveries did this famous doctor make? (5)
7 What do the coronary arteries do? (6)
8 What may happen to someone who has coronary heart disease? (6)
9 What sort of things should you do in order to try to avoid getting coronary heart disease? (6)
10 What operation can be done when someone has a badly blocked coronary artery? (7)

Chapter 12   Human population

1 How long does it take for the world population to increase by one million people? (1)
2 In which year does the world population seem likely to reach 5 billion? (2)
3 What is likely to be the figure for world population by the year 2000? (2)
4 During which 25 year period was world population growing at the fastest rate? (Look for the steepest part of the curve in Figure 12.2.) (2)
5 Read the notes in the Reference Section for Chapter 12. The prediction says that the human population will level off at about 10.5 billion people by the year 2110. What does this mean?
6 Which country has the largest population in the world? (2)
7 Look at the factors listed in Section 4. Which of these factors are beyond our control?
8 The human population cannot go on growing for ever. What factors could stop it from increasing? (4)
9 What does the FAO do? (5)
10 Why do the rich and poor nations need each other? (5)

Chapter 13   Human reproduction

1 What does the word menstruation mean? (2)
2 How many days always pass between the moment when an egg is released from a woman's ovary and the moment when her next period begins? (2)
3 If a woman's period began on the 26 March, on what date was her last egg released? (2)
4 At what age, roughly, do women stop producing eggs? (2)
5 Where are sperms made? (3)
6 Make a list of the differences between sperms and eggs (2 and 3)
7 What does the word fertilisation mean? (4)

8 What is the purpose of courtship? (4)

9 Whereabouts in the female does the male release the sperms? (5)

10 Whereabouts does the sperm normally fertilise an egg? (5)

11 In what sense are our birth certificates misleading? (5)

12 Men produce two types of sperm. What is the difference between them? (6)

13 About how old is the human embryo when it reaches the uterus? (7)

14 How many weeks after fertilisation does the baby become known as a foetus? (7)

15 Draw a line to show how long the baby is when it is two months old. (7)

16 Draw another line to show how long the baby is at four months. (7)

17 What is the purpose of the contractions which take place during the first stage of labour. (8)

Chapter 14   Diseases

1 What are the leading killer diseases in Britain today? (1)

2 Name four of the most serious diseases in the world today. (1)

3 Why is smallpox such a terrible disease. (2)

4 Imagine that you are Edward Jenner. You have vaccinated the 8 year old boy with material from a cowpox sore. The boy has had cowpox and has recovered. You now want to complete the experiment by deliberately trying to infect the boy with smallpox. What would you say to his parents? (2)

5 What are the three things about smallpox which made health workers confident that they could wipe out this disease? (3)

6 What was the name of the last person to get smallpox (outside a laboratory)? Where did he live? (3)

7 Smallpox could break out again in the world. How might this happen? What should be done to try to prevent this from happening? (3)

8 What is a parasite? (4)

9 Why are many of the worst diseases in the world today more difficult to wipe out than smallpox? (4)

10 How can you catch malaria? (5)

11 Why is malaria such a serious disease in the world today? (5)

12 Make a list of the reasons why malaria is so difficult to control. (5)

Chapter 15   Pollution

1 Why might some people try to ignore or to hide the effects of pollution? (1)

2 Explain why we can use the animals which are found in a sample of water to tell us how polluted the water is. (2)

3 Why did the Thames become an open sewer? (3)

4 When was the Thames Conservancy set up? (3)

5 Explain why the Victorian sewer system did not solve the problem of pollution in the Thames. (3)

6 Explain why you would not have enjoyed visiting Westminster in the 1850s. (3)

7 How do we know that the River Thames is much less polluted than it used to be? (3)

8 Why was the tanker *Scenic* banned from returning to the Sullom Voe oil terminal? (4)

9 How many tons of oil escaped into the sea when the Ixtoc I oil well blew out? (4)

10 Use a table to make a summary of the estimated cost of the Ixtoc I disaster. Put 'cost not known' by items for which there is no information. (4)

11 What happens to people who suffer from mercury poisoning? (5)

Chapter 16   Conservation

1 Give the names of three animals which became extinct during the 19th century. (1)

2 During which period did the Texas Grizzly Bear become extinct? (2)

3 Give two reasons why some plants and animals become extinct. (2)

4 Why are some people worried by the disappearance of hedges and woods in the British countryside? (2)

5 Which will contain the larger number of different plants and animals: one hectare of tropical forest or one hectare of British woodland? (2)

6 Why does man cut down and clear rain forest? (2 and 3)

7 Give an example of the way in which a wild animal can be useful to man. (3)

8 Make a list of the reasons why the continuing destruction of tropical rain forest might cause problems for man. (2 and 3)

9 What is a beefalo and why could this animal be useful to man? (4)

Chapter 17   Classification

1 Why do we arrange plants and animals into groups? (1)

2 Why do we need a scientific system for naming plants and animals? (1)

3 Make a list of the differences between viruses and bacteria. (1)

4 The following groups are used by biologists for classifying animals: class, family, genus, order, species. A class is divided into several orders. What is each order divided into? What is each family divided into? (3)

5 Write out the full classification for the snow leopard. (3)

Index